PIPE FITTINGS

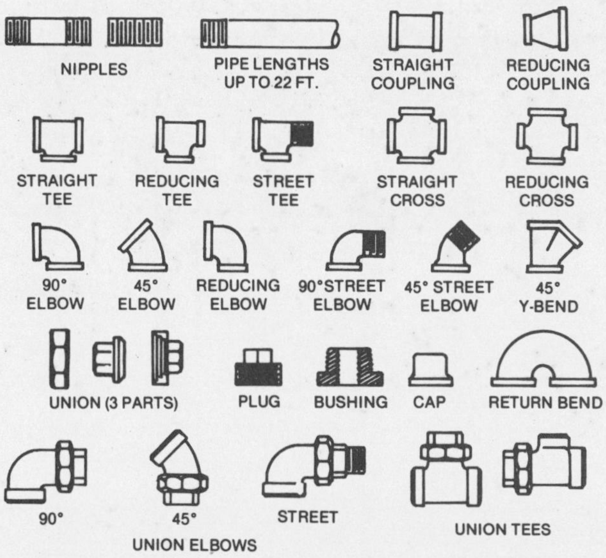

Here are the common steel pipe fittings. Nipples are simply short lengths of pipe threaded on both ends. Reducing fittings join two different sizes of pipe.

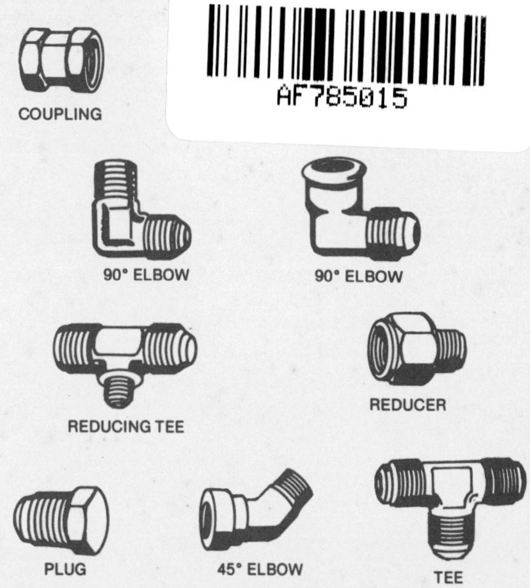

Compression fittings of the flared-tube type are the easiest for the novice to handle when working with copper tubing.

STANDARD STEEL PIPE
(All Dimensions in Inches)

Nominal Size	Outside Diameter	Inside Diameter	Nominal Size	Outside Diameter	Inside Diameter
1/8	0.405	0.269	1	1.315	1.049
1/4	0.540	0.364	1 1/4	1.660	1.380
3/8	0.675	0.493	1 1/2	1.900	1.610
1/2	0.840	0.622	2	2.375	2.067
3/4	1.050	0.824	2 1/2	2.875	2.469

SQUARE MEASURE

144 sq in = 1 sq ft
9 sq ft = 1 sq yd
272.25 sq ft = 1 sq rod
160 sq rods = 1 acre

VOLUME MEASURE

1728 cu in = 1 cu ft
27 cu ft = 1 cu yd

MEASURES OF CAPACITY

1 cup = 8 fl oz
2 cups = 1 pint
2 pints = 1 quart
4 quarts = 1 gallon
2 gallons = 1 peck
4 pecks = 1 bushel

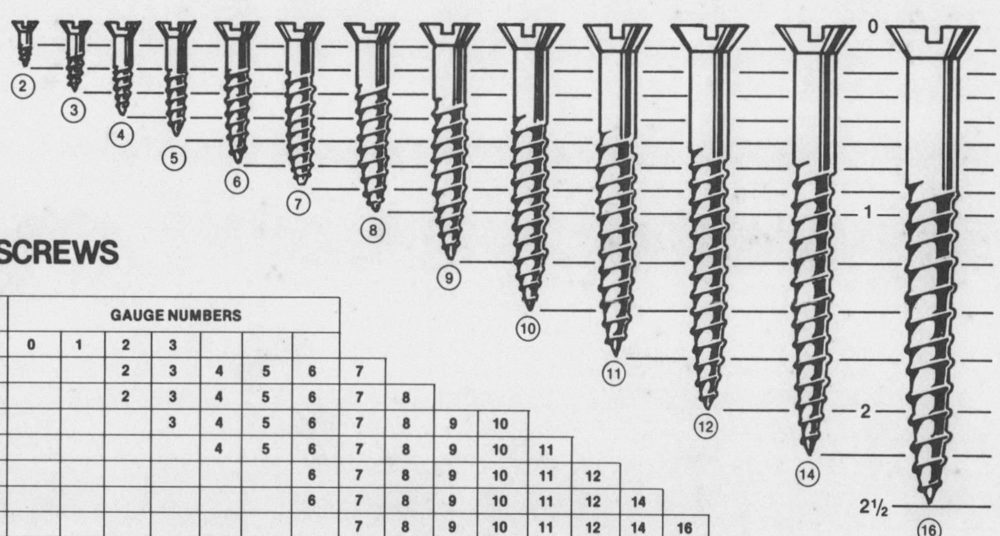

WOOD SCREWS

LENGTH	GAUGE NUMBERS																
1/4 INCH	0	1	2	3													
3/8 INCH			2	3	4	5	6	7									
1/2 INCH			2	3	4	5	6	7	8								
5/8 INCH				3	4	5	6	7	8	9	10						
3/4 INCH					4	5	6	7	8	9	10	11					
7/8 INCH							6	7	8	9	10	11	12				
1 INCH							6	7	8	9	10	11	12	14			
1 1/4 INCH								7	8	9	10	11	12	14	16		
1 1/2 INCH							6	7	8	9	10	11	12	14	16	18	
1 3/4 INCH									8	9	10	11	12	14	16	18	20
2 INCH									8	9	10	11	12	14	16	18	20
2 1/4 INCH										9	10	11	12	14	16	18	20
2 1/2 INCH													12	14	16	18	20
2 3/4 INCH														14	16	18	20
3 INCH															16	18	20
3 1/2 INCH																18	20	24
4 INCH																18	20	24

WHEN YOU BUY SCREWS, SPECIFY (1) LENGTH, (2) GAUGE NUMBER, (3) TYPE OF HEAD—FLAT, ROUND, OR OVAL, (4) MATERIAL—STEEL, BRASS, BRONZE, ETC., (5) FINISH—BRIGHT, STEEL BLUED, CADMIUM, NICKEL, OR CHROMIUM PLATED.

HERE ARE TWO great decks you can build. The rugged deck above is built for years of outdoor living. The perimeter railing includes benches that provide ample seating for large gatherings. The deck at left was kept as simple in appearance and construction as possible. Container plantings add visual interest. The steps are thick wooden slabs. See page 2098.

In this volume . . .

BEAUTIFUL DOWEL PLANTER is one of four projects from Scandinavia. See page 2106.

TWO MORE PROJECTS from Scandinavia are shown above: a large standing planter (foreground) and a bottle rack stored in a bench of concrete blocks. See page 2106.

AN ELABORATE GARDEN WALKWAY—or a simple path—not only is a convenience, but can set off your home in beautiful style. See the suggestions on page 2084.

BUILD THESE exciting projects from Plexiglas. This cutting board is durable, sanitary and nonabsorbent.

THIS NOVEL stepladder displays favored plants in fine style. It's easy to build, and can be moved to follow the sun.

COFFEE TABLE is easily made by combining your favorite wood with a pair of U-shaped legs fashioned from clear plastic. The result is an airy, floating effect. You'll find instructions for making these and other projects on page 2339.

Popular Mechanics

do-it-yourself encyclopedia

in 20 volumes

a complete how-to guide for the homeowner, the hobbyist—
and anyone who enjoys working with mind and hands!

All about:

home maintenance
home-improvement projects
wall paneling
burglary and fire protection
furniture projects
finishing and refinishing furniture
outdoor living
home remodeling
solutions to home problems
challenging woodworking projects
hobbies and handicrafts
model making
weekend projects
workshop shortcuts and techniques
hand-tool skills
power-tool know-how
shop-made tools
car repairs
car maintenance
appliance repair
boating
hunting
fishing
camping
photography projects
radio, TV and electronics know-how
clever hints and tips
projects just for fun

volume 14

ISBN 0-87851-079-6
Library of Congress Catalog Number 77 84920

MANUFACTURED IN THE UNITED STATES OF AMERICA

contents

VOLUME 14

Handsome garden paths and walkways

By PETER OLDALE

BREAK UP top soil and scoop out narrow trenches for wooden curbs treated with a good preservative.

SEE ALSO
Asphalt driveways . . . Concrete . . . Gardening . . . Landscaping . . . Lawns . . . Patios . . . Retaining walls . . . Steps . . . Transplanting . . . Trees

CAREFULLY POSITION slabs over the loose soil. It's a worthwhile idea to chart your layout of slabs first.

TAMP THE SLAB firmly into place by using the handle of a hammer—never pound it with a hammer's head.

A GARDEN PATH made from blocks of stone or concrete is strong, durable, easy to lay (apart from the actual labor of carrying the slabs) and can be done in colors, materials or patterns to blend with almost any style of house or garden.

Yard for yard, slabs of concrete are on the low-cost side, but stone is a different matter. Dressed York Stone slabs are one of the most expensive materials obtainable.

Steps for garden paths can be plain gray concrete (the cheapest), colored concrete, textured concrete cast to imitate the irregularities of natural stone, or concrete that's topped with inlaid pebbles or stone chips. Common shapes are square, rectangular, hexagonal or octagonal, all suited for layout in many patterns. Great care must be taken with the colored slabs, however, or unnaturally garish effects may be produced. A single slab, viewed in a building supply yard, may seem subdued in shade, but a whole path or drive in this same material could appear impossibly bright.

Before ordering, lay a few slabs together on the ground and, if possible, wet them down—the color of wet slabs is markedly deeper than that of dry ones, and a path that looks restrained in summer may darken unpleasantly in winter rains.

Slabs are usually sold by the piece, thus the actual cost *per square yard* will be greater for small slabs than for larger ones. Paths and drives should be planned for widths that can use standard-sized slabs, thus eliminating a need for cutting.

Where a pattern of various-sized slabs is desired, work out beforehand the exact number of each size needed. In general, avoid patterns using large numbers of small pieces. These are hard to lay, susceptible to wear and expensive.

Octagonal and hexagonal slabs will not make a straight-edged path by themselves, so halves (for edges) and quarters (for corners) are needed. Again, detailed planning will give the required number of each kind. Paths laid out with these slabs should have only parallel edges and right-angled or 45° corners. Other angles are very difficult to lay satisfactorily.

Inlay stones in a concrete bed

POUR A BED of concrete and beat the mix down with a length of lumber. Make sure the form is level.

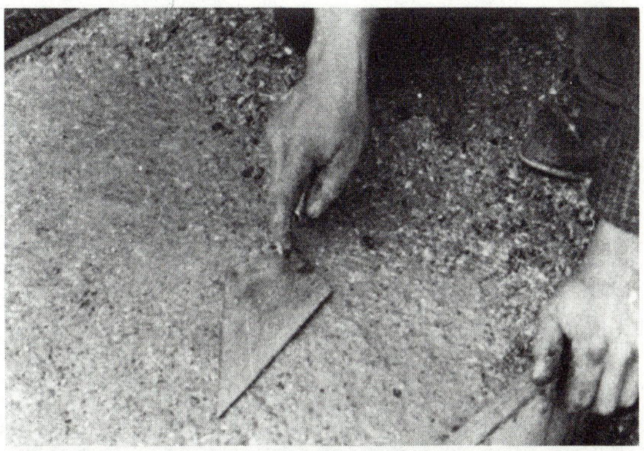

USE A TROWEL in pounding fashion to bring fuzzy finish to the surface. Smooth walks can be dangerous.

WHILE CONCRETE is still setting up, scoop out portions and inlay stones, slabs or other material.

TAMP DOWN until level. The cement will be forced up between the joints to be flush with the surface.

Lay a path with built-in greenery

POSITION EACH STONE carefully on a bed of soil and sand. It's best to start with the edge stones.

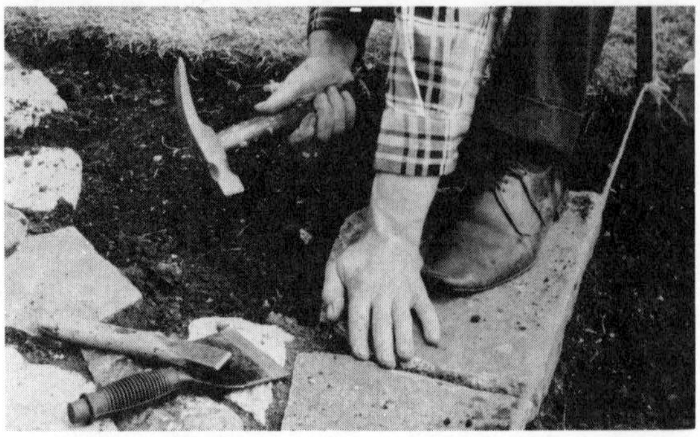

STAND ON THE STONE and pound the soil under its edges to consolidate soil and level the stone.

BE VERY CAREFUL when tamping stones around small plants. Otherwise you can damage the roots.

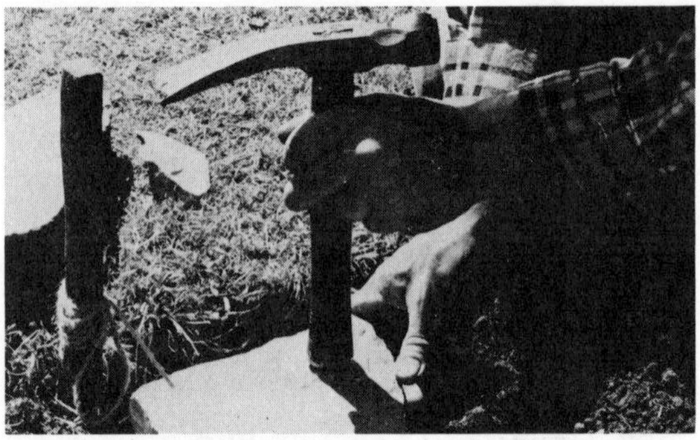

CORNER STONES should be as square as possible to maintain clean lines of the path or walkway.

Use hexagonal slabs for a truly distinctive touch

CONCRETE BLOCKS of this size require a high standard bed of pure sand or sand/cement dry mix. It's important to smooth the bed carefully for every concrete slab you lay, making sure it's perfectly level.

INSERT CREEPING plants, such as thyme, or small plants, such as rosemary, as the work progresses.

IF NECESSARY, you can chip stone to fit awkward-shaped areas, but always wear safety goggles.

SPREAD FINE SOIL over the completed walkway. It often is advisable to sift all of the topsoil first.

BRUSH THE SOIL into all the cracks and crevices at the butt joints to produce a well-defined walkway.

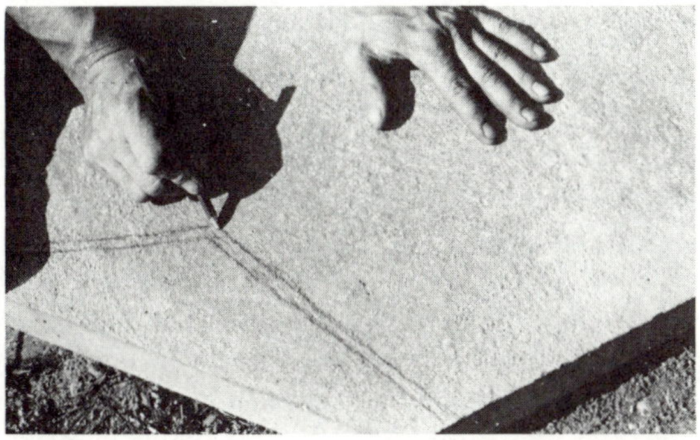

WHERE A BLOCK must be cut, make a pair of guide lines; each should be about ¼-in. off the desired cutline.

USE A MASONRY saw to cut between the drawn lines, applying water liberally to lubricate the saw.

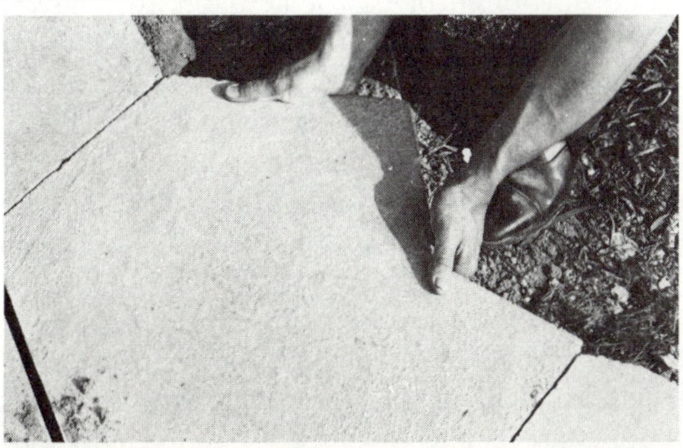

LOWER THE CUT block gingerly into place on the bed, making sure that the smooth bed isn't disturbed.

FINE, SIFTED SAND is then brushed into all the cracks until every joist in the walk is completely filled.

continued

Laying an asphalt path

POUR A GENEROUS AMOUNT of gravel on top of a firm foundation and rake it until it's spread evenly.

BREAK OPEN the bags of asphalt and pour this on top of gravel bed. Asphalt comes in several colors.

RAKE OUT asphalt at once. Heating the head of the rake over a low flame makes the raking task easier.

A SPRINKLING of colored chips will break the solid color and improve the appearance. Then roll the path.

Stone paving can be *random-squared* (various irregular squares or rectangles fitted together in patterns), or it can be *crazy paving*—broken flat stones fitted together in the manner of a jigsaw puzzle.

Squared slabs can be bought by the square yard, but most stone is bought by the ton. The area a ton of stone will cover depends on its average thickness and its type. Sandstone, in particular, varies somewhat in its weight per cubic foot. The most direct method of finding out the amount to order is to telephone the materials dealer and ask how much of his particular stone will be needed for the area you wish to cover.

Delivery costs can account for a large part of the price since most quarries will not deliver less than a full truckload—say five tons. If this quantity is not needed, it may pay to seek a neighbor who also is thinking of laying a stone path, and share the load.

Small orders can be collected direct from quarries at a comparatively low price—and if a truck can be borrowed, this is the most economical method of purchase. Do not be tempted, however, to overload a small truck with great heaps of stone. Five or six hundredweight of crazy paving doesn't look very heavy, but it is better to make extra trips than to ruin the suspension or springs.

Garden centers, on the other hand, will deliver almost any amount, however small, but the cost per ton is high. The cheapest solid material is broken concrete slabs, often available from public works authorities, and these can be laid down as "crazy paving" in the same way as stone.

Unquestionably the simplest of all paths to make is the plain gravel type, which consists essentially of a layer of gravel spread between some sort of curbing. The actual gravel may be either shingle (pebbles) or stone chips; both are available in various sizes and colors. There are also a number of gravels (known as *self-setting*) containing coarse clean stones and a high proportion of finer material. This causes a well-rolled layer of this material to set much like soft concrete.

Loose gravel can be rolled to consolidate it, but it will never become truly firm. However, this has its advantages, for even paths in a very poor state can be vigorously reraked to look almost new. Loose gravel should be about 2 in. deep for chips, less for shingle.

Tool flagstone joints in concrete

MAKE A scoring tool out of a long piece of ½ or ¾-in. copper tubing by bending it in an S-shape. Use it to score a random flagstone pattern in the still-wet concrete (above left). Once you notice that the water sheen has completely disappeared, float and trowel the surface (center), and finally, use a short bristle brush to touch up all of the joints to give a finished appearance (above right).

Decorative effects cost little, add much

STONES SET into square of concrete will create a novel pattern to offset a path otherwise made of gray-colored concrete blocks or plain-looking slabs.

SIMPLE CIRCLES can be made to add life to a walkway made of cement. After the surface has been troweled smooth, use a can to make the impressions.

How to build a brick-in-sand patio

Looking for an extremely attractive patio? For good reason, the brick-in-sand patio has become very popular. It's easy to install and maintain

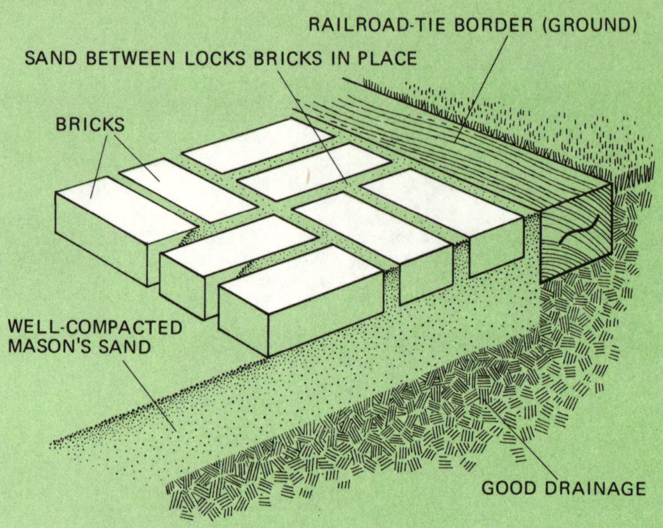

TOOLS YOU'LL NEED	TOOLS THAT MAKE THE JOB EASIER
HAND TAMPER MATTOCK OR PICK 2-FT. SPIRIT LEVEL MASON'S LINE (HEAVY) HAMMER SAW ROAD BROOM MASON'S CHISEL SHOVEL RAKE	BRICKLAYER'S HAMMER PORTABLE ELECTRIC SAW SLEDGE HAMMER

Types of borders (grounds)

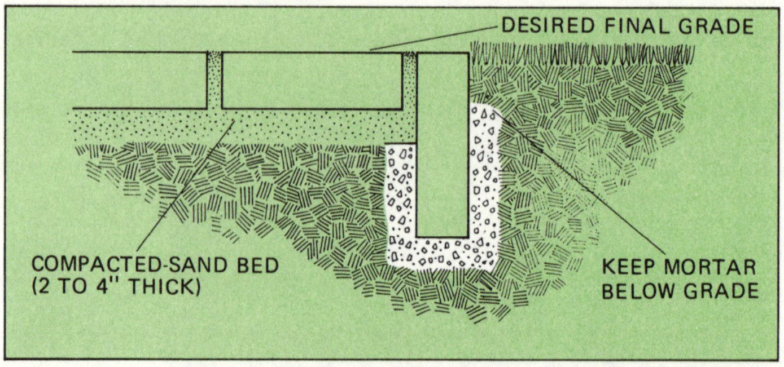

FOR A BRICK-ON-END border, bricks are set in a mortar footing placed in a trench that's at least 6 in. wide and 10 in. deep. Pour the mortar in the bottom of the trench and set the bricks in place. Tap the bricks gently to seat them in the mortar and check the row occasionally with a spirit level. Then place mortar on both sides of the bricks and tamp it firmly with a short length of 1x2 lumber.

THE DICTIONARY says that a patio is a "walled-in courtyard open to the sky." But today, perhaps, that description doesn't exactly fit the typical American patio. Walled-in? Yes in some cases, with shrubbery or privacy screens. Open to the sky? Sure, but many homeowners add a roof to gain use during rainy weather. A better, and contemporary, description is that a patio is an outdoor living room.

Of the many types of patios you can choose from, a brick-in-sand patio—no matter which border you prefer—remains attractive throughout the years. Unlike concrete, it won't crack or settle, and because water will drain through rather than run off, it can be perfectly level. That's a plus when it comes to arranging your

SEE ALSO
Barbecues . . . Benches, deck . . . Carpeting, outdoor . . . Concrete . . . Cookout bars . . . Decks . . . Firepits . . . Garden shelters . . . Grills . . . Picnic tables . . . Planters . . . Retaining walls . . . Yard lighting

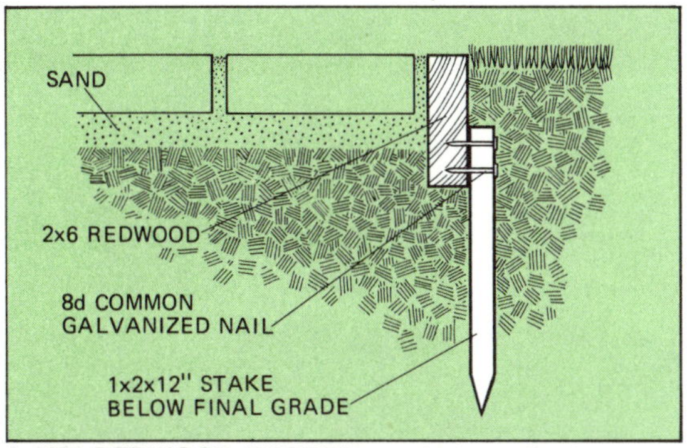

A 2X6 REDWOOD BORDER needs less digging once the grade has been determined. Set a stake, establish the grade at that point and nail the 2x6 to the stake. Level the 2x6 and nail to a second stake at the other end. If the 2x6 hangs in the air at either point, prop it with a brick to the desired level and backfill outside of the border with soil. Gentle sloping of the soil may also be required or a second border can be added.

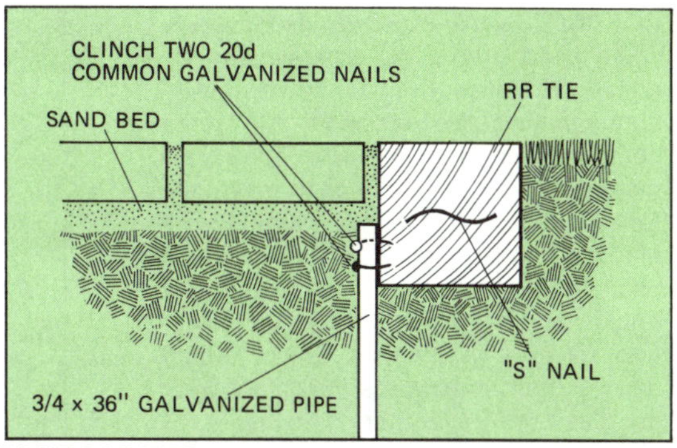

RAILROAD TIES may be set in an excavated trench to be flush with the grade and the inside area excavated for the sand bed. To prevent ties from "rocking," drive in galvanized pipes as shown and clinch a pair of 20d galvanized nails around the pipe. Ties come in 6x8 and 7x9-in. sizes, each 8 ft. long. They're heavy—approximately 210 pounds each—so make certain you have help available on the day that you set them.

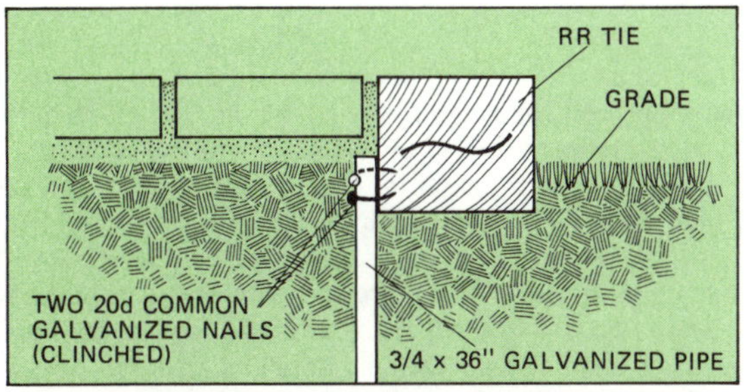

FOR A STEP EFFECT, a single course of ties can be set in a very shallow trench. If the ground slopes away sharply, the ties may be stacked at the low point two ties high. Again, a minimum of interior excavation is required, but you should dig down to assure good drainage before placing the sand bed. Pipe "stabilizers" are a must here—every 4 ft. at least.

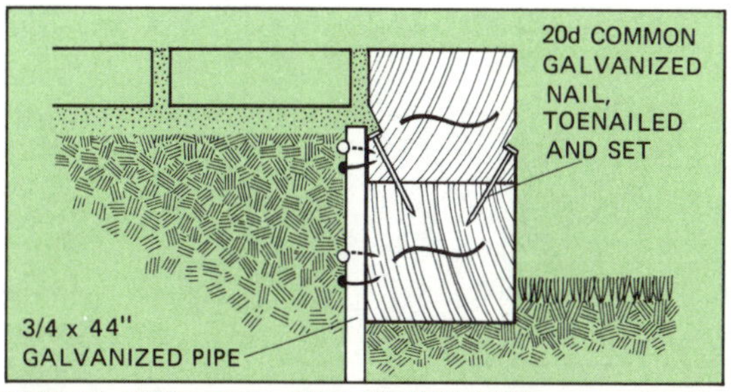

NOTICE THAT THE PIPE STABILIZER on a double course border spans both ties with nails driven into each of them. The ties should also be toenailed at the sides using the same-size nails. Since this wood is very dense, drilled pilot holes may be needed. Nailheads can be set flush with a heavy nailset, but with a rustic effect, this is of minor concern.

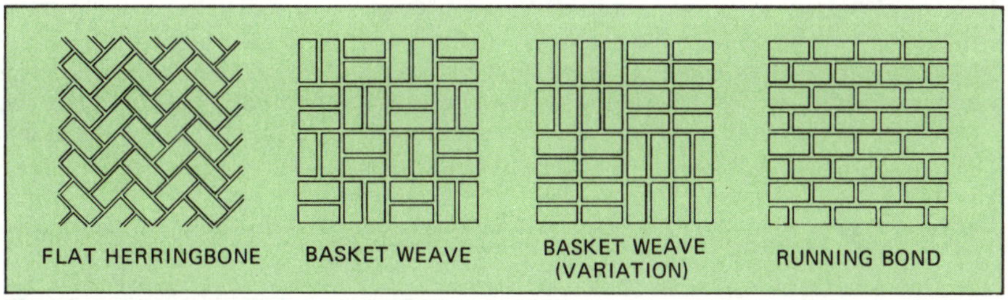

FOUR OF THE most popular brick patterns are shown in the drawing at the right. No matter which you choose, you'll have a bit of "make-up" (adjustment) to keep the proper consistency of pattern. The only way to tell is to experiment.

patio furniture. Still another advantage is that damaged bricks are easily replaced in short order.

The bricks you choose can be either new or used. But for attractiveness, the latter hold an edge because of color variation and mortar stains. New common brick costs about the same as used brick.

Your first step is to select the patio site. Because it is considered as an outdoor family room, the patio should be placed near a door. This will prove to be convenient when you are entertaining or dining outside.

Borders are a personal choice; railroad ties hold a slight edge among homeowners. You can buy ties from most large nurseries; also check your local classified directory under "Ties, Railroad." Though you can use new ties, used ones are more pleasing to the eye when placed stone-pocked side up.

IN ADDITION TO BORDER MATERIALS, you'll need bricks, mason's sand, sharpened 1x2 stakes about a foot long and 8d common nails. Use the chart at the right to compute your brick and sand. Quantities may vary slightly, but the chart is a guide for 100 sq. ft. of finished patio area. Bricks may be 3/8 to 1/2 in. apart or butted. To cut one with minimum waste, use a bricklayer's hammer or a 20-oz. hammer and mason's wide chisel. Bricks should rest on a flat solid surface. For safety, wear goggles and be sure there is no one in the path of flying chips.

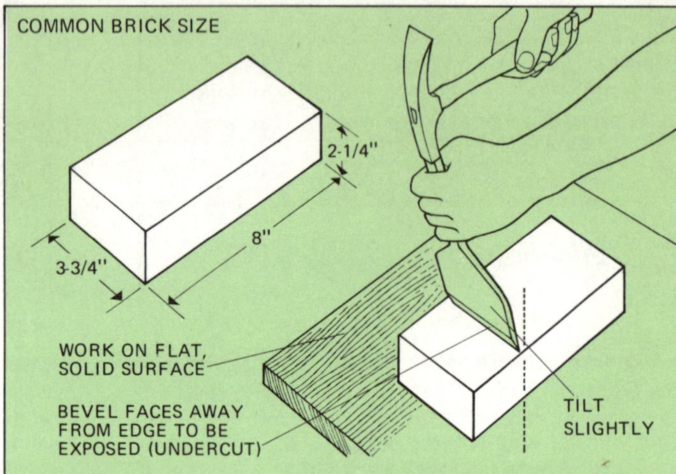

MATERIALS FOR 100 SQ. FT.	CLOSED JOINT (BRICKS BUTTED)	3/8"-1/2" JOINT
BRICKS	500	450
SAND PER 1" DEPTH	1/3 CU. YD.	1/2 CU. YD.

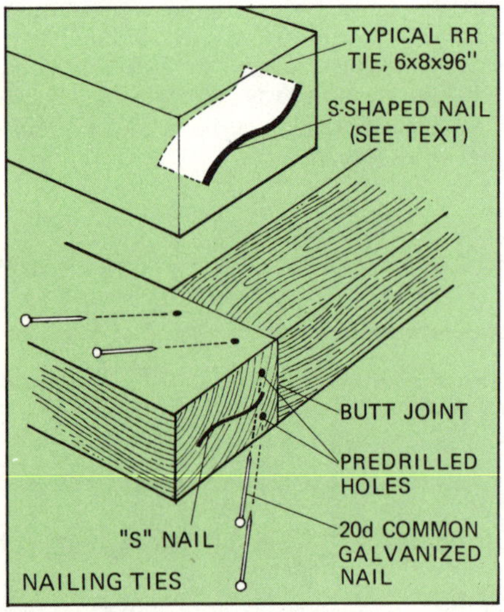

RAILROAD TIES (left) can be cut with a two-man saw or a portable circular saw equipped with a coarse-set or rip blade. Since this blade will not cut fully through the tie, mark cutting lines on all four sides; then make the four cuts, flopping the tie after each pass of the saw. When you're cutting near one end of a tie, make certain that you remove the "S" nail driven into the end grain. In most cases, you can pry it out with an awl and pliers. *Caution:* Railroad ties are creosoted clear through, so wear goggles while you are cutting them. Butt the corner joints as shown; no need to miter them. To keep the corner closed tightly, toenail the joint with hefty nails.

AFTER CHOOSING YOUR PATIO SITE, lay out the area by driving stakes at all points where the direction changes. Fasten a mason's line from stake to stake; then study the proposed patio before you put a spade into the earth. When you're satisfied with the shape and size, start excavating for the border. Level the trench as you go from stake to stake using a straight 2x4 (no more than 12 ft. long) and a spirit level to transfer marks from one stake to another. Where stakes are over 12 ft. apart, drive in an intermediate stake for grade purposes. Tip: As you dig, try to throw soil well away to avoid having to move it a second time. It is important that you check your work carefully at this stage so that you have the proper symmetry for your bricks.

ONCE YOU HAVE LEVELED the trench where the railroad ties will rest, stretch a mason's line to align ties as you place them. Use a pry bar with bricks for a fulcrum for easy lifting where you want to add soil to raise a tie. After leveling each tie, anchor it with 3-ft. lengths of galvanized pipe driven at 2-ft. intervals and attached as shown. Excavate the area with the border of the ties and fill with mason's (mortar) sand. Thorough tamping is a must.

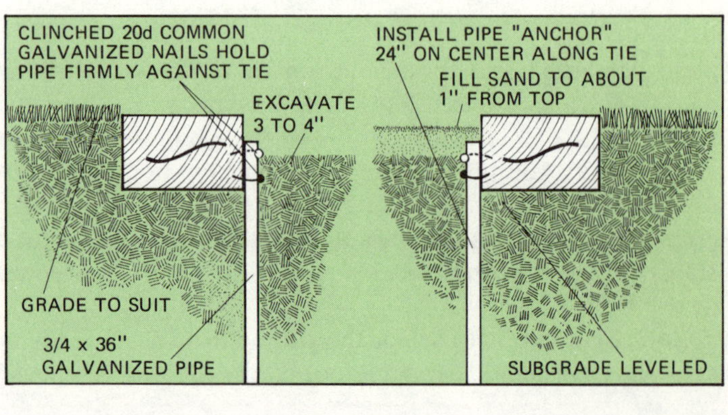

WHEN ALL BORDERS ARE IN PLACE, the interior can be excavated. You should remove all topsoil to provide good drainage (see bottom drawing). Next, fill in this interior area with mason's (stone-free) sand to the top of the borders. After hand-tamping the backfill, screed the sand fairly level using either a 2x4 with shim or a notched 2x6 as shown below. On narrow walks, borders can be used for screeding. For wider spans, you must install a temporary, intermediate ground for screeding. To screed, strike the board side to side to drag sand ahead as you go. Fill low spots from the pile you're dragging ahead of the screed. Finally, compact sand with an overnight soaking from a lawn sprinkler.

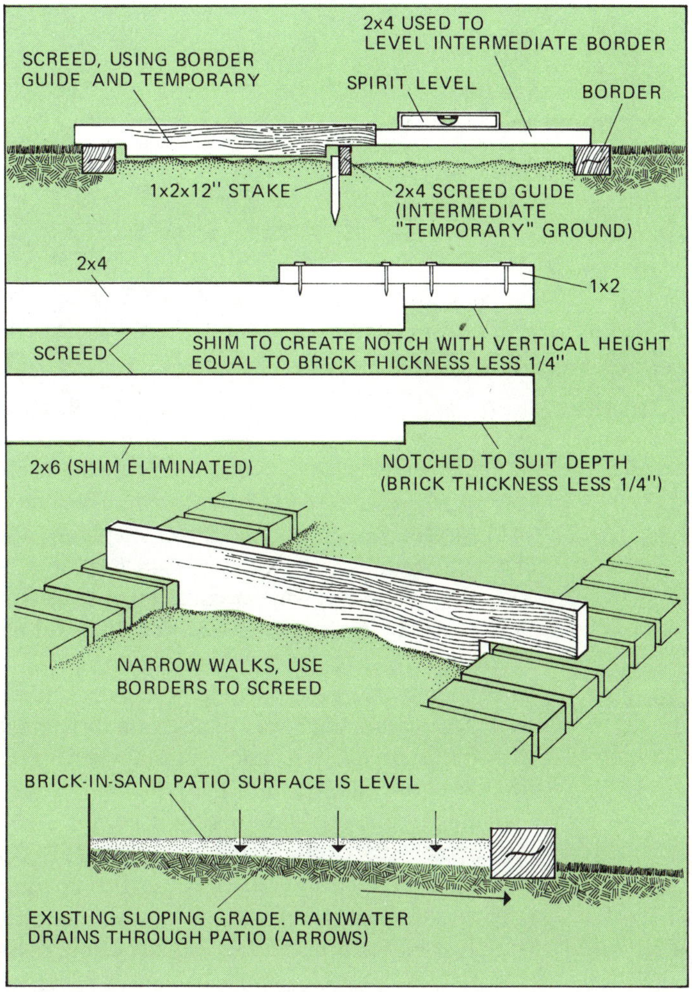

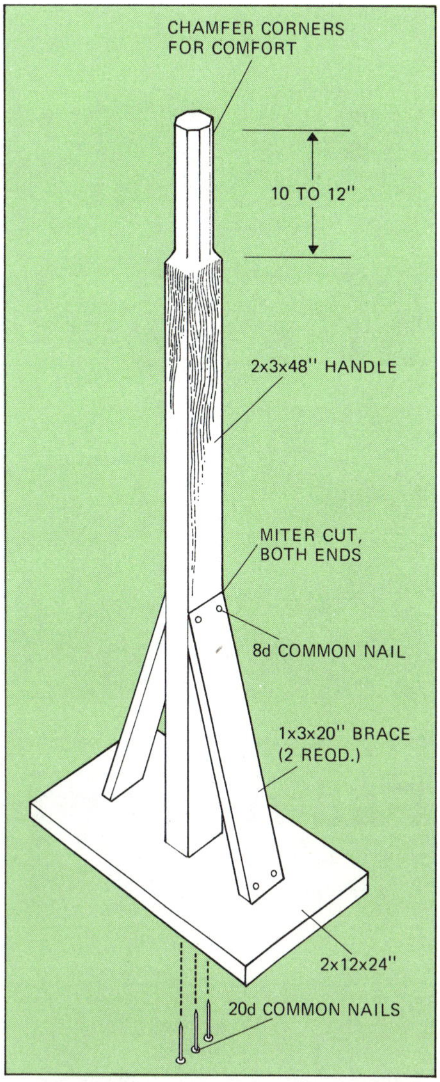

COMPACTING the sand bed is essential so you must have a tamper. While you may rent one from most tool-rental shops, you should consider making yours for permanent ownership. You'll find it a handy thing to have for landscape work.

START LAYING BRICKS in the pattern of your choice. As you set each brick, tap it firmly with your hammer handle to "set" it level. After you have covered about 10 sq. ft., shovel on some mason's sand and brush it in place with a firm street broom to lock in the bricks. Repeat this step until all bricks are laid; then give the entire patio a thorough second sanding and brooming. Soak your patio for several hours with your lawn sprinkler. When it's fully dry, sand and broom it again to fill in voids, and repeat until no voids develop in the joints when the patio is soaked. When the patio is completely dry, clean it and, for aesthetic reasons, creosote the wood border. When using creosote, follow the instructions on the can and wear a long-sleeved shirt, gloves and goggles. Save some sand and bricks until your patio is fully weathered. Further sanding may be required and, quite likely, some split bricks will need replacing. You'll have these answers within two months of the day you completed your patio. If the weather does reveal some spots that need work, you should repair them in the same manner you laid the original work. Repeat the sweeping and filling until the repair is made.

Patio on the roof

By ANNETTE I. SUKOR

SEE ALSO

Benches, deck . . . Decks . . .
Gutters and downspouts . . . Planters . . . Roofs

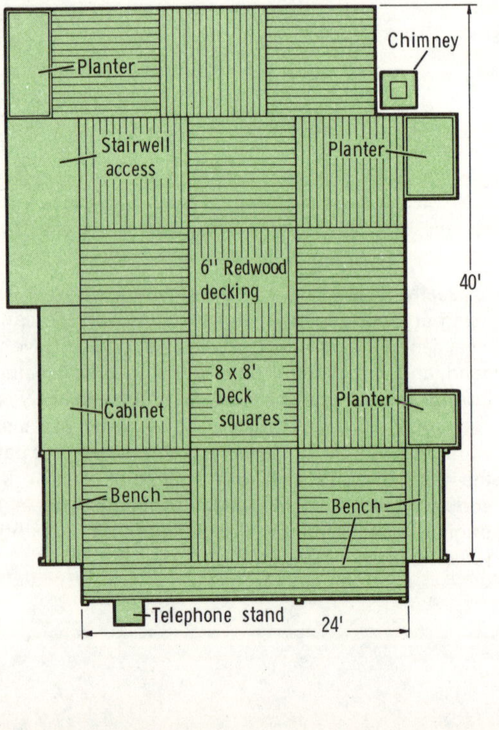

■ HERE'S ONE FAMILY'S SOLUTION to the problem of where to put the patio—it's on the roof!

Complete with a roof garden, telephone and electrical outlets, and built-in benches of redwood, the patio has truly become an outdoor living center for the Ray Hedelson family of Edina, Minn.

Originally designed as a redwood deck to be used for sunbathing, the patio soon became a high-traffic relaxation and entertainment area for the entire family.

Though your roof-line may not permit building a patio atop your home, the handsome design could be used in your back yard or possibly atop an attached garage. Redwood decking 6 in. wide is used to form 8 x 8-ft. squares, like oversize parquet flooring. Similarly, you can borrow ideas on bench and cabinet construction from the photos and drawing.

BENCHES FACE inboard to discourage children and visitors from venturing near the roof's edge.

FIBERGLASS GETS stripes and a new angular rib for extra variety in applications.

Roof your patio with glass

By W. CLYDE LAMMEY

WHAT TO DO about that patio roof? A much-to-be-desired privacy fence? A room divider? Perhaps a hideaway for the garbage can? A backdrop for a flower planting or maybe an "eyebrow" awning over an exposed door?

Fiberglass panels can be the answer to the problems posed by these sample questions.

Fiberglass is a tough, colorful material, takes the weather without crumbling, peeling or flaking away. It lets in light, but you can't see through it; it filters infrared and lets ultra violet through. It sheds water like a duck's back, comes in rainbow colors and in big sheets that cover a lot of area in an hour or two of weekend time. You can drill the stuff, nail it, saw it, even bend it one way within reasonable limits.

The popular and perhaps the most useful pattern is a corrugated panel similar to metal corrugated roofing. This and other configurations such as flat sheets in plain colors or with embedded fibers in various designs in outline are available almost anywhere you might ask. Any of these can be framed into colorful fencings, room dividers, indoor planters, door panels and, well, you'll think of other uses, indoors and out.

Handling and working fiberglass panels calls for only a few minor precautions. You don't have to baby the stuff in the handling; you just avoid throwing it about or hitting it hard with a hammer. You don't drive nails through it without first drilling a nail-size hole. You stay at least ⅜ in. away from any edge of the panel with a drilled nail hole; better ½ in. or more if there's space. And you always use the approved nails and neoprene washers when attaching the panels to any framing. Of course, you can always use screws or even wood clips or other improvised fastenings, also the ready-cut moldings in structures where there is no undue stress on the panel. Otherwise you handle and work the material much as you would plywood.

Your materials dealer will have work sheets and other data that will help you plan and install any form of fiberglass panel in any project in which the use of such panels is suitable.

continued

SEE ALSO

**Barbecues . . . Benches, deck . . .
Carpeting, outdoor . . . Cookout bars . . . Decks . . .
Grills . . . Planters . . . Privacy screens . . . Roofs**

roof your patio, continued

ALWAYS PAINT, stain (and rotproof) any lumber to be used out of doors with fiberglass paneling. The job will be neater, fiberglass free of drips and spatters.

USE A LINE, level and spacer when placing vertical supports for fiberglass paneling. Careful accuracy is important, prevents trouble later on.

Photos courtesy Filon Division, Vistron Corp.

PRECUTTING grooves in framing posts and rails makes assembly run smoother. The rails can be toenailed or, better, notched into posts.

IF YOU DO toenail the rails, set nail heads below the surface and fill with putty. Corrugated panels can span greater distances unsupported.

CORRUGATED panels in roofs, sidewalls or fences should be held in place with matching molding. It's available from the paneling dealer.

A FENCE can present a handsome appearance plus light and color to those on either side. Such a structure also makes a good windbreak.

WHEN YOU nail through into end grain, be sure to aim the nail dead center for best holding power. Note the zigzag spacing of these center supports.

ALWAYS HEED manufacturers' specs for panel lap on roofs. Always drill the nail holes. And always use approved nails with neoprene washers.

CAREFUL with that hammer! Fiberglass can stand almost anything but hammer blows; they can cause it to "craze" and eventually to break up around the nail.

SPECS usually call for weatherstripping the lap joints of roofing. It's easy to apply and prevents wind-driven rain from leaking between panels.

WHEN A patio roof joins siding, flashing is vital. Get the kind preformed to corrugations and ready to install for good waterproofing.

A SEGMENT of the out of doors becomes part of the house during the most enjoyable time of the year. You'll wonder how you got along without it.

Two great decks you can build

A well-built deck quickly becomes the center of activity in warm weather. Here's how to add value to your house by designing and building one of your own

By HARRY WICKS

RUGGED REAR DECK (above) on this home is built for years of outdoor living. Perimeter railing incorporates benches to provide ample seating for large gatherings. The front deck was kept simple; the focal point is the group of planting containers along the house wall. The steps are thick wooden slabs.

SEE ALSO

Benches, deck . . . Carpeting, outdoor . . . Decks . . . Kitchens, outdoor . . . Outdoor tables . . . Picnic tables . . . Planters . . . Railings . . .

■ IF YOU HAVE THE SPACE, a well-designed, solidly built deck or patio will add a great deal to your home. Besides improving the looks of many homes, a handsome deck can alter a family's life style during the warm-weather months. And a well-built deck increases a home's value. If it is do-it-yourself built, the investment will probably be returned in full if you decide to sell your house.

The decks shown here made handsome additions to this vacation home. If you are contemplating building a deck, take a drive around your

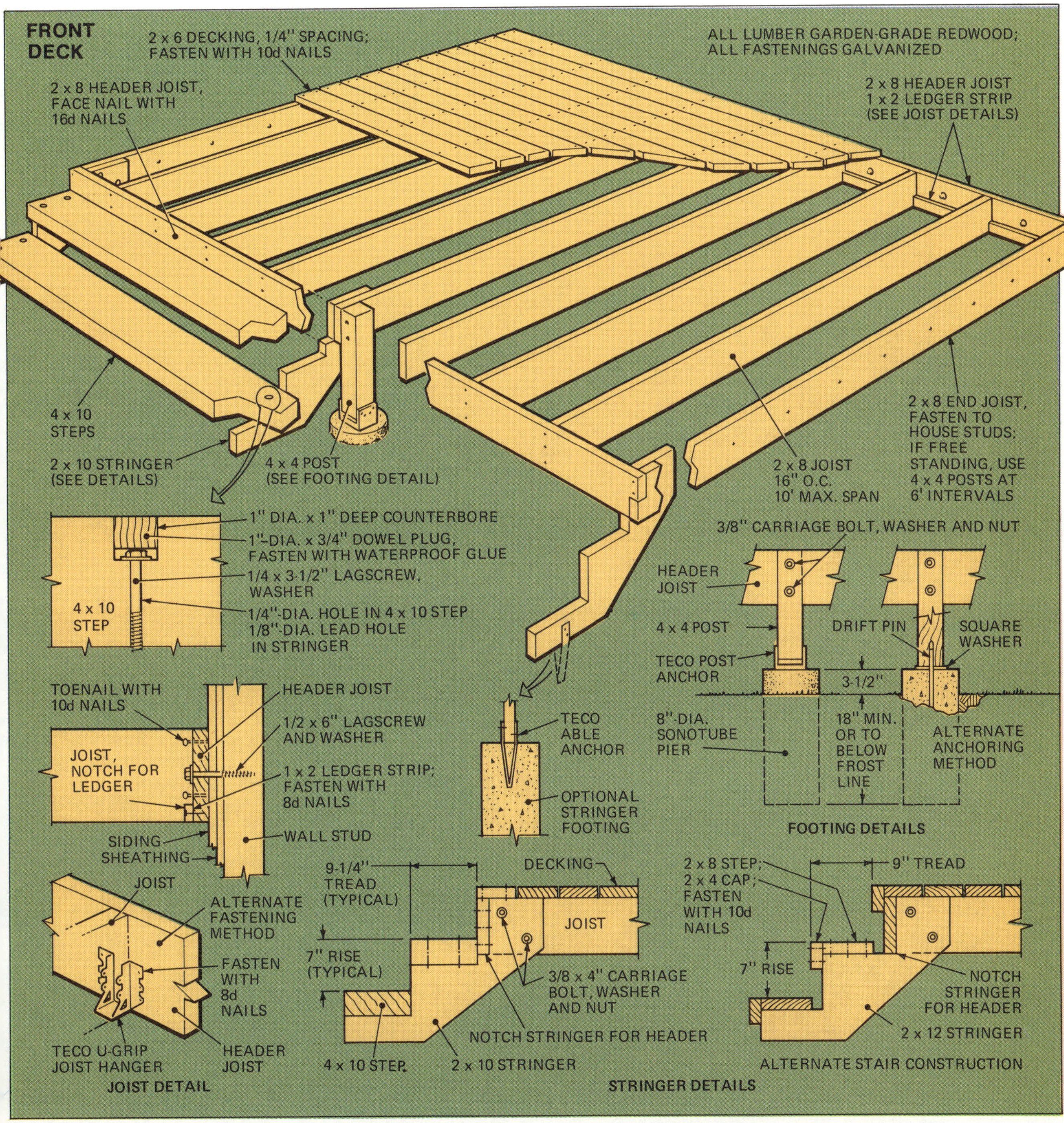

area and see what others have done. Frequently, a good deck design is nothing more than a combination of ideas taken from other decks and adapted to your special needs. Use the plans presented here as the starting point for your own design.

For longevity, as well as appearance, be a little choosy about the wood that will make up your patio. You should settle for nothing less than Wolmanized (pressure-treated) or redwood lumber.

The first is pressure treated to assure many years of resistance to rot and decay, while redwood has a natural resistance to insect infestation. The latter is frequently chosen for use on decks because of its beauty. When treated peri-

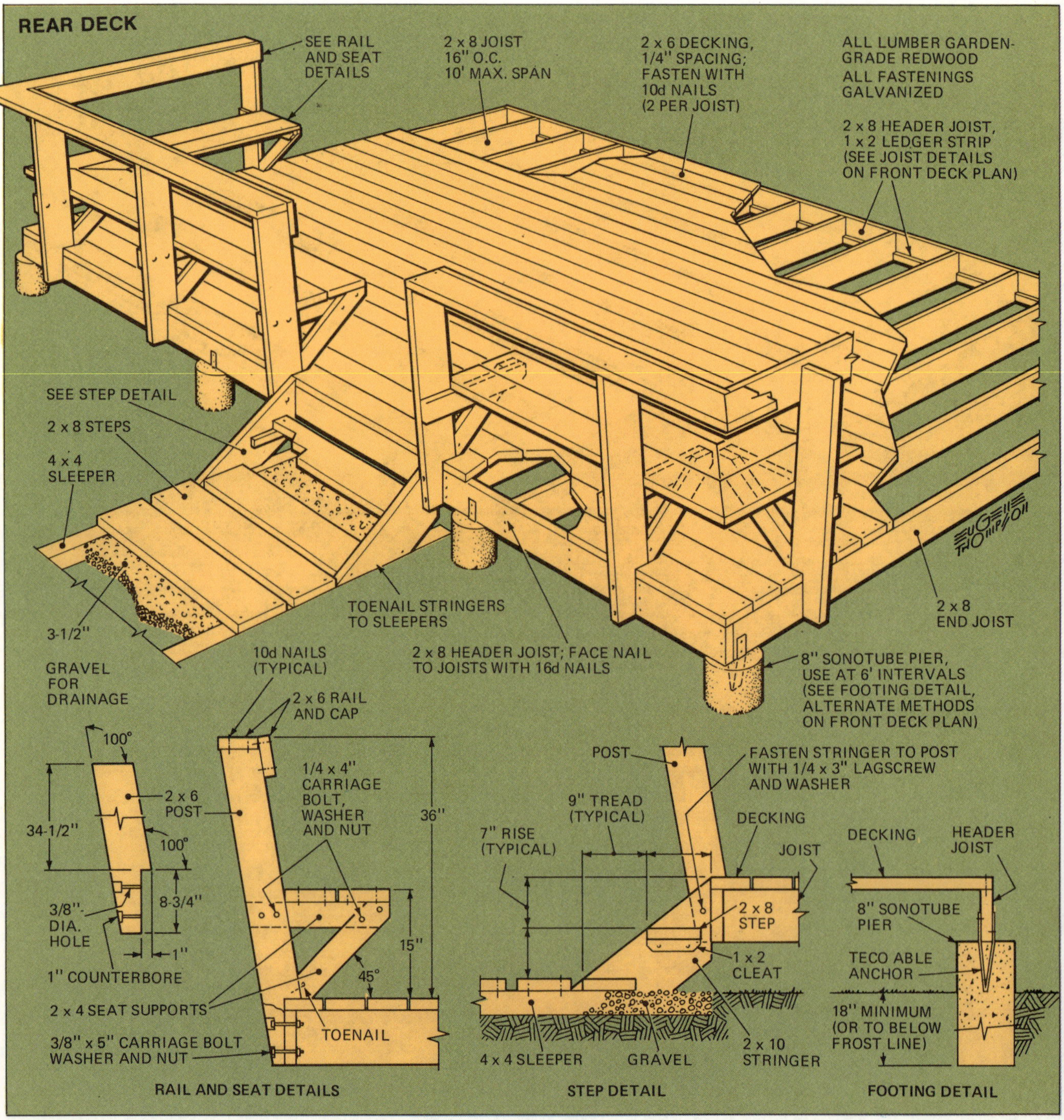

odically with the recommended clear preservative, redwood ages to a handsome silver gray patina.

Both types of wood (even the pressure treated, with its slight greenish cast) can be stained to suit the decor you plan for your yard. A sensible lumber choice might be to use Wolmanized material for the understructure—piers, joists, etc.—and redwood for deck and railings.

planning your deck or patio

It's easiest if you start by sketching your planned deck on ½-in.-scaled graph paper. Though the temptation may be great to make the deck extra large, keep in mind that as its size increases so does the cost to build.

When you are satisfied with your floor plan sketch, move out to the actual job site. Carry along a number of 1x3 wooden stakes, a ball of mason's line, a tape measure and a hand sledge. Using the tape, lay out the perimeter of the deck, using the stakes and mason's line. Check corners for square, using the 6, 8 and 10-ft. method (when one leg of a corner is 6 ft. and the second is 8 ft., the corner is perfectly square when the hypotenuse equals 10 ft.).

When the deck has been staked out, step back and take a long, hard look. If you're dissatisfied with the shape, size or appearance, rearrange the lines until you find a deck shape that seems to be compatible with both house and yard.

Rework your sketch, if necessary, and take it to your local building department to learn if a permit will be required. Local requirements for such decks vary. There may be restrictions on the location of the deck (away from lot lines), the materials to be used, and how the deck is fastened to existing structures. In some cases you will want to exceed local codes. For example, concrete piers are not always required to meet the law, but are a must if your deck is to be well-anchored and last for years.

deck-building hints and tips

In general, building a deck is a chore well within the skills of the average do-it-yourselfer. But there are exceptions: If yours will be on steeply pitched ground, or well up in the air, you may be well-advised to call in a qualified professional contractor for some assistance in pouring the footings and the like. Hillside construction is tricky, at best.

You can build a deck with mostly hand tools—hammer, saw, square, brace and bit, level, and shovels, but a couple of the right power tools will make the job go faster and save your back. A portable drill and circular saw will save many arm-wearying hours when building a deck.

Since dimensional lumber is the best bet when building a deck, we designed ours to make use of such readily available stock. With the exception of the 4x10 steps on the front deck, all materials are carried by well-stocked lumberyards and home centers. To save frustration and hunting for the 4x10s (such stock may be hard to come by in some areas), we show an alternate step construction that gives the same slab appearance, except that you make the treads using 2x4s and 2x8s. (See detail in lower right-hand corner of drawing on page 2099).

There are several ways of fastening a deck to a house. We decided to use the header joist-and-joist-hanger method. The header joist is well secured to the house with hefty lagscrews through siding and into wall studs. (*Note:* Lagscrews *must* be anchored in studs, or the header joist may separate from house wall.) On the model house we used metal (Teco) hangers to secure joists to header joists; but you can avoid buying the connectors by fastening ledger strips to header joists as shown in the drawing. In this case, every joist should be carefully notched to assure its seating squarely on the ledger strip.

use rustproof hardware

You do not need a great deal of hardware to build either deck. So spend a couple of more bucks and buy only galvanized hardware. It is worth the extra cost to avoid the rust stains that will appear if you use ordinary steel hardware and expose it to the weather. And, do take time to bore pilot holes for nails when fastening near the end of a board; this will prevent splits in your expensive lumber.

about the deck floor

The deck floor is the most visible part of your deck. Take your time when installing the floor to make certain it will have a craftsman-like appearance. Our pattern is a simple one—the same-width deck boards are laid parallel with ends staggered over various joists. You may opt for a herringbone design, or experiment with alternate widths to come up with a look of your own choosing. No matter which pattern you elect to use on your deck, make it a point to lay each board with its bark side up.

■ OUTDOOR LIVING has become a way of life for the typical American family. Moderate seasons and temperate climates especially stimulate the desire for an "outdoor family room." The cost to build a deck is substantially lower than that of a same-size addition and, considering the use that the entire family will get from the new space. it's money well spent.

We've rounded up three particularly handsome decks—including the double-tiered variety for hilly sites (facing page) designed by Saint Paul, Minnesota, landscape architect Marion Fry. In addition, you'll find all the basics you need to

Deck and patio ideas you can borrow

DECKS ARE OFTEN the only means for outdoor living on steep building plots (top photo) and are popular for homes on level ground as well. The older home shown in the snapshot at the left was redesigned by architect Russell Zenk of Minneapolis. The house-coordinated deck plays an important role; it provides an adult entertainment center at night and a play area for the children by day.

SEE ALSO

Barbecues . . . Benches, deck . . . Cabanas . . . Cookout bars . . . Decks . . . Firepits . . . Garden shelters . . . Gazebos . . . Lumber . . . Picnic tables . . . Planters . . . Stairs . . . Yard lighting

THIS HUGE double-tiered deck extends along the entire length of the house at the rear.

TYPICAL PATIO CONSTRUCTION

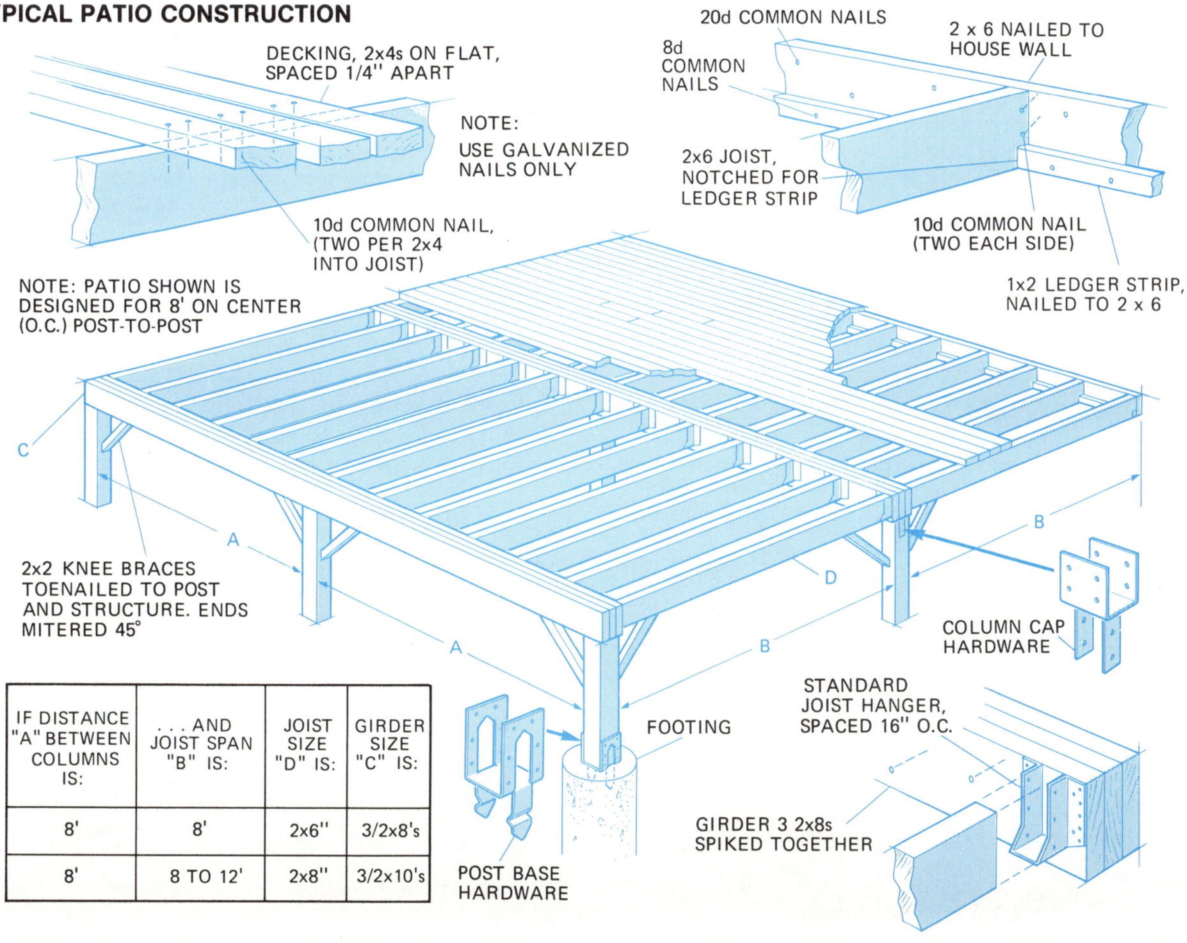

IF DISTANCE "A" BETWEEN COLUMNS IS:	. . . AND JOIST SPAN "B" IS:	JOIST SIZE "D" IS:	GIRDER SIZE "C" IS:
8'	8'	2x6"	3/2x8's
8'	8 TO 12'	2x8"	3/2x10's

HOW TO LAY OUT STAIRS

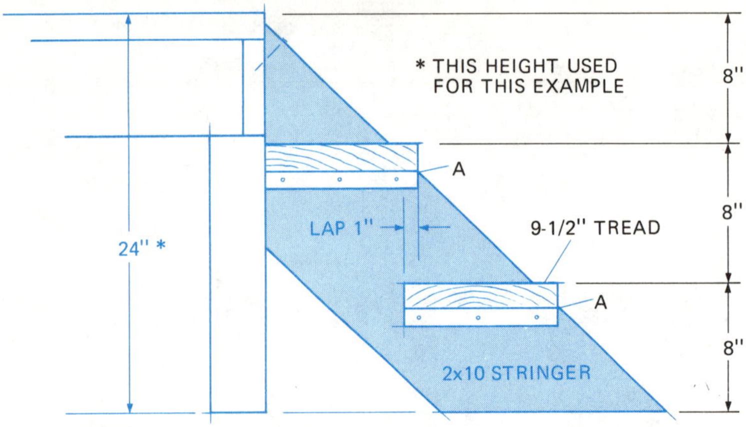

STAIR DESIGN is tricky, but not beyond a do-it-yourselfer. The important point is that the riser height should never exceed 8½ in.—ideally, riser times tread (width) should equal 72. Thus, with an 8-in. rise, the tread should be 9 in. For best results, lay out the stairs actual-size on plywood or a clean garage floor. Measure the height from the deck to the ground and try a riser height of 8 in. A deck height of 24 in. divided by 8 equals three spaces. Since ground and deck are not counted, that means two treads will be required to make the 24-in. rise above.

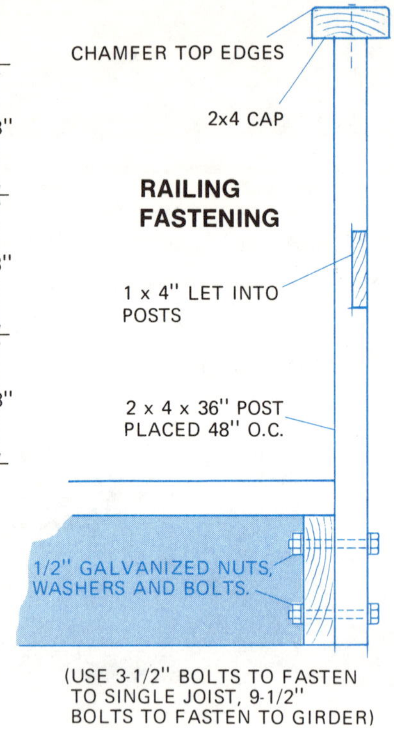

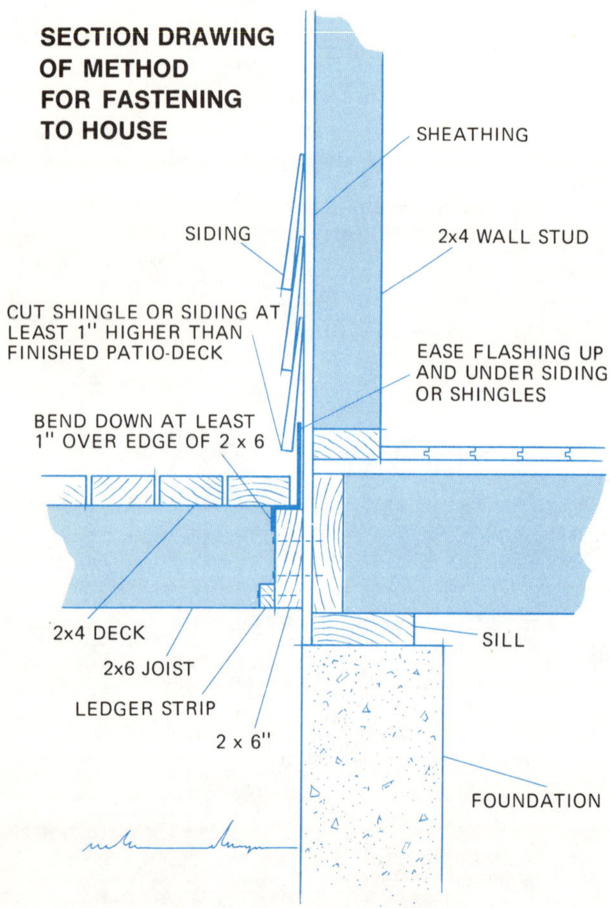

* NOTE: FINISHED PATIO-DECK SHOULD BE LOWER THAN INTERIOR FLOOR

know for good deck construction shown in the drawings on these pages. Even if you decide to have a contractor build your deck, the information given in the drawings will let you determine whether the job is being done properly.

The type of materials you use is important. Usual decking requirements are wood that offers a high decay resistance, nonsplintering, good stiffness (for strength), wear resistance and minimal chance of warping. Woods with heartwood that combine these characteristics—from a good to a high degree—include: southern pine, cedar, redwood and cypress.

Open decking, as shown in the sketches, is usually nominal 2x4s spaced ¼ in. apart over joists. Here, because rainwater will run through the deck, good drainage below—away from the house—is a must. For a solid deck, which will be covered by outdoor carpet, use only exterior-grade plywood over the joists. Keep in mind that a solid deck must be pitched to provide positive water runoff. Flashing, installed as shown, is imperative.

Preservation treatment of wood decking is also important in extending the life of the deck. So, if possible, use wood that has been pressure-treated and, for longevity, treat your decks annually with preservative.

Local building codes vary on requirements for decks of this type.

Buzzing faucet

There's a peculiar buzzing sound when the cold-water faucet of my bathroom is opened. When it's opened wide the sound sometimes stops, but not always. It's not a hammering, but rather a high-pitched buzz. I have an expansion chamber on the plumbing. What causes this and how can I silence it?—C.T., Ill.

Among the more likely causes are a loose washer or worn threads on the valve stem. Sometimes you can cure this by repacking. Shut off the water at the meter, unscrew the faucet handle and packing nut directly underneath it. Replace the washer and, if the packing (washer or string-type) is worn, torn or otherwise damaged, replace it. This simple repair often cures a noisy faucet. If not, it's usually best to replace the faucet.

If you have an unusually long run of pipe in the basement to the faucet, the pipe may vibrate slightly to cause the noise. Such vibration can often be stopped by wrapping cardboard around the pipe at each hanger.

Repairing sewing cabinet

I have what used to be called a Martha Washington sewing cabinet, with half-octagonal end storage pockets. Several pieces of veneer have come off the flats. How can I glue them back? There seems no way to apply clamps.—George Tilman, Madison, Wis.

You won't need clamps if you use contact cement. Scrape off all old glue to the bare wood on the areas originally joined, on both the veneer and the panel to which it is fitted. Then coat both surfaces uniformly with the cement, spreading it to the edges, but be careful not to get any on finished surfaces it can damage. Allow it to dry as package instructions require, then locate veneer exactly as it was. Press the veneer into full contact and go over it with a roller or wood block and hammer to assure good adhesion to the surface. By the way, there are now nonflammable contact cements on the market; you might look for one of these to use.

Bright spot in a bad spot

I spilled a small quantity of gloss varnish on an asphalt-tile floor. Although I wiped it up as quickly as possible, there's a glossy area remaining. How can I remove it?—Mrs. G.A. Whiteside, St. Paul, Minn.

It's too late, I'm afraid. On some floor tiles, you can use paint remover, but *not on asphalt.* You might as well wax the entire floor, using wax suited to this composition tile.

Digs and gouges

I have tile-faced hardboard wall paneling in a powder room. Two of the "tiles" have been accidentally damaged. The digs, or gouges, don't go all the way through, but both tiles must be replaced. Can I do this, or must I install a new tileboard?—F.D., Ga.

If, as you say, the board has not been broken, it may be possible to make a repair by spackling, over which a white or matching enamel can be applied after the spackle is dry and has been lightly sanded flush with the surrounding surface. Carefully remove all loose material from the damaged areas, making sure you remove all loose chips or pieces of the original finish. It may be a good idea to drill several small holes clear through the board within the depression so that some of the spackle will be forced through to provide an anchor.

Then press spackle into the depression with a wide putty knife, taking care to strike the surface of the patch smooth and flush with the surrounding surface. Use sufficient pressure on the putty knife to make sure the spackle is forced into all irregularities. Then allow the patch to dry thoroughly, mask around the edges of the affected tile with painter's masking tape and finish with a semigloss enamel, coating the whole tile and taking care to avoid any brush marks. A second coat may be required to obtain a good, smooth finish. Strip off the masking before the enamel is entirely dry. Treat the other affected tile in the same manner.

Burn out a tree stump

A year ago an elm tree was cut down in my yard and the stump is still there. I'd like to get rid of it, but how? It was cut close to ground level and seems quite dry and dead. I once tried to burn it out, but had little success. What else can I do?—E.L., Iowa.

With a little extra doing it can be burned out, or at least reduced sufficiently below ground level to permit covering with new topsoil and grass. One way that's quite effective is to bore a random pattern of 1-in.-dia. holes 6 to 10 in. deep in the wood. Then fill the holes with fuel oil (the grade used in oil-burning furnaces). Cover the stump to keep it from getting rain-soaked. In three weeks to a month, the oil will have been absorbed into the wood. Then build up a good, hot fire on top of the stump, if possible, using hardwood as fuel. Keep the fire going until the stump is fully aflame. Thereafter it will usually burn out without adding more fuel.

Four patio projects from Scandinavia

THE FOUR SIMPLE PROJECTS shown on these pages will add a little more charm to your back-yard living.

trellis planter

To build the planter, cut all parts to the dimensions provided in materials list. Then carefully lay out, centerpunch and bore dowel holes in trellis top and bottom (C).

Cut notches for the posts in the planter bottom (H) and you are ready for assembly. If you intend to stain or paint your planter, do it now.

Start assembling by nailing cleats to sides (D) and ends (E) as required. Then nail the sides and ends to the posts (A and B). Fit in the bottom (H) and make certain you bore at least eight evenly spaced drain holes.

Next, nail the trellis bottom pieces (C) to the inside of the box as shown in the plans. Insert the dowels in the predrilled holes. Finally, align tops of dowels with holes in the trellis top (C), insert the dowels, and then nail the last C piece into place.

DOWEL WALL (left) makes this planter ideal for climbing vegetables or vines and serves as a privacy screen. Standing planter (above) is large enough for holding your potted favorites. Bottle rack (above in bench) keeps beverages handy.

SEE ALSO

Benches, deck . . . Cookout bars . . . Decks . . . Gazebos . . . Grills . . . Insect traps . . . Kitchens, outdoor . . . Picnic tables . . . Planters . . . Privacy screens . . . Screened summer rooms

hanging cage planter

To build the hanging planter, rip ¾-in.-wide strips from nominal 1-in. stock and cut to lengths given in the materials list for A and B. Then cut the side and bottom dowels (C and D).

Bore holes for leather thongs in top of uprights A as shown. Start by gluing dowels into two pairs of uprights A to form two panels with 10 side dowels left over. Then glue the bottom dowels between pieces B.

When the glue is dry on the three panels, apply glue to the remaining dowels and assemble the three panels by nailing uprights A to bottom pieces.

Attach the leather thongs.

large capacity floor planter

Start by cutting all members to size. Then bore the drain holes in the bottom piece (D). Fasten the cleats (C) first to four of the sideboards (B).

AN EASY-TO-MAKE, airy and suspended planter is created from ¾-in. strips of wood and dowels.

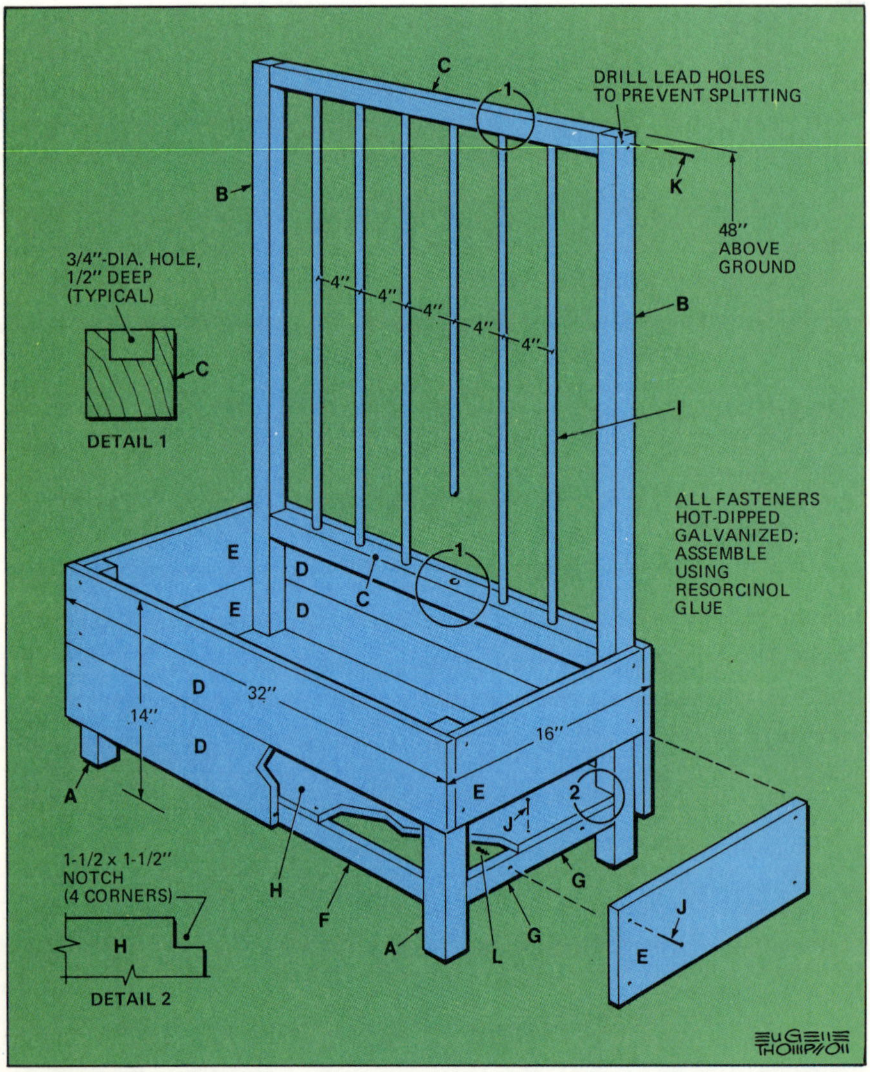

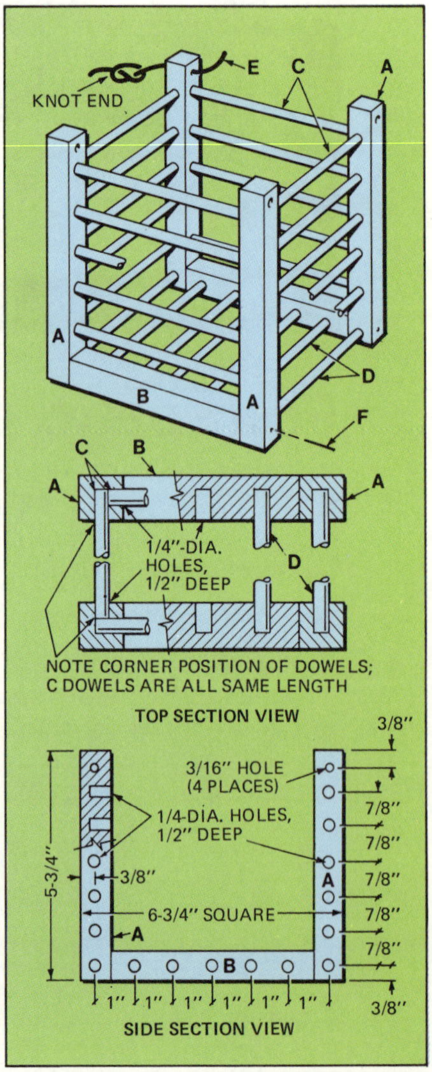

Then nail and glue the side boards to the legs (A).

Join the four sides together with screws. Counterbore and plug for a finished appearance. Finally, drop in the bottom of the stand (D) and use finishing nails through the sides to secure it firmly.

patio wine rack

This rack will hold six bottles and prevent trips in and out of the house once your party gets started.

After all the members have been cut and holes bored, apply a small amount of glue to each hole and assemble. Make certain that you allow the glue to dry.

To prevent the rack from pulling apart under stress, drill lead holes at each joint and pin the dowels in place with ½-in. brads.

MATERIALS LIST—TRELLIS PLANTER

Key	No.	Size and description (use)
A	2	1½ × 1½ × 14″ redwood (front leg)
B	2	1½ × 1½ × 48″ redwood (rear leg)
C	2	1½ × 1½ × 27½″ redwood (crosspiece)
D	4	¾ × 5½ × 32″ redwood (front and back)
E	4	¾ × 5½ × 14½″ redwood (sides)
F	2	¾ × 1½ × 27½″ redwood (front and back cleats)
G	2	¾ × 1½ × 11½″ redwood (side cleat)
H	1	½ × 14½ × 30½″ exterior plywood (bottom)
I	6	¾″-dia. × 34″ dowels
J		6d casing nails (as reqd.)
K		10d casing nails (as reqd.)
L		No. 10 × 1¼″ fh screws (as reqd.)

MATERIALS LIST—HANGING PLANTER

Key	No.	Size and description (use)
A	4	¾ × ¾ × 5¾″ pine or redwood (corner posts)
B	2	¾ × ¾ × 5¼″ pine or redwood (bottom rails)
C	20	¼″-dia. × 6″ dowels (side)
D	7	¼″-dia. × 6¼″ dowels (bottom)
E	2	36″ long, or to suit, leather thongs (to hang planter)
F		6d casing nails (as reqd.)

Misc.: Resorcinol glue.

MATERIALS LIST—STANDING PLANTER

Key	No.	Size and description (use)
A	8	¾ × 3½ × 24″ redwood (leg)
B	12	¾ × 3½ × 21¾″ redwood (side)
C	4	¾ × 1½ × 20¼″ redwood (cleats)
D	1	½ × 21 × 21″ exterior plywood (bottom)
E	8	No. 10 × 2″ fh screws
F	12	No. 10 × 1¼″ fh screws
G		10d casing nails (as reqd.)
H		6d casing nails (as reqd.)

Misc.: Resorcinol glue.

MATERIALS LIST—WINE RACK

Key	No.	Size and description (use)
A	8	⅜″-dia. × 8¼″ dowels (crosspiece)
B	6	⅜″-dia. × 12¼″ dowels (uprights)
C	12	¾ × ¾ × 8¾″ pine (rails)

Misc.: Resorcinol glue.

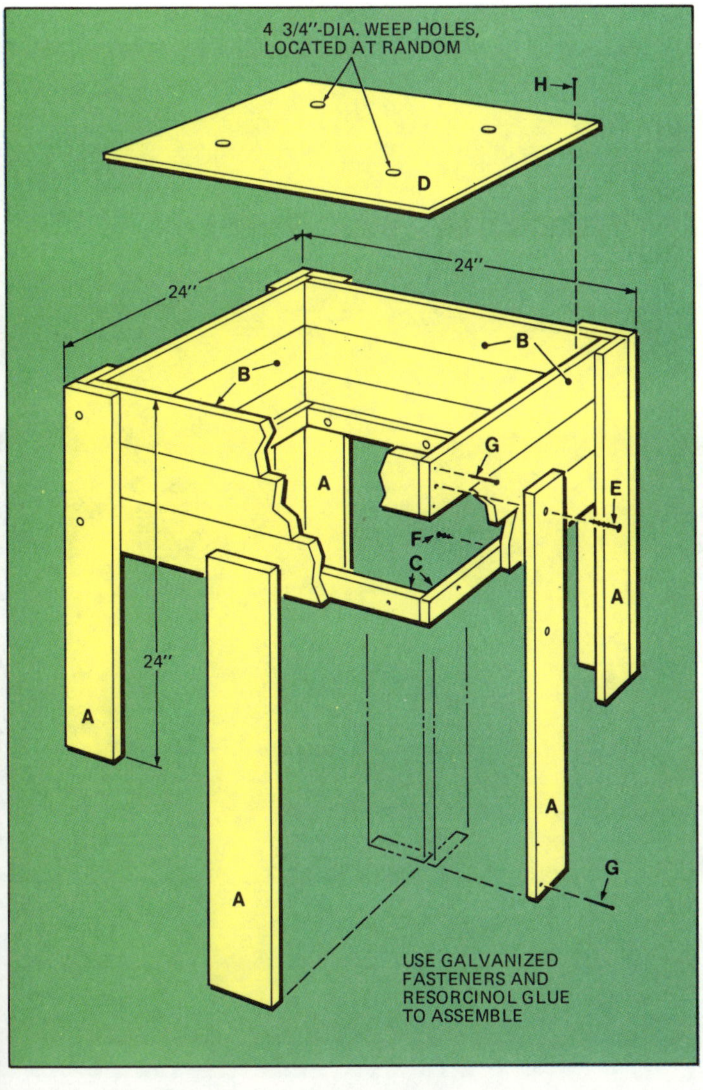

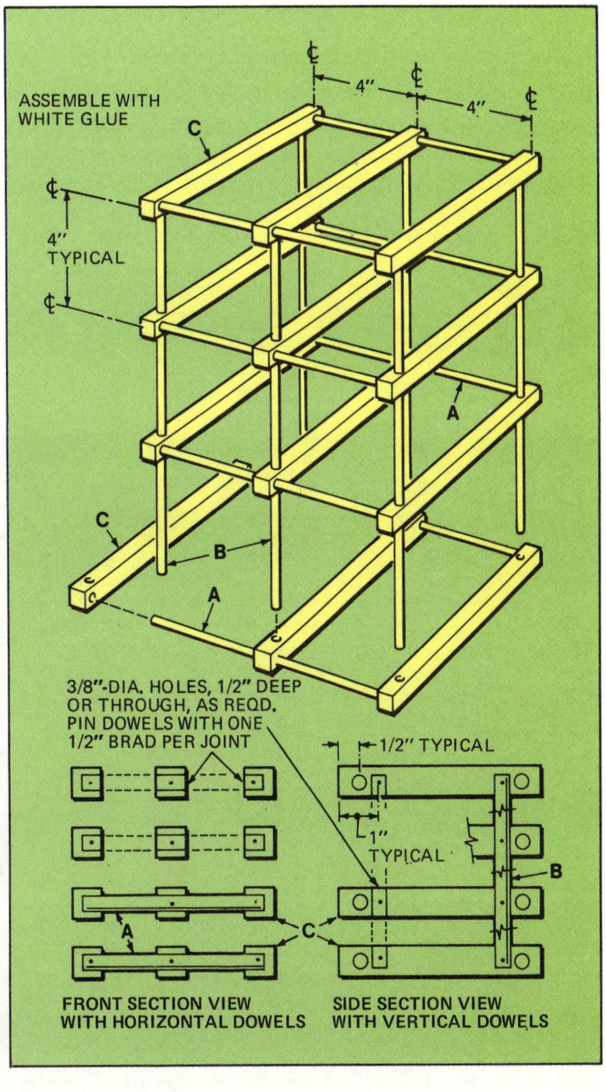

Patio partners you can make

Striking and easy to build, these structures add a special touch to your yard. All are weekend projects

By HARRY WICKS

■ UPGRADING YOUR DECK, patio or back yard is a sure way to guarantee more enjoyable use of that space. To help provide ideas you can use, we've rounded up nine attractive projects that dress up any outdoor area.

The usual woods used for outdoor construction include redwood, Douglas fir, ponderosa pine and Idaho white pine. Each has a color of its

Planter

QUICKLY BUILT, this planter's bottom and sides can be of 1½-in.-thick (actual) tongue-and-groove construction lumber such as Douglas fir or ponderosa pine. Join parts as shown using 8 and 16d galvanized nails. Finish the planter with either latex or oil-based stain.

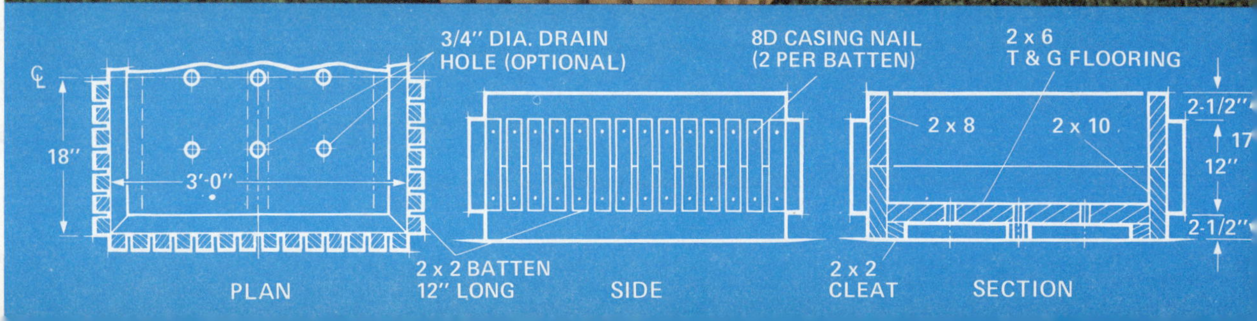

Storage gazebo

THE KEY to construction of this gazebo is the simplicity of the roof design—the joining of two metal hoods or awnings. Since the metal roof will dictate the gazebo's overall dimensions, have it fabricated at your local sheet-metal dealer and determine your building's size from it.

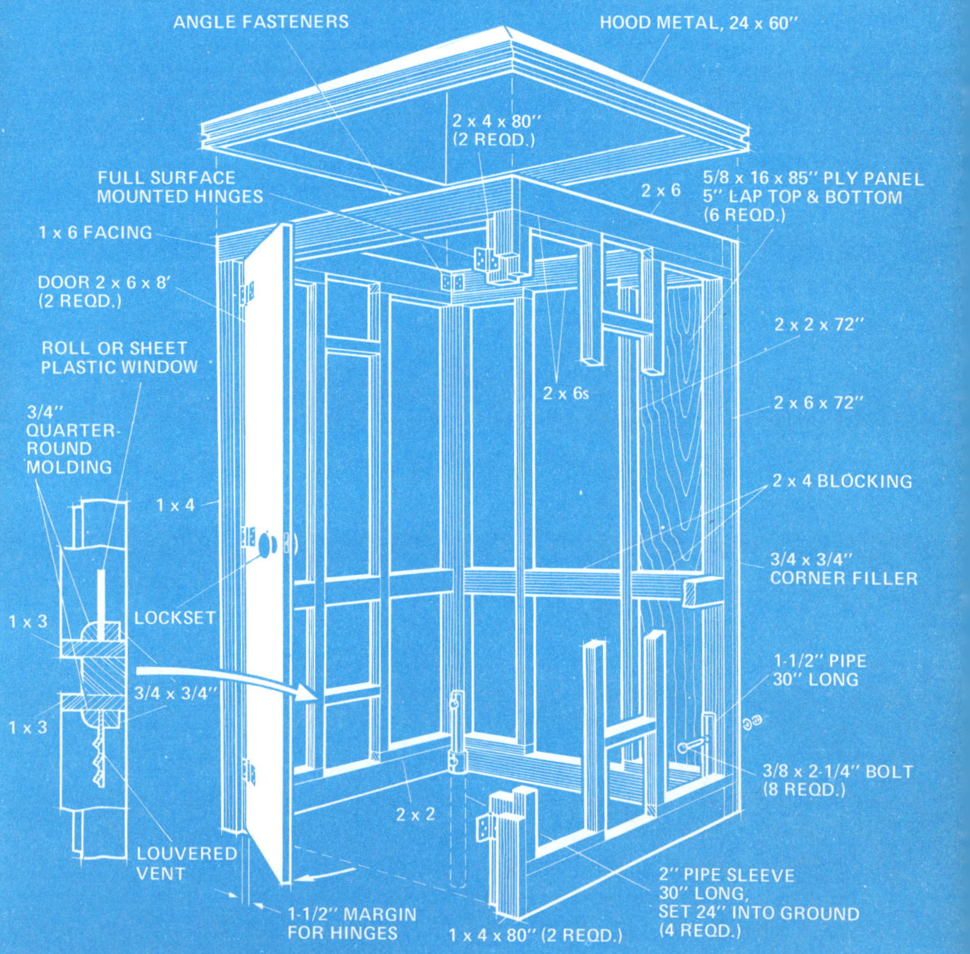

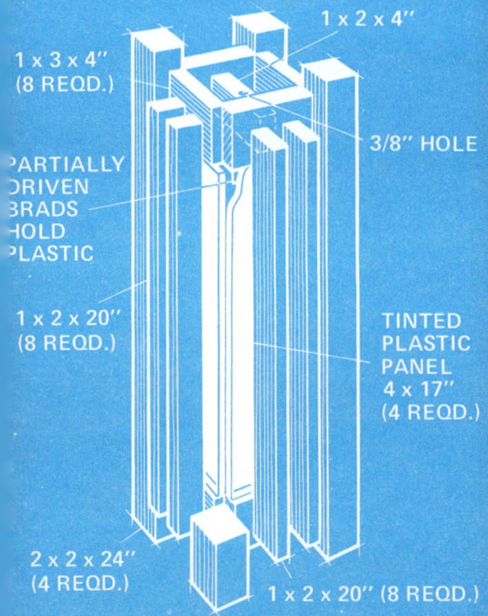

Electrical Materials: swag kit with chain; light socket; coupling, 1/8 in. dia.; threaded tube or pipe, 1/8 in. dia.

Hanging lamp

THIS contemporary lamp of redwood adds a bright note to a patio or entry. Use clear window glass or, for a softer light, frosted glass or opaque sheet plastic.

SEE ALSO

Barbecues . . . Benches, deck . . . Decks . . . Gazebos . . . Picnic tables . . . Planters . . . Post lamps . . . Privacy screens . . .

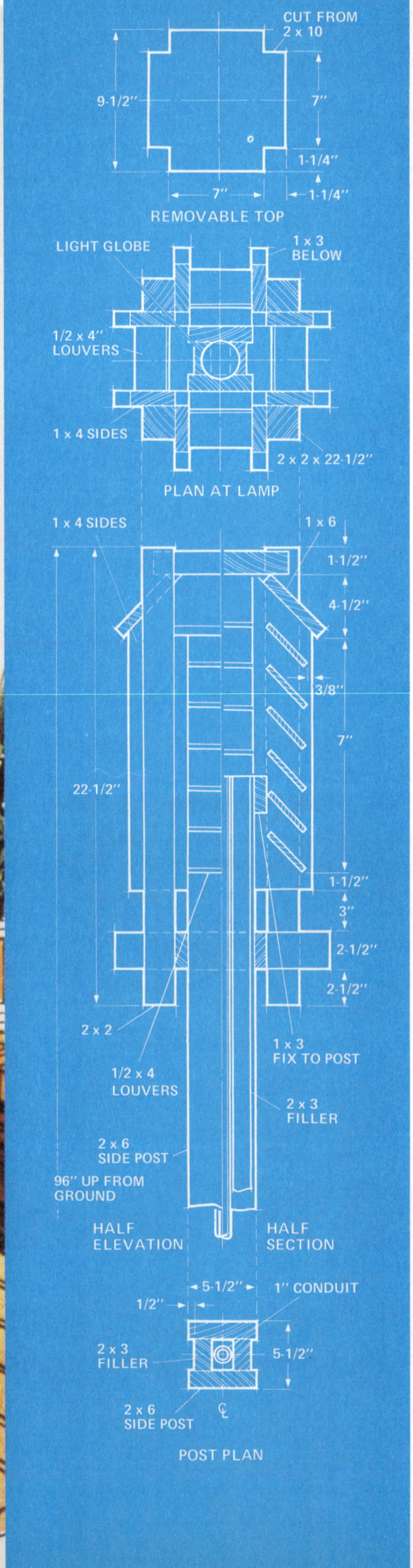

View divider

THE CLEAN LINES of this redwood fence make it adaptable to almost any back yard. The cutouts in the privacy screen serve a dual function—they let breezes pass and provide a place to display potted plants.

Post lamp

GOOD LIGHTING is essential for any deck. If the lamp is entirely of wood, it's sure to go with any outdoor decor. Simply stain the wood to blend with the patio.

Grille fence

THE GEOMETRIC pattern created by the latticework is pleasing to look at but doesn't block airflow.

Redwood planter

SIMPLICITY is the design key here. One pair of box sides is framed with heavy 1½-in.-thick stiles and rails, while the second pair of sides is without decoration.

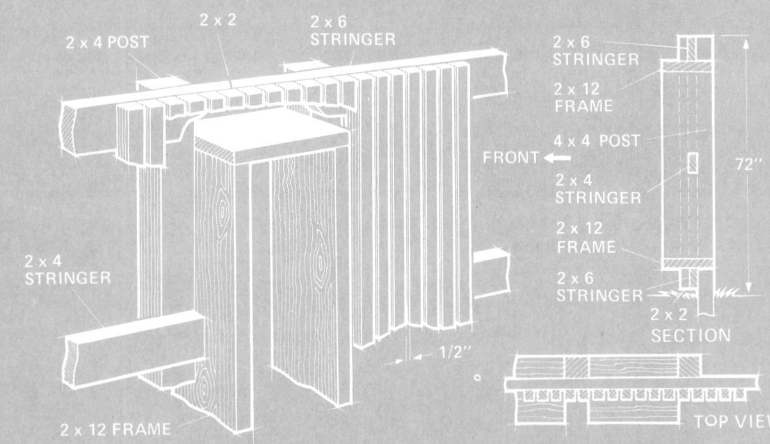

2 x 2
2 x 4 POST
2 x 6
STRINGER
2 x 6
STRINGER
2 x 12
FRAME
4 x 4 POST
FRONT
2 x 4
STRINGER
72"
2 x 12
FRAME
2 x 4
STRINGER
2 x 6
STRINGER
2 x 2
SECTION
1/2"
TOP VIEW
2 x 12 FRAME

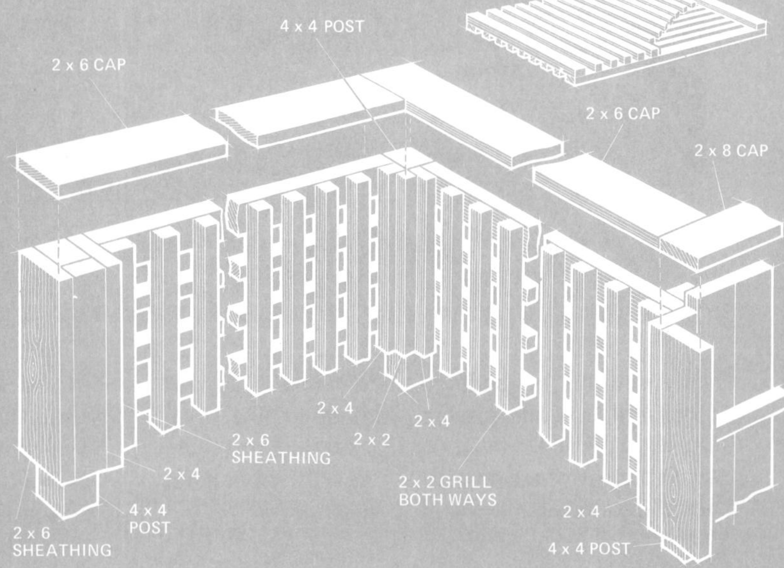

4 x 4 POST
2 x 6 CAP
2 x 6 CAP
2 x 8 CAP
2 x 4
2 x 4
2 x 6
SHEATHING
2 x 2
2 x 4
2 x 2 GRILL
BOTH WAYS
4 x 4
POST
2 x 6
SHEATHING
2 x 4
4 x 4 POST

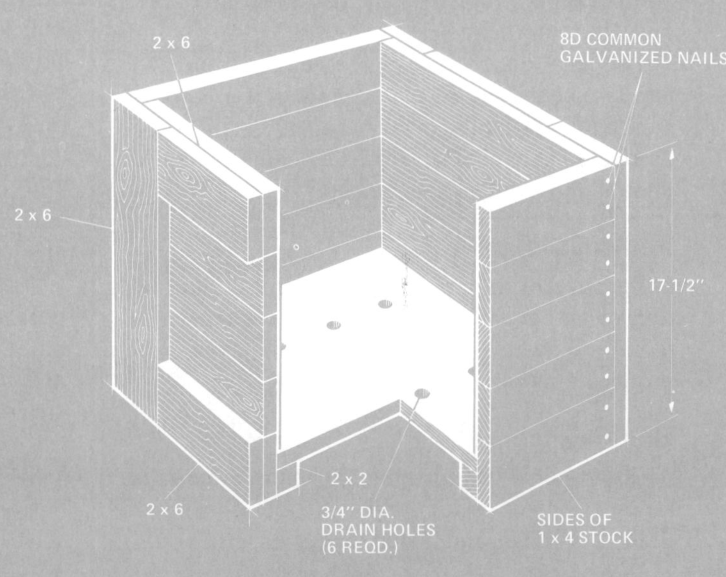

2 x 6
8D COMMON
GALVANIZED NAILS
2 x 6
17-1/2"
2 x 2
2 x 6
3/4" DIA.
DRAIN HOLES
(6 REQD.)
SIDES OF
1 x 4 STOCK

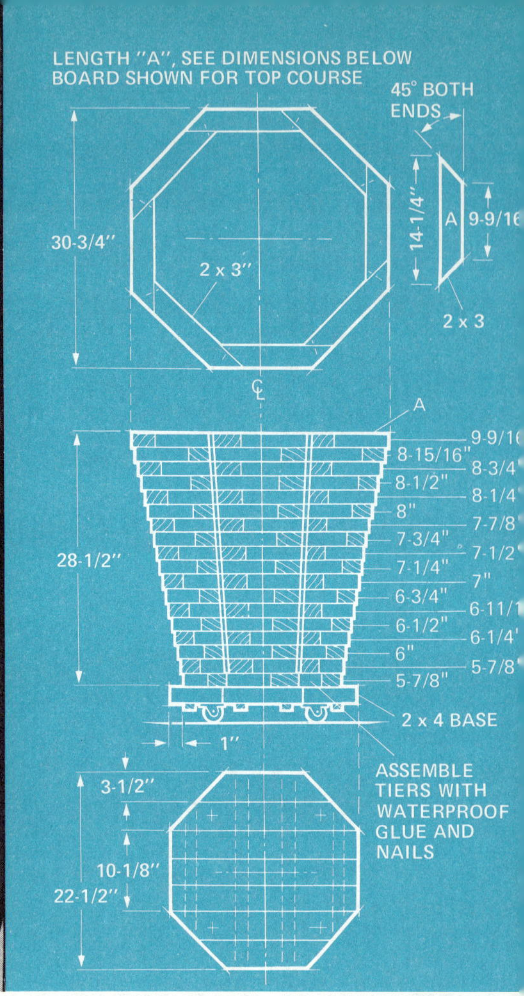

own and this, probably more than any other factor, will determine which lumber to use. You might well apply stain or treat outdoor projects with a clear water repellent. Use only galvanized or aluminum nails for all construction.

Storage gazebo

The roof dictates the overall dimensions of the shed. The length of the gazebo will be the length of the hood minus material thickness, while width is double the awning projection. Height, of course, is determined by the pair of 80-in. doors plus the door header above.

The least expensive way to get the roof is to join two metal hoods or awnings that are commercially available, or you can have the roof fabricated at a local sheet-metal dealer using the photos and drawings as guides.

Redwood planter

Because of its large size, this box is built of tongue-and-groove stock. Assemble as shown in the drawing using galvanized nails; weatherproof glue is optional.

Hanging lamp

Constructed of redwood, this lamp is perfect for entryway or patio. Set plastic or glass behind the 1x2 verticals and fasten the panes with brads partially driven into the horizontal members (1x3s) at top and bottom. Attach the 2x2 corners by drilling and nailing to the horizontal members as well. Drill a hole in the spacer block to accommodate the electrical threaded tube, and nail the block in place. Install electrical components as shown, and finish with clear sealer intended for outdoor use.

View divider

Garden grades of redwood—construction heart and construction common—are ideal for building this privacy screen. Use the former for posts and bottom stringer and the latter for all remaining parts. Posts are set at 4-ft. intervals; posts also flank each window. Since the width of each window is 15½ in., set the flanking posts 15½ in. apart or 19 in. on center. Plant posts at least 2 ft. in ground (or below area frost line) and anchor them in concrete.

Nail top and bottom stringers to posts and position the 2x4 stringer midway between. Finally, predrill holes in the 2x2 vertical members and nail them to stringers using a nail at each stringer. Fasten all members with 16d nails.

Grille fence

Construction is similar to the previously described fence. Open latticework is spotted here

Octagon planter

It can be built of western red cedar for less than $50. The planter shown has a 30½-in. dia. at the top and stands about 32 in. high on casters. The 18 courses that form the sides are 2x3 (nominal lumber). Note dimension "A" for each course: This is the inside measurement as shown. The easiest way to assemble the planter is to work upside down, starting with the top course and proceeding downward

←

Stained planter

Well suited for holding shrubs or plants, this box has sides capped by 2x6s. The outside edges of the 2x6s are chamfered for a pleasing effect

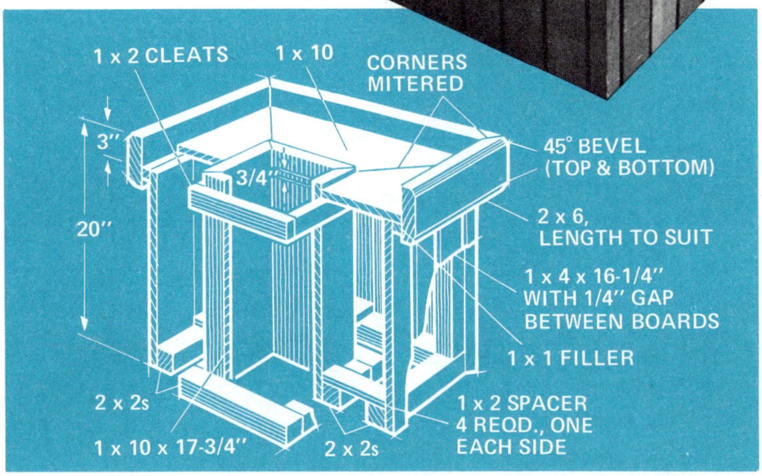

and there in a closed fence to guarantee passage of cooling breezes. Build the lattice section as shown in the drawing on page 2113.

Post lamp

This design is particularly well suited for construction with clear Idaho pine followed by a stain to suit patio or entry decor. Construction of the lamp is easier than it may appear. Start by marking and nailing louvers and top pieces to the sides to create four units. After adding the 1x1 filler strips to inside edges of two of the louver units, secure units together by nailing through the filler strips. Next, toenail the four lengths of 2x2s into the four corners formed by the louver units. Fabricate the post, install in ground and slip in lamp. Collar of 1x3s at top of post and 1x3 strips below hold lamp assembly in place.

Redwood planter

This is basically a simple box. Complete plans for building it are shown on page 2265. Notice that the box design includes two different pairs of sides. Construction of redwood planters requires two basic precautions to make them maintenance-free. First, be sure to drill holes in, or leave narrow spaces between, bottom boards to assure adequate drainage. Second, use only corrosion-resistant nails and fasteners.

Octagonal planter

The 18 courses that form the sides of this planter are cut from nominal 2x3 cedar lumber. Measurements are easy—see the example of one length (A) shown for the top course. Measurements in the drawing are for the dimension shown in the example—that is, the short length between the 45° miter cuts at both ends.

To build the planter shown, you'll need 144 linear feet of lumber for the sides. Two galvanized 12d nails in each piece hold it firmly to the piece under it. Though it's optional, it would be wise to use waterproof glue. Vertical grooves at corners help to hide uneven cuts. Making them requires careful use of a portable circular saw and a tacked-on guide. Painting is not advised for this planter; rather, stain it to match house or patio. For simplicity, assemble pieces with planter upside down.

Stained planter

Basically a box, this planter can be made of either construction grade (knotty) or clear pine. As seen in the construction drawing, a second box is created on the inside to receive the plant container. This box, of course, can be sized to suit the plant of your choice. If desired, a shelf can be added here to raise the pot height.

Hints for photographers

Many and ingenious are the ways photographers have found to ease their tasks, become more versatile, and beat the high cost of photographic equipment—often by building their own

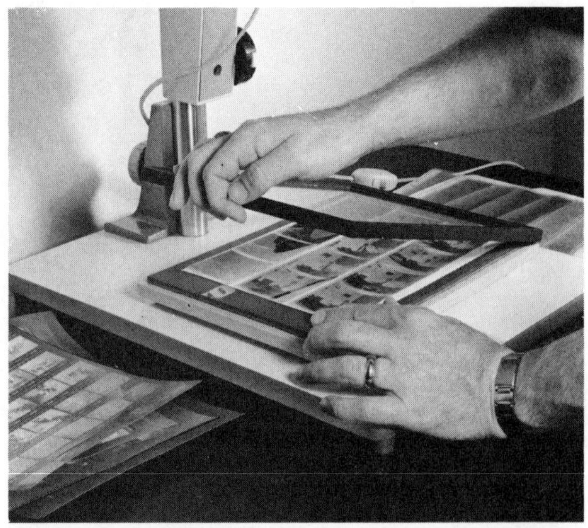

A PICTURE FRAME makes a low-cost photo proofer: The quickest, easiest way to evaluate your shooting is by contact-printing a proof sheet for each roll you shoot. But commercial proofing easels cost $10 or more, and the cheapest, simplest alternative—a sheet of plate glass—is likely to collect finger-prints, or slip out of your hands and shatter on the floor.

But you can build your own proofer for under $3. Materials are just a 9x12 picture frame with glass, a piece of ½-inch plywood cut to the frame's outside dimensions, a 12-inch square of indoor-outdoor carpet, plus hinges and tack bumpers.

To start, remove the small nails or wires which hold the glass in the frame and take out the glass. Then line the frame's inside rim with glue, replace the glass and weight it with a heavy book till dry.

While that's drying, paint the bottom and edges of the plywood (but not the top), and put a tack bumper on each corner of the bottom. When the paint dries, place the frame on the base and secure the hinges. Then glue the carpet square—face down and foam backing up—to the plywood base. Trim away the excess. A bulletin-board pushpin in the frame side opposite the hinge makes a good lifting handle.

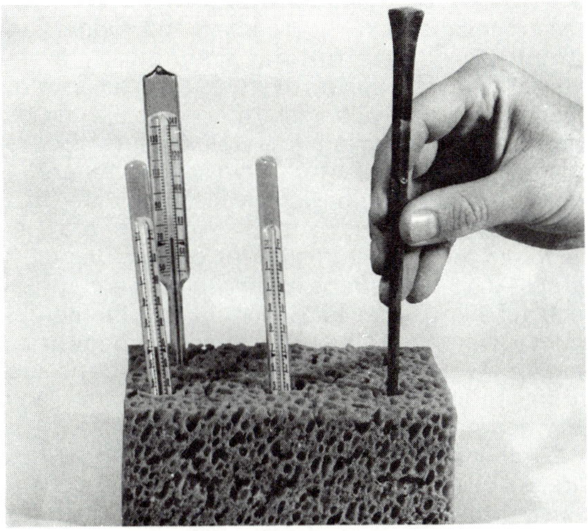

SPONGE HOLDS DARKROOM THERMOMETERS: Need a safe, convenient place to hold your darkroom thermometers? Cut holes in a large plastic sponge, using a sharpened piece of quarter-inch copper tubing as a cutter. The holes in the low-cost "rack" will hold the thermometers and stirring rods conveniently—and you can still use the sponge for wiping up darkroom spills.

DATA SHEET A HANDY FILM REMINDER: You won't forget what's in your camera if you fold the film's data sheet and tuck it into your camera case with the film's name showing. What's more, that leaves the data sheet right there when you want it for checking exposure, filter factors or anything else you may suddenly want to know about before you push the button.

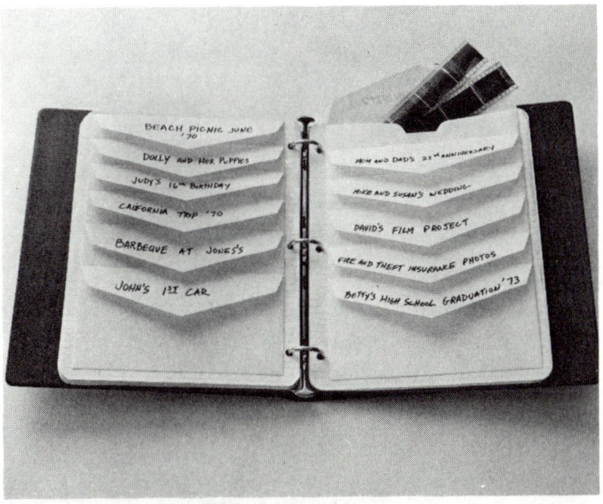

HERE'S AN EASY WAY TO FILE your negatives where you can find them again. Glue No. 6-¾ (3-⅝ x 6½ in.) envelopes to loose-leaf notebook pages, four or five to each side of the paper, overlapping them so that only the flaps are visible. Identify the negatives in each envelope by writing the subject name or film number on the flaps. Then file in a ring binder. If you have a lot of negatives, you can restrict each page to negative subjects starting with the same letter, then file them between alphabetical index separator pages.

SEE ALSO

Camera bags . . . Camera care . . .
Close-up photos . . . Darkrooms . . .
Developing, photo . . . Dryers, photo . . .
Filters, photo . . . Lightboxes . . . Photography . . .
Prints, photo

continued

A SIMPLE EFFECTIVE VIGNETTER may be made by cutting a toilet paper roll in two, painting its interior flat black, and carefully slipping it over the lens (or into a filter adapter ring) of a reflex camera. For a twin-lens reflex, use two identical vignetters. To vary the effect, change tube lengths: a longer tube will vignette more, a shorter one will vignette less.

ENLARGING LENS SLIPS under shelf: If you use more than one size of film, you'll need more than one enlarging lens—and a place to store whichever lens isn't in use. Two slotted lumber scraps under a darkroom shelf will hold the lens handily, complete with lens board. The shelf will help keep dust off the lens, but if you have lens caps, use them.

PLASTIC "FERROTYPE" FOR COLOR PRINTS: Do your ferrotyped color prints have measles? Those stains are due to pits and scratches in the ferrotype plate's surface. For foolproof color ferrotyping, cut a new plate from clear plastic "window glass," sold by builders' supply stores. In hot or dry weather, cover the prints with old newspapers once they're on the plate, so drying will be slow and even.

GUITAR STRAP EASES CAMERA LOAD: Ever need relief after carrying a camera and gadget bag around through a full day's shooting? Most weekend photographers overload themselves with gear, then suffer aches and pains from muscles they don't use during the week unless they're postmen. A touch of arthritis made one shutterbug look for something easier on his shoulders than the narrow straps and pads now sold for photo use. He found the answer in colorful, extra-wide guitar straps—two-inch straps for his camera and three-inch for his gadget bag—distributing the equipment's weight over the largest possible body area, and relieving muscular strain. The straps are strong enough to carry your equipment safely, and they can cost less than a good strap pad.

To mount them, cut your camera and gadget-bag straps down to three-inch stubs, and have a shoe-repair shop stub-rivet the stubs to the guitar strap's leather tab end.

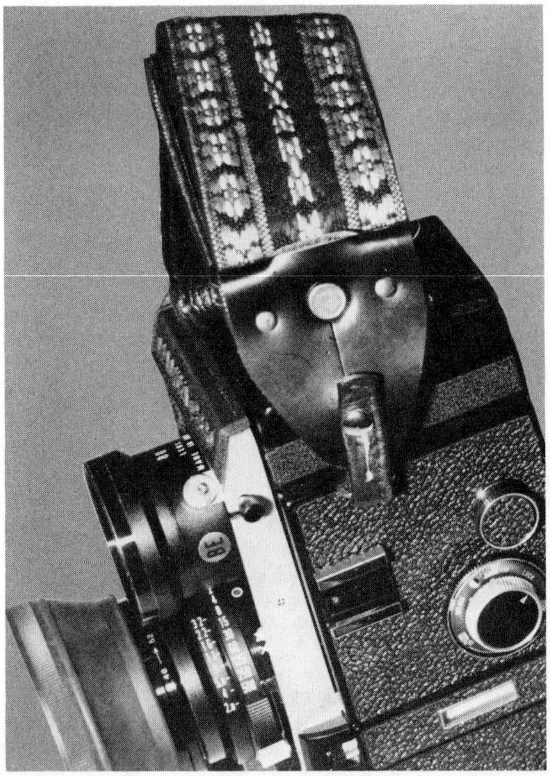

AIDS TO EASIER PRINT-SPOTTING: Print-spotting gets a lot less tedious if you work on only one section of a print at a time, blocking off the rest of the area with a sheet of white or yellow construction paper. This paper also doubles as a blotter for removing excess spotting fluid from your brush. And a plain, white, 4-inch-square tile from the hardware store is great for mixing the spotting dyes.

DARKROOM SHELF FITS ON LAUNDRY TUB: If you're using a laundry tub, either single or double, for a darkroom sink, here's a shelf that will stretch your effective counter area—and will drain off easily into the tub.

Attach three 5-inch shelf brackets to a suitable piece of scrap lumber, as shown, so the brackets will fit snugly over the side or divider of the tub. A coat of epoxy paint will make it waterproof and stain-resistant. It's handy for holding trays or developing tanks, and for mixing chemicals.

ENVELOPE KEEPS TEST STRIPS HANDY: Photographic test strips left lying loose in your enlarging paper box can be hard to find in the dark. Keep them in a manilla envelope, cut open as shown above, and glued to the inside of the enlarging paper box lid.

continued →

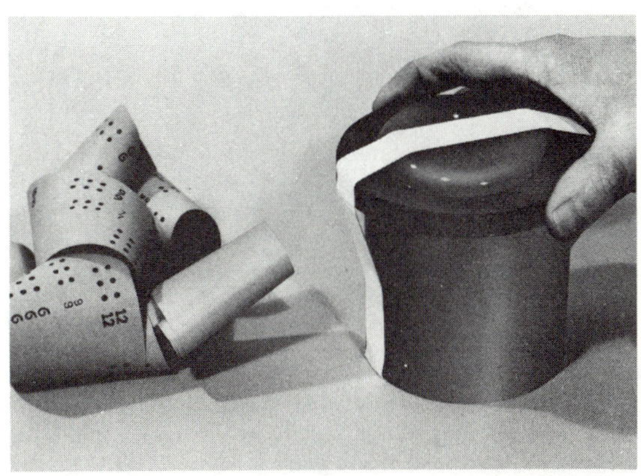

TAPE OVER FILM PREVENTS MISTAKES: If you don't develop your film right after you load it into your film tank you may forget you've loaded it—or forget what type of film you've loaded. Fastening a piece of tape around the lid will remind you (and others) that the tank is loaded. Write the film type and developing time on the tape.

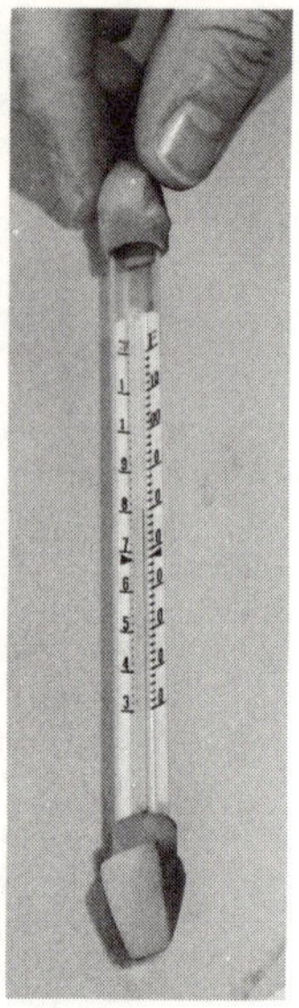

ERASERS CUT DARKROOM ERRORS: The rubber erasers that slip onto pencils can slip helpfully into your darkroom, too. They can give you a better grip on the knobs of some photo timers (above, left), while keeping the timer's metal from contamination by any photo chemicals on your hands. And erasers over the ends of glass darkroom thermometers (above, right) help protect them from breakage, without interfering with temperature measurement.

HOW TO RESTRAIN A CABLE RELEASE: Cable releases have a way of swinging in front of your lens just as you shoot, but they may bind if you wrap them around the camera to prevent this. An easy way to keep your cable release where you want it is to restrain it with a plastic cable tie, or with one of the plastic ties often supplied with plastic trash bags. On some cameras, the tie will pass through the camera's neckstrap slot or "D" ring; on most others, it can be pierced to fit over the camera's strap lug or some other projection.

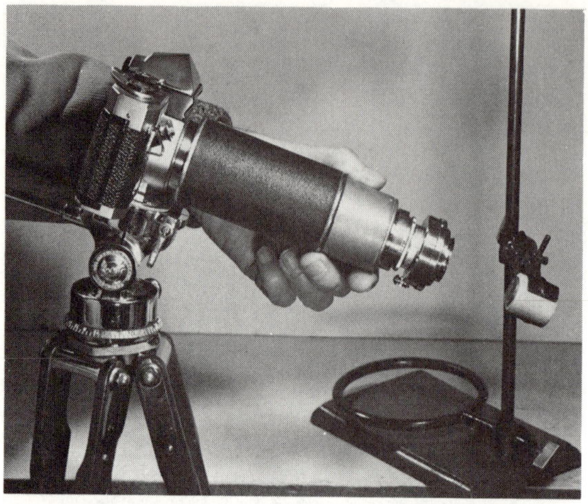

SHOOTING COIN (see below); note reversed lens.

INTERCHANGEABLE inside tubes add versatility; here, to hold one lens normally and another reversed.

SHARP CLOSE-UP made with setup on opposite page; this token has been enlarged four or five diameters.

REVERSIBLE-LENS FOCUSING TUBE

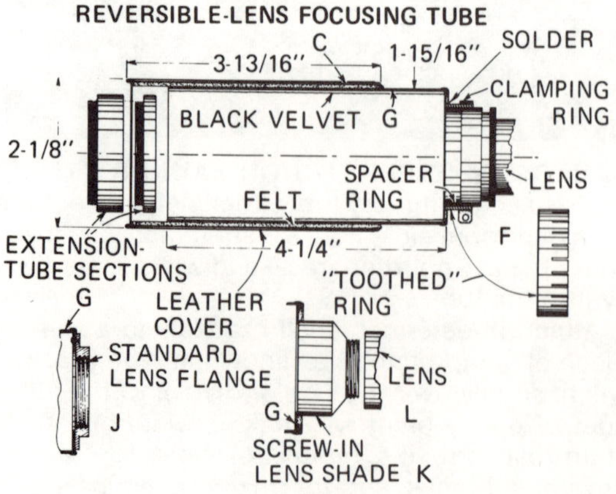

INSTEAD OF A BELLOWS close-up attachment for my single-lens reflex, you can build an adjustable focusing tube—from junk parts. Basically, it's just two tubes, one sliding within the other (see diagram at left). Make the outer tube (C in the diagram, also in photo above) from a small frozen-juice can, with one end removed. The inner tube (G in diagram and photo) could be another can, if you have one that fits, or a cardboard tube with a metal end cap.

Cement a lining of dark felt inside the outer tube, to provide a light-tight seal and a cushion for the inner tube to slide in without play. Cut a carefully centered hole in the back end of the outer tube, just large enough to clear your lens mount; then screw two short, extension-tube sections through the hole (see diagram) so you can mount the completed focusing tube to your camera.

Line the inner, sliding tube with black velvet, or other nonreflecting material. Make another carefully centered hole in this tube's end cap, for a fitting to hold your lens. This could be a standard lens flange (J in the diagram); it would either bolt on or screw on with a retaining ring. Reversing adapters, also available for many lenses, allow you to reverse the lens end-for-end for a little added sharpness in extreme close-ups; if you can't find one, you could make a clamping attachment like that shown as "F" in the diagram. Cut a ring from brass tubing, saw slots to form a series of clamping fingers, line it with plastic electrical tape and compress with a screw-tightened ring or hose clamp, to hold it on the lens barrel. This ring can be soldered or welded to the end cap. Or you can fasten a lens shade to the tube, and screw on the lens, reversed.

FOCUS-TUBE PARTS: Extension tubes (A) hold juice-can outer tube (C) to camera; lining of felt (H) inside C seals and cushions slide of inner cardboard tube (G). Lenses (D, L) can be fastened with lens flanges (not shown), with reversed lens-hood (K) to fit lens (L), or with toothed ring (F) made from brass pipe (B) and clamped to lens with clamping ring (E). For details, see diagram on page at left and text.

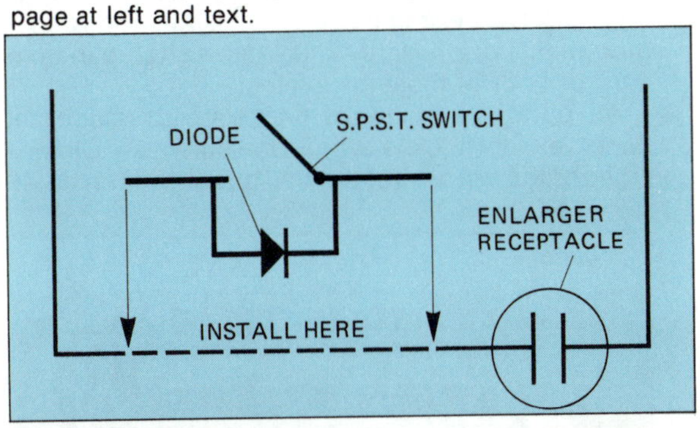

DIODE DIMS ENLARGER: Printing "thin" negatives requires either stopping down your enlarger lens to f/22 (not its sharpest aperture), using exposure times too short to allow dodging and burning-in, or both.

This simple intensity switch can help by allowing you to cut your enlarger's light output in half whenever you need to. It's simply an s.p.s.t. toggle switch placed in parallel with a silicon diode and wired into your timer's enlarger socket. With the switch open, the diode allows only half of each a.c. cycle to power the lamp. Closing the switch restores normal operation. The diode should have a rating of at least 2 amps. at 400 PIV. Polarity is unimportant.

If there's no room in your timer for the switch, you can mount the switch, diode, and a duplicate receptacle in a minibox. Remember to connect the box between the timer and the enlarger, not between the timer and the a.c. line.

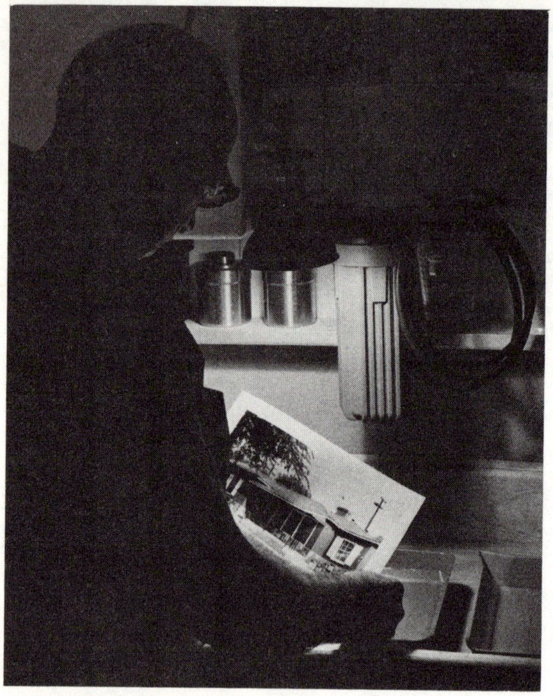

AN INSPECTION LIGHT above the fixing tray is convenient; here's how to switch it on easily.

KNEE SWITCH for print-inspection light: The best way to judge the quality of your prints is with a white light over the fixer tray. But turning that light on and off as needed can be both a nuisance and a potential shock hazard. This knee switch can take care of both of those problems.

All parts are standard hardware or electrical items, except for the wood pressure bar. Dimensions of the bar are not critical, but its ¼-inch holes

NUDGE THE BAR (arrow) with your knee and the light goes on. Release it and the light goes off.

should be counterbored ¾ inch to receive the washers on the switch actuator (4, on photo, facing page) and spring assembly (3). Locate the bar at knee level on your sink or counter front, near the fixer tray. The light may be turned on safely once the print has been in the fixer 20 seconds.

Parts are shown in approximately their assembled relationship. The switch (6) is a normally open type, mounted in a standard receptacle box, with

WALL-HANG YOUR EASEL: Two pieces of molding, one turn-button and four mounting screws can solve the problem of storing enlarging easels out of the way when not in use.

The easel actually rests behind the lip on the upper edge of the lower molding; the turn-button on the upper molding (which has no lip) holds it

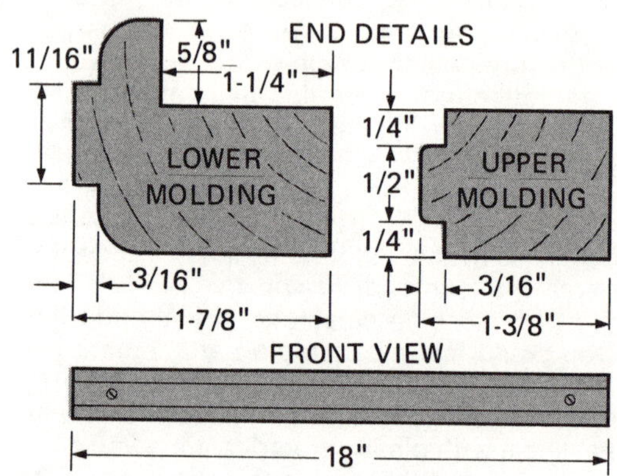

securely. Exact dimensions should be determined for your easel—the ones indicated here are for the 16x20 easel shown. With an easel of this size and weight, the moldings should be attached to your wall's studs; with smaller easels, the moldings can be mounted to a ¼-inch-plywood back and attached with two screws to a single stud.

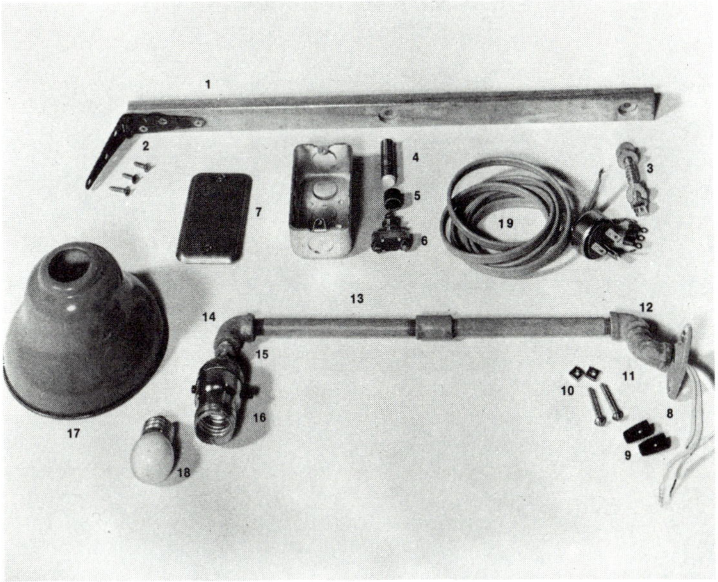

EXACT PARTS NEEDED will depend on your darkroom's layout, dimensions and other requirements. But as the picture shows, all parts can be made from standard switches and electrical hardware, stock pipe and pipe fittings, wood, metal rod, and other normal odds and ends from your shop. Even the guide bolt and compression-spring assembly (3) is made up from common, easy-to-find hardware.

List of parts for inspection light

1. Pressure bar, 13/16 x 1¼ x 20" hardwood.
2. 3" strap hinge and screws.
3. Guide bolt, compression-spring nuts and washers.
4. ½ x 2" metal rod with rubber bumper at switch end.
5. ½ x ¾" bronze bearing.
6. Momentary switch N-O (normally open).
7. Receptacle box and cover.
8. ¼" pipe waste nut and thread nipple.
9. Solderless connectors.
10. 3/16 x 1½" mounting bolts plus nuts.
11. ¼" elbow.
12. ¼" elbow and thread nipple.
13. ¼ x 12" pipe.
14. ¼" elbow.
15. Reducer ¼ to ⅛" pipe, plus ⅛" pipe thread nipple.
16. Standard switch socket.
17. Bell-type reflector.
18. 7½-w. frosted lamp.
19. Three-wire cord with grounding plug and crimp connectors.

washers holding it in place in one of the box's knockouts. Locate this box under the sink, where it won't get splashed, and make sure it's properly grounded to the third wire of the three-wire plug, or directly to a waterpipe.

Where you mount the light fixture will depend on your darkroom setup. My light is mounted with pipe fittings to the side of a cabinet, so it can be swung out of the way when not in use. The wire runs through the pipe, then inside the wall to the box under the sink. Make sure everything is solid and protected from moisture, and ground the light assembly either to the third wire or a water pipe. It's wise to use a socket with a switch you can turn off when loading film, so an accidental nudge of the knee switch won't cause a darkroom disaster.

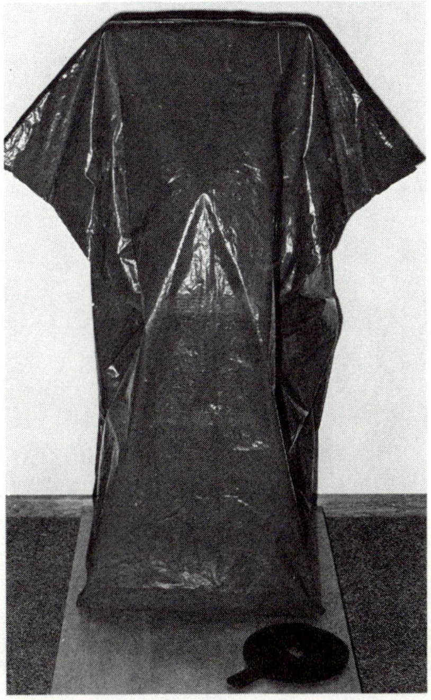

CHEAP ENLARGER DUST COVER: Keeping your enlarger dust-free can save you hours of print-spotting. But enlarger dust covers are expensive and not readily available as few dealers stock them. Plastic trash bags can do the same job for just a few cents. Here, a 30-gallon trash bag covers a big Beseler 23C. Smaller bags can store chemical trays and other darkroom items.

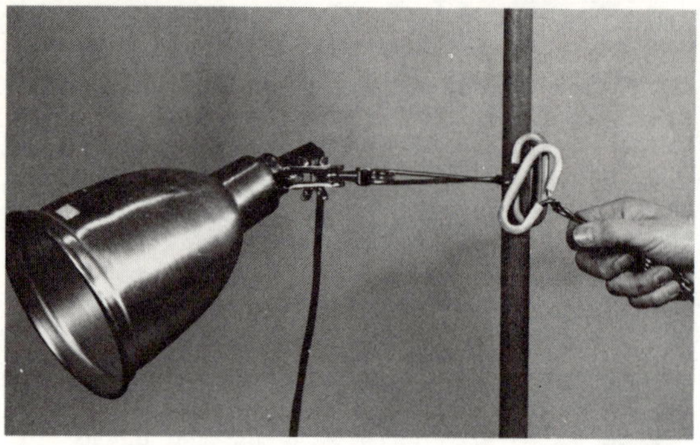

DOUBLED CLAMP IS TWICE AS STEADY: If your clamp-on photo lamps slip because their clamps are loosening, you can hold them in place by placing another spring clamp over the first one.

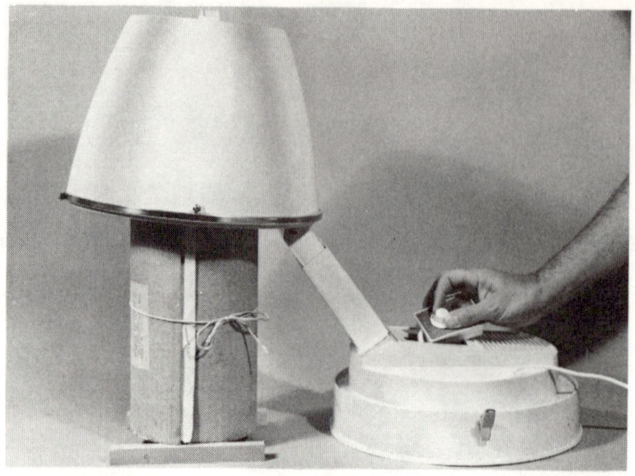

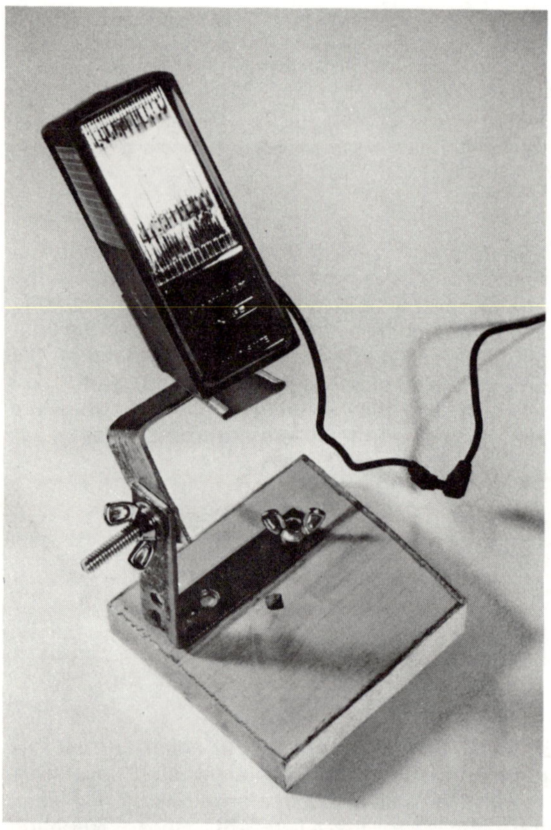

EASY BRACKET HOLDS FLASH: Holding the flashgun away from your camera, or adding off-camera extension flashes, gives your shots more interesting illumination. But how do you hold the camera and still aim a flash—especially a flash beyond arm's reach?

This simple stand can do it for you. It can be made in minutes from a small square of scrap ¾-inch lumber, plus a pair of standard 3-inch angle irons and a pair of ¼-inch bolts with wingnuts.

The mounting shoe for the flash is cut from a tin can, then formed with pliers and its sharp edges filed. A ¼-20 nut epoxied into a hole in the wood base (or a ¼-20 T-nut) also permits tripod mounting when required.

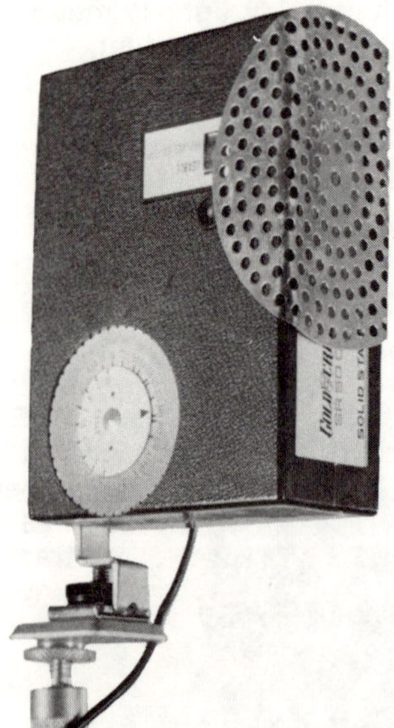

STRAINER FILTERS FLASH: The effective output of shoe-mount or other small electronic flash units can be reduced approximately two f-stops for close-ups, by bending a 3-inch flat sink strainer to fit over the flash head. Spring tension will hold it in place. Since strainers vary, make some tests first.

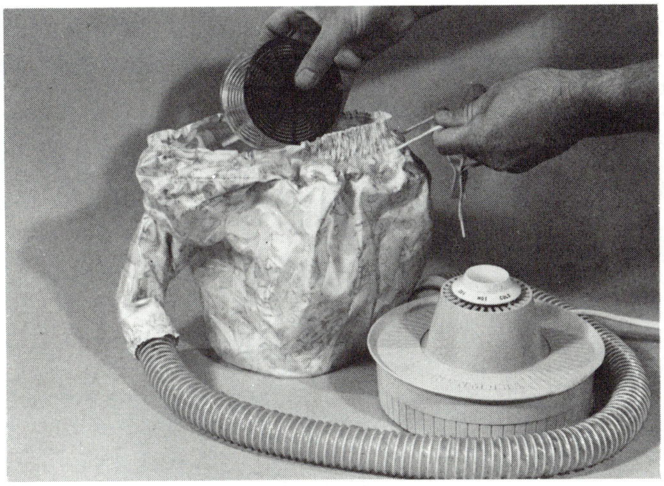

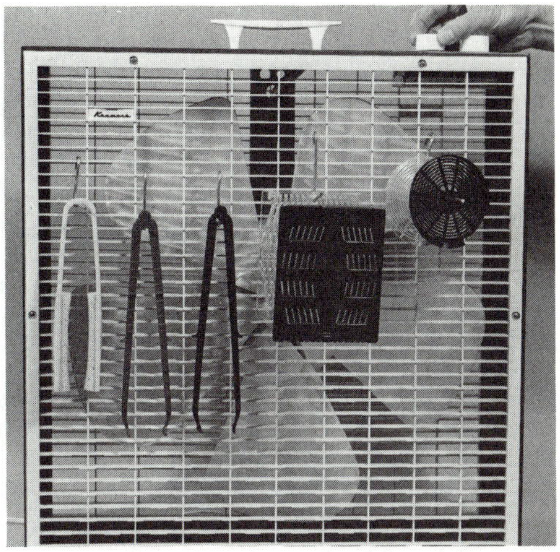

HAIR DRYERS, FANS EASE DRYING: Women's hair dryers have a lot of uses in the darkroom. The hard-hood type is an excellent device for quickly drying prints in a blotter roll; just be sure you prop up the roll as shown so air can circulate beneath it. With a coathanger wire beneath the hood, it also dries 4x5-inch sheet film. For roll film, place the dryer at the edge of the counter, and let the film hang down. If your film curls, use a lower heat. A soft-hooded dryer dries plastic developing tank reels quickly after one reel's developed, so you can load the next roll of film without its sticking. And the modern square type of household fan make an ideal dryer for reels, print tongs and other paraphernalia. Just make hanger clips from light wire to hold everything to the grille, and place a damp towel over the back of the fan to filter out dust.

DARKEN YOUR DOOR with weatherstripping. Close your darkroom door and stand there long enough to let your eyes accustom themselves to the darkness. You'll probably find it's not that dark, after all. Few doors make really light-tight fits into their frames.

But there's an easy way to seal your darkroom door and make it really light-tight: Use automotive weatherstripping. Because the adhesive that comes on the back of the stripping is messy and doesn't hold well if moved, first lay down a strip of double-sided masking tape which is clean, efficient and moveable. Then run the black automotive stripping on top of this. The tape can be pulled off later, if need be, without marring the finish of the wood.

continued

CLOSE-UPS of low-lying flowers and the like—or low-angle shots of larger objects—are easy with the Flatpod (shown in use above) and the Spikepod (upper photo at right). Flatpod construction (lower photo at right) is simple; the only materials are a ¼-20 screw and a piece of hardboard; unit works indoors or out. The Spikepod is for use in soft ground.

THIS INDOOR-OUTDOOR CAMERAPOD provides low-level close-ups, which normally aren't easy. Tripods which can hold a camera close to the ground often require accessories, or hold it upside down. And why tote two feet of tripod to hold a camera at a two-inch elevation? These solutions—the Flatpod and Spikepod—fit in your pocket, and can be made for less than $2.

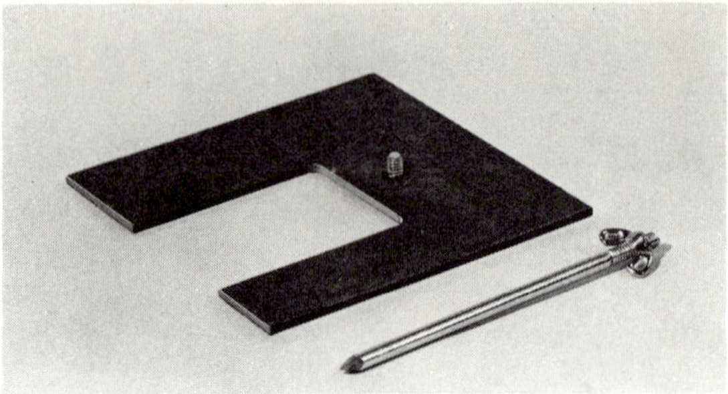

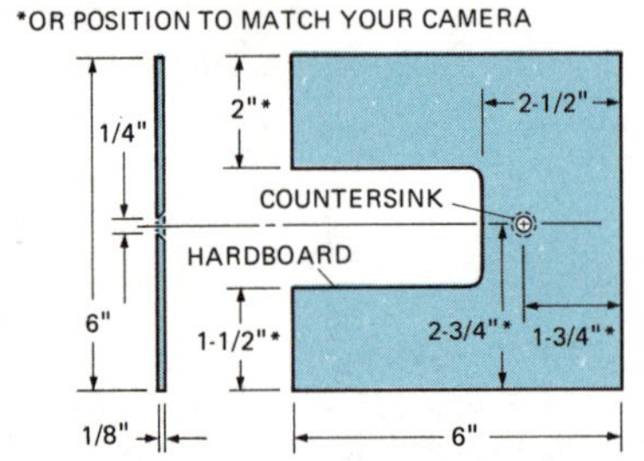

The Flatpod is made from a 6x6-inch scrap of hardboard. Cut a slot as shown for lens clearance, drill and countersink ¼-inch hole for a ¼-20 x ⅜-inch flathead bolt, and you have a low-level stand that will hold your camera and most macro lenses steady on any reasonably level surface. The lens clearance slot and tripod screw positions shown are for a Nikon; you may have to adjust them to fit other cameras.

The Spikepod is even simpler: just hacksaw off the head of a long ¼-20 carriage bolt and file the cut end to a point. Add a wingnut to tighten the spike to the camera. To use, just jam the spike into the ground. You can use three, four or six-inch bolts.

FILM HOLDER ENDS FUMBLING: Tired of groping for film in the bottom of your gadget bag? This easy-to-make film holder will end that. All you need is a 1x5-inch strip of hardboard, three 4-40 screws with nuts and lockwashers and six extra film cans. Drill a ⅛-inch hole in the bottom of each film can, and in the hardboard strip at the middle and ½ inch from each end. Attach two cans opposite each other at each hole. The new plastic film cans can be spaced closer together, but washers should then be used. If you like, you can drill an additional hole between two cans for a string to hold the strip on your belt or shoulder strap.

MAKE A BROOMSTICK UNIPOD: Add one more leg to the two you have already, and you're a tripod. That's the unipod principle. And while you and the unipod together aren't quite as shake-free as a true tripod, the unipod's much easier to carry.

A homemade version doesn't telescope like the commercial ones, but it's a lot cheaper, and at least as light and sturdy. All you need is a length of 7/8-inch dowel, a 7/8-inch cane tip, a bicycle handlegrip, and a camera-case retaining screw (available from photo dealers).

To put it all together, tape the retaining screw to one end of the dowel securely; then coat that end with glue and push the handlegrip down tightly over that end till the screw threads extend through the grip's end hole (most grips have one, but if yours doesn't, it's easy to punch or cut). Seat the cane tip on the dowel's other end, and you're done.

Length is up to you: A dowel long enough to raise your camera's finder to your eye level is steadiest, but most awkward to carry. This one is 36 inches high so it will double as a walking stick, and you squat or sit to use it. A tripod hanger ring helps keep the screw threads clean when not in use, and lets you attach a rawhide thong as a wrist strap. Another useful option is a golfshoe spike in the bottom, covered by the cane tip when it's not in use.

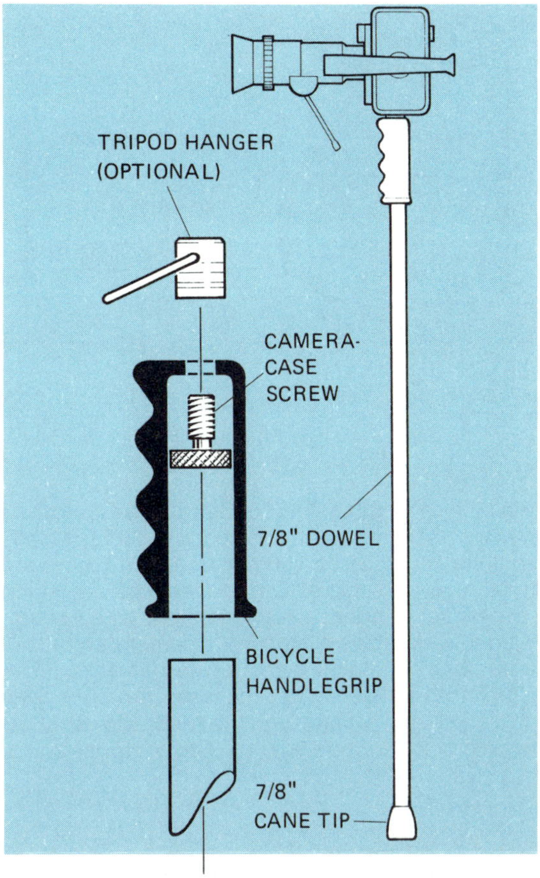

REMOVING CAMERA-CASE FROM TRIPOD: If you keep your camera in its case when it's on a tripod, you've probably found that turning the tripod screw often just turns the case screw around and around, loosening the camera, but leaving the case stuck to the tripod. And you can seldom get tools in between the case and the tripod head to grip and hold the screw.

A preventive is to drill, beforehand, one or more holes in the case screw's knurled edge, to take a nail that can act as a gripping level. Try to position the hole so it will be accessible when the camera is screwed down, and angle it away from the tripod-screw hole.

continued

KEY-CHAIN TAB IMPROVES ZIPPER: If the zipper on your gadget bag is sticking, stop fighting with it. Just attach a key chain with an ornamental tab of your choice, and you'll be able to get a good grip on the zipper tab for a strong pull without fumbling.

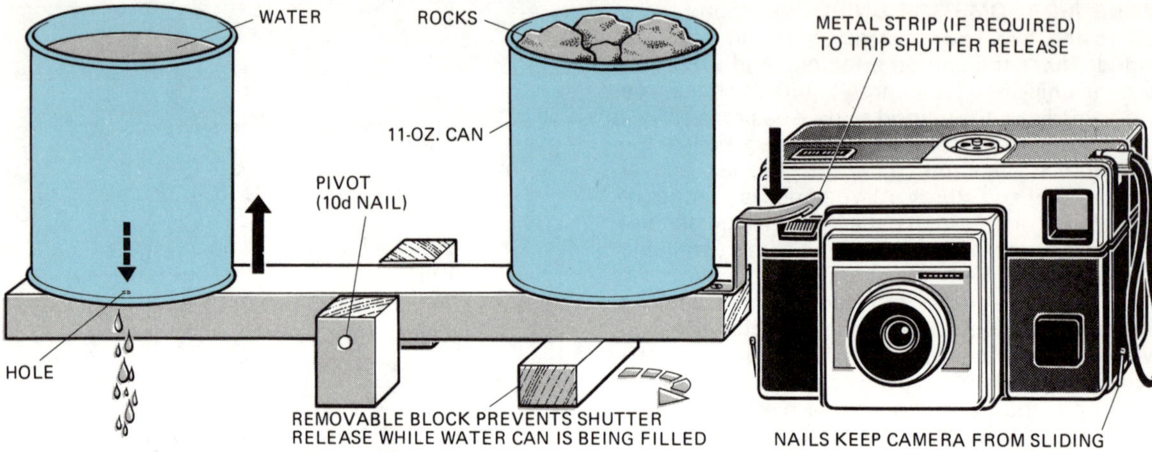

WATER-DRIP SELF-TIMER: Simple cameras don't have self-timers—and often lack cable-release sockets for accessory timer units. But here's a timer you can make. On one end of a 15-inch seesaw stick, mount a soup can filled with enough weight in pebbles to trip your camera's shutter. The other can holds a greater weight of water. A small hole in that can lets the water run out slowly until the balance shifts and the rocks trip the shutter. A block of wood under the can of stones keeps the shutter from tripping accidentally until you remove it.

You can calibrate the water can for different delays, but 10 seconds seems best; too much more time, and the subjects get restless and change expressions—too little time, and you can't get into place before the shutter snaps. A bonus: most subjects are too fascinated by this weird gizmo to think about getting stiff and self-conscious.

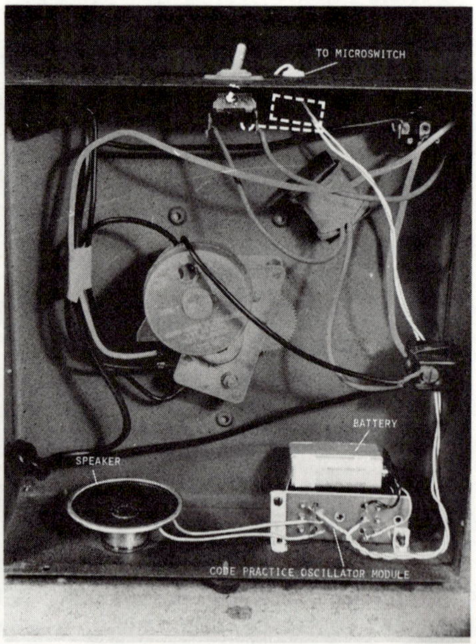

BEEPER IMPROVES LAB TIMER: One man uses his Gra-Lab timer for both printing and film developing. Since he can't always look up to see when he should agitate the film or paper, he added a "beeper" to sound off once per minute while the timer hands are moving. Parts used were a lever-type microswitch, mounted to contact the second hand as it passed the 60 second mark, a small speaker, and a Radio Shack code oscillator module with its battery taped on; but any equivalent parts should do. The oscillator is mounted inside the timer case with aluminum brackets, and the speaker is epoxied directly to the case. (There is adequate sound without baffle holes). The microswitch is mounted on a small wood spacer, so it won't interfere with the minute hand's operation.

DETAIL OF CROSSPIECE

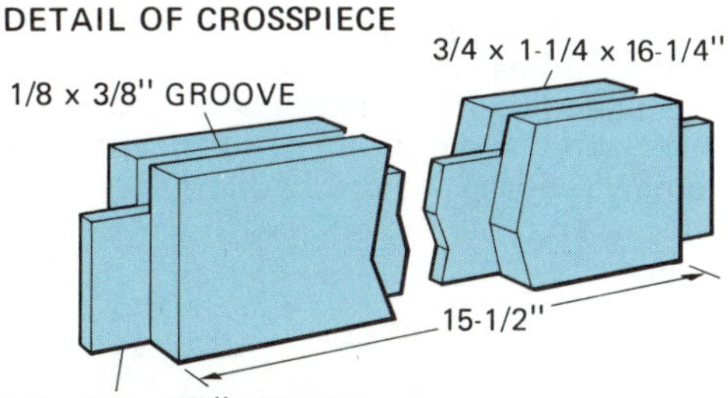

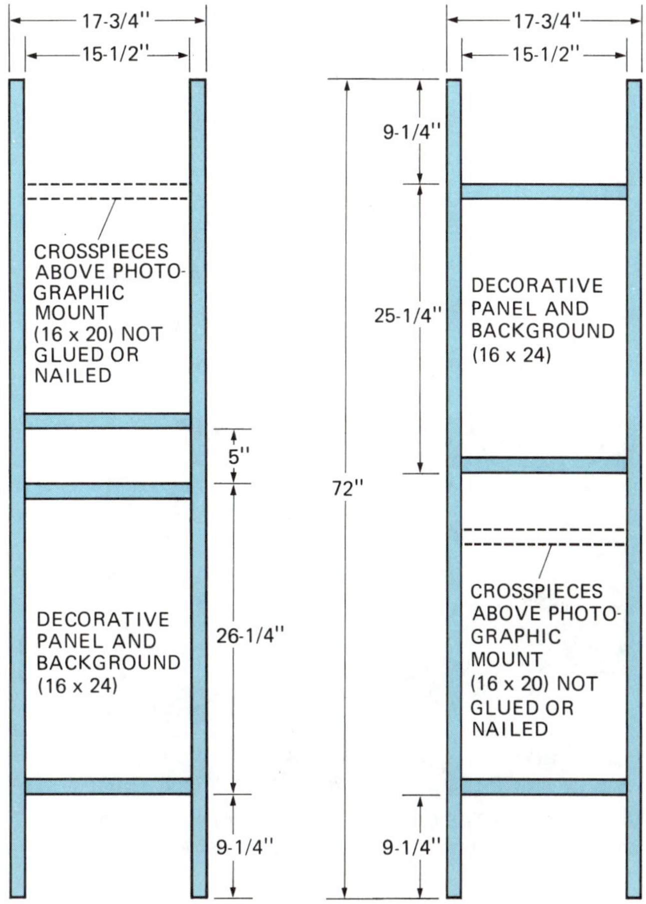

CENTER PANEL, 1 REQD.

SIDE PANELS, 2 REQD.

FOLDING SCREEN DISPLAYS PHOTOS: This folding screen serves as both a room divider and a display for photographs—and the photos are easily changed.

Construction is simple, with each section built individually, then attached with folding screen hinges. Materials are readily cut from 1x2 stock, and can be cut for you by a lumberyard. Both the vertical and horizontal pieces have grooves ⅛ in. wide by ⅜ in. deep along one edge to hold the panels; the horizontal pieces also have ⅜ x ⅛ x ⅞ in. tongues to fit grooves of vertical supports.

Each section was assembled with glue and small brads, but the horizontal pieces above the photos were not glued or nailed, so the photos could be changed easily. Decorative panels are of ⅛-in. plywood or hardboard filigree, stained or painted before the watercolor-board backing is applied. Photo panels are 16x20-in. print mounts; the prints are attached by dry mounting.

A VIGNETTING LENS HOOD: Your lens hood should be matched as closely as possible to your lens' angle of view. Too wide a hood admits stray light that can cause flare; too narrow a hood darkens or "vignettes" photo corners.

To check for vignetting, mount the hood, open your lens to its widest f-stop, lock the shutter open, and look through the lens from behind each corner of the film framing aperture in the back of the camera. Darkened areas in one or more corners indicate vignetting.

To cure it, hold a pencil against the hood's inner edge and move it back slowly until its sharp point disappears from view. Mark that spot, trim hood back to the mark with a hacksaw, then file smooth and repaint the edge black to prevent reflections.

PRINT ON THE RIGHT HALF, leave the left half blank, and fold the paper on the centerline.

EMULSION ON THE OUTSIDE carries the picture, while paper's back surface, inside, is easy to write on.

PHOTOS MAKE NOTE CARDS: Turn your favorite photos into photo notes, and you'll get a lot more mileage from them. Cut 8x10 single-weight, matte paper into 5x8-inch halves (double-weight or glossy papers are more likely to crack), and print your picture as a vertical or horizontal on the right half of the sheet, so that it makes the front of the note when folded; mask off the unexposed half of the paper during exposure, to avoid fogging it. If it's a shot you're especially proud of, you can print it across the entire sheet and fold the picture in the middle; the recipient can fold it out again.

Since unmounted, single-weight paper has a tendency to curl, use print-flattening solution (or print on Kodak's "RC" resin-finished papers) and keepyour finished note cards flattened between blotters until you use them.

FILM-TYPE REMINDER: Trace a film box's end flap on a scrap of aluminum flashing, and cut with metal snips (or scissors), leaving enough metal around the outline to allow three bent edges as shown (box end flaps slip in the open end). Bend with pliers, sand, and glue or epoxy on. When you put in a new roll, slip the box end into the slot on your camera, and you'll never have to wonder what you're shooting.

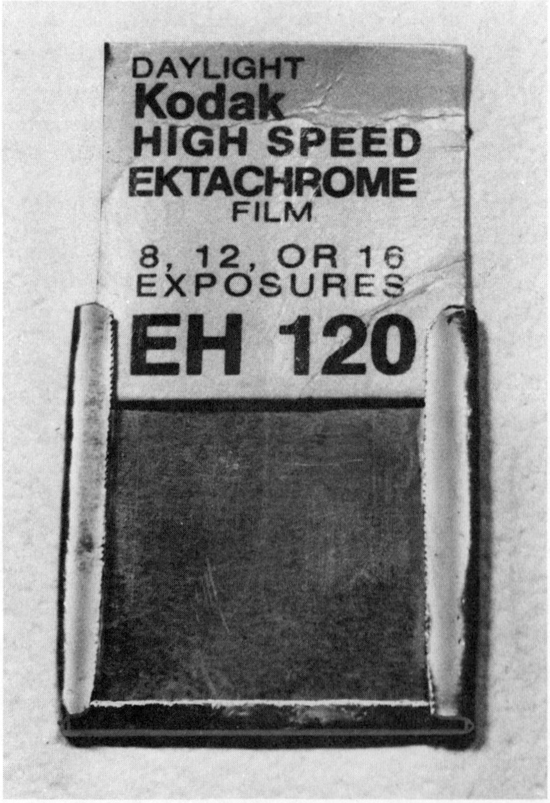

SLIP-IN EASEL (above and right) can be made to fit any size paper, is easy to load in the dark or under safelights. Black paint keeps reflections from fogging paper and reminds you to focus on blank sheet. Detail (above) shows how molding holds down paper edge.

MAKE A LOW-COST 16x20 EASEL: Easels for 16x20 enlargements are rather expensive—especially if you don't make such big enlargements very often. So I made my own for less than $4, and in approximately two hours' time. It's just a piece of half-inch plywood that is cut two inches wider and two inches longer than the paper size it's designed for. (If you cut your paper to custom sizes—for full-negative prints from 35 mm, for instance—you can build the easel to fit them, too.) Cut three strips of No. A-749 metal edging (available from most of the better hardware stores) to fit three of the paper's sides, and mount them, flat-side down, on the plywood base with 3/8-in. x No. 4 sheetmetal screws. This will leave a small groove between the wood base and the metal edging that's intended for the paper to slide into. Paint easel flat black to prevent flare in printing.

continued

EASEL BECOMES COPY FRAME: An enlarging easel and a copy frame have the same basic purpose: to hold a piece of paper flat. So if you have an easel, you have a ready-made copy frame, too. To get the even lighting that copying requires, you can use soft daylight—wait for an overcast day, or prop your easel up in the shade of a building where it gets even skylight, not direct sun. The easel borders needn't appear in your final print. Normally, I move in closer with my camera to crop out the easel border, and crop out whatever is left of it when I make my enlargements.

SINK STOPPER STOPS STAINS: A large, flat rubber sink stopper, like the one shown here, makes a good coaster to catch drops of developer that may run down the sides of your tank or beaker and stain your darkroom benchtop. (Regular coasters are far too small for this.) Look for a stopper with a flat top, as many have central humps which you must otherwise cut off.

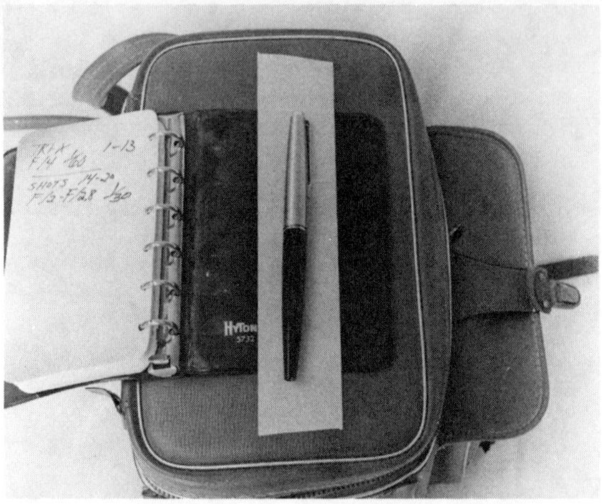

TAPE HOLDS PHOTO NOTEBOOK HANDY: Keep a notebook for recording exposures, filters, locations and other picture-taking information handy by taping it to the top of your gadget bag. The notebook is always easy to find, and the bag's top makes a good, portable writing desk. When in a hurry, you can take notes without even taking the bag from your shoulder.

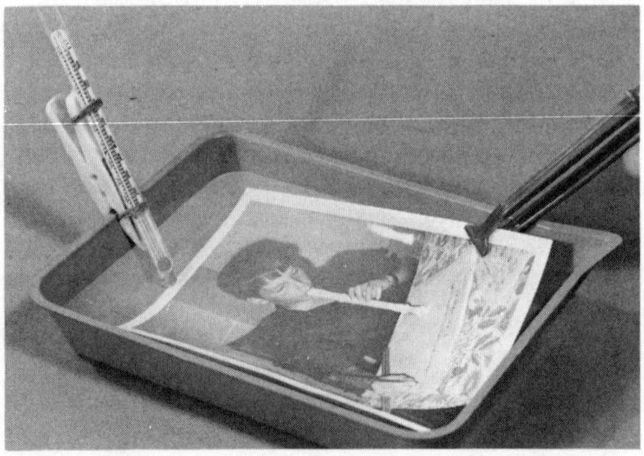

CLOTHESPIN CLIP FOR THERMOMETER: A darkroom thermometer is easier to see if it's fastened with rubber bands to a plastic clothespin (wood ones absorb chemicals) and clipped to the side of your tray.

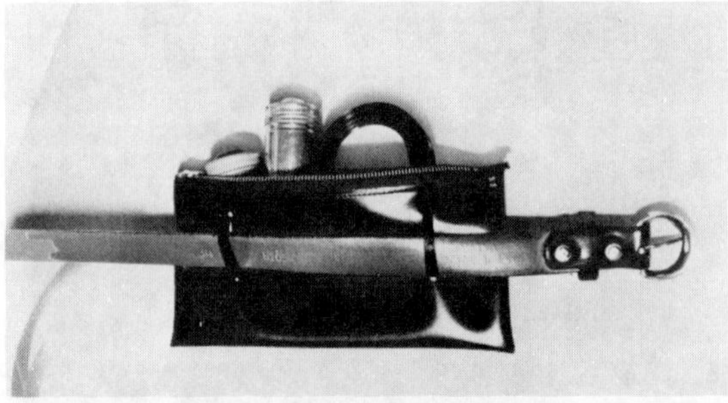

BELT CARRIER FROM A PENCIL CASE: A plastic pencil case makes a fine belt holder for small camera items such as extra film, filters, shades, cable releases. Cut two slits near each end to form loops to slip the belt through. The zippered case is easy to open and close with one hand while holding a camera with the other.

BLEACH BOTTLE SPEEDS TANK FILLING: Cut a thoroughly washed plastic bleach bottle in half, and the bottom makes a container big enough to fill your developing tank. Use a graduate to measure out the proper amount of solution, then draw a fill mark and label the volume on the outside with a brush pen or felt marker. The thin plastic feels flimsy, but when you pour, it conveniently deforms to make its own pouring lip. The bottle's upper half makes a handy funnel, complete with a convenient handle. Two gadgets from one bottle!

JUG KEEPS FILM COOL: A wide-mouth, insulated jug can keep your film cool in the summer and warm in the winter. The plastic-foam type is best because of its light weight. Just keep the jug open in your airconditioned or heated room at night, and close it in the morning.

MAKESHIFT COPY STAND: A vise and clipboard make a good, impromptu copy stand. Use a rubber band to hold the bottom of the paper flat to the board.

continued

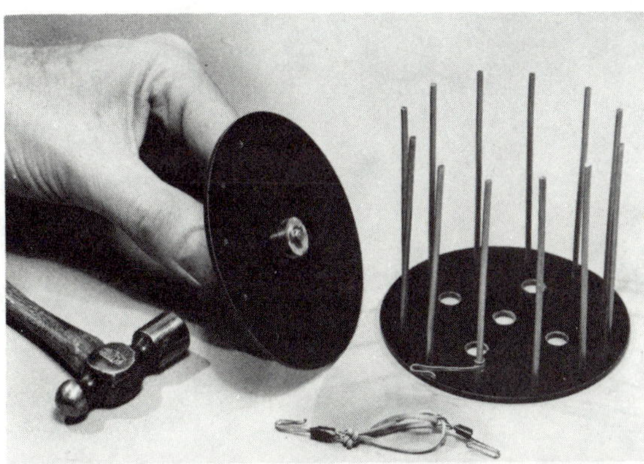

MINI-REEL FOR SMALL FILM: If your camera collection includes a subminiature pocket type using 16-mm film, you may find developing difficult without a special tank to handle such narrow strips in short lengths. An easy compromise is to make your own mini-reel to fit in a standard 35-mm tank. The one at left is 3⅜ inches in diameter and holds 34 inches of 16-mm film. Cut the end discs from Bakelite or similar material and the rods from ⅛-inch noncorroding wire. A short length of brass tubing or wood dowel makes a handle. The handle and rods can be cemented into holes in the discs with epoxy. Drill extra holes in the bottom disc to let developer circulate freely.

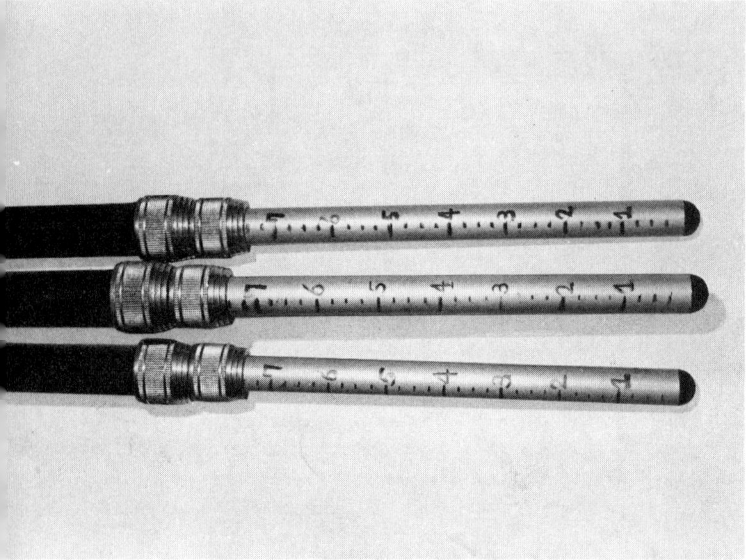

GETTING EACH TRIPOD LEG to come out exactly the same length can drive you up a wall. To eliminate this frustration, lay a ruler along your tripod's legs and lightly mark off measurements with a pencil. Using a small, pointed brush and quick-drying acrylic, paint each mark on permanently. If the legs are a tight fit, score the marks with a triangular file before painting; the paint will then be below the metal surface and won't rub off.

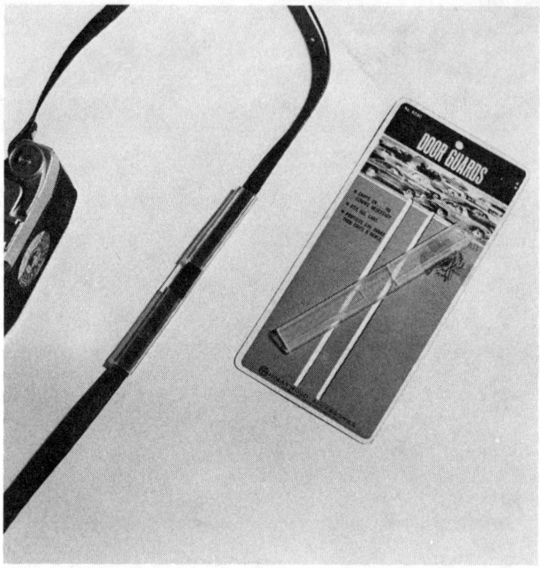

THE SHORT PLASTIC STRIPS sold in auto-supply stores as door-edge guards make good cushions for your camera neckstrap. Just insert the strap into the doorguard as shown, making sure the doorguard is centered on the strap and that the guard's cut area faces away from your neck. It will rest securely in position. Since the guards come in pairs, you'll have one for a friend, too, or for another camera.

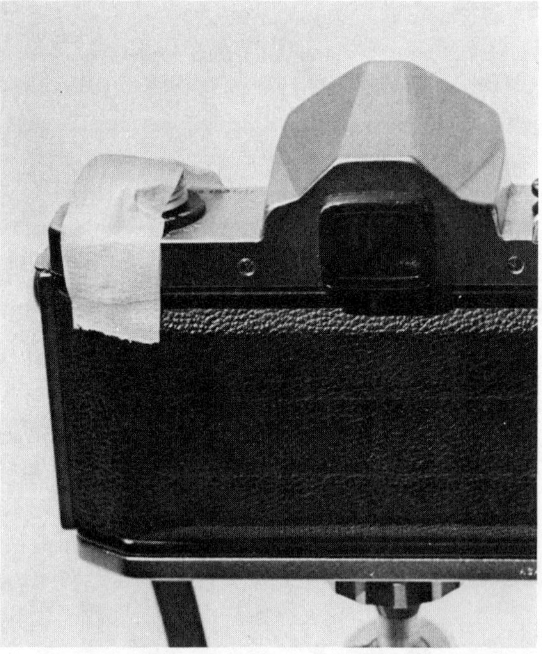

NOT ALL 35-MM cameras let you take deliberate double exposures; but those that do usually require that you hold down the rewind knob while winding the shutter for the second exposure. It helps if you draw up the slack film, then tape down the rewind knob *before* making the first exposure. Masking tape is fine for this purpose.

ATTACH YOUR SAFELIGHT to a pull-down reel of the type made for household light fixtures, and you double its utility. You can lower it over a tray for better inspection of developing prints, or raise it for more general illumination and to avoid fogging high-speed papers. This one is attached to a ceiling outlet, using a commercial type twist-lock electrical plug, but you can also mount it permanently, if you prefer.

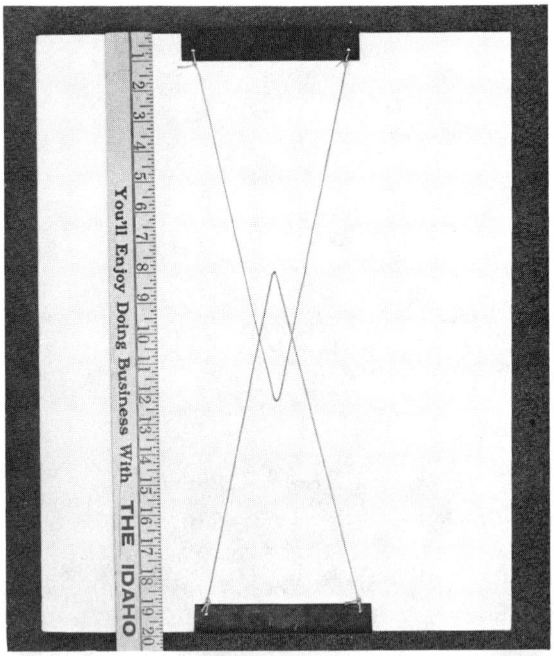

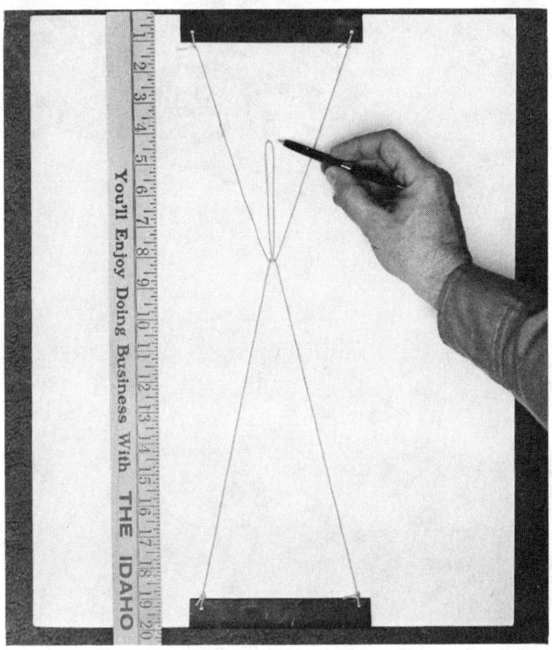

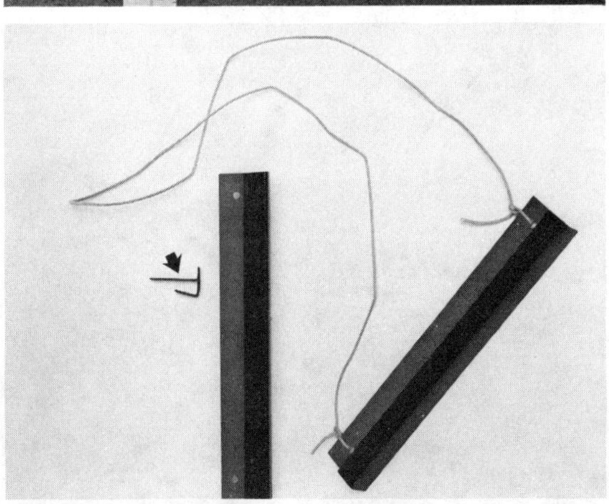

SALON PRINT FRAME: No need to frame your photos and display them under glass. You can show them more effectively, informally and inexpensively by borrowing a tip from the salon exhibitor.

First, dry-mount your photo on mounting board (16x20 is a good size). Then buy a strip of outside-corner plastic molding as shown (arrow) in the photo below. This usually comes in several decorator colors. An 8-foot piece—enough for about eight pictures—should sell for around $1. Next, saw the molding into 6-inch strips, and drill or punch out two small holes in the long leg of each, as illustrated.

Cut two pieces of cord, each 6 inches longer than the mounting board, and tie them to the holes as shown below. Center the plastic molding on the top and bottom edges of the board, turn the print face down, and pass the loop of the top cord through the loop from the bottom cord (left). Now pull the cord tight, and hang the print from the tip of the top loop.

If you standardize on one mount size, you can change photos easily.

The outside-corner molding shown will hold the print about ¼ inch from the wall. If you prefer the picture to hang closer to the wall, you can use edging, which lacks the outside corner molding's rear projection. For hanging pictures high on your wall, use an outside corner molding at the top of the picture, and edging at the bottom, to angle the picture downward.

Simple cameras can take good pictures

By IVAN BERGER

THINK YOU NEED a fancy camera to get good shots? You don't.

But what you do need is a mind that's alive to what makes good pictures and that flashes a warning signal when you're about to take a bad one.

A $400 camera doesn't make you a good photographer. It just lets you shoot equally good (or equally bad) photos under a wider range of picture situa-

PANNING with action simplifies the background by blurring it while the subject stays sharp. The trick can work even if your camera has a slow shutter.

BACKGROUND AND foreground are equally sharp with most simpler cameras. Using backgrounds that are as clean and simple as possible can make that general sharpness pay off with satisfying snapshots.

SEE ALSO

Camera care . . . Cameras . . .
Candid photography . . . Close-up photos . . .
Montages, photo . . . Mountings, photo . . .
Night photography . . . Outdoor photography . . .
Prints, photo . . . Used cameras

EVER ready, a simple camera can help on quick shots like this. But you, too, must stay alert for such appealing photographs.

SOFT, directional window light is fine for portraits.

BACKLIGHTING puts a softer light on faces and highlights hair. And it saves the strained look of squinting eyes.

FOCUSING cameras can simplify a complex background by blurring it.

GOOD snapshots put subjects against a non-distracting background and show them living instead of posing.

COMMON GOOFS abound here. The foreground at top left is nice and sharp, but there's far too much of it, leaving the center of interest remote and fuzzy. The moral: Move in close and check the focus. Close-ups (above) have their own problems. Arms and legs that project toward the camera swell disproportionately. The horizon line through the head, the harsh facial shadows and eyes squinting into the sun are other problems the photographer could have avoided. The higher angle at right simplifies the background and the better pose corrects the subject's proportions, cuts the distracting shadows and softens light on the face.

EMPTY FOREGROUNDS (left photos) may be easy to fill. I just waited for a ferry boat and maneuvered to get fellow tourists into the shot. (New Yorkers will spot this as an old photo: Manhattan's 110-story World Trade Center is missing.)

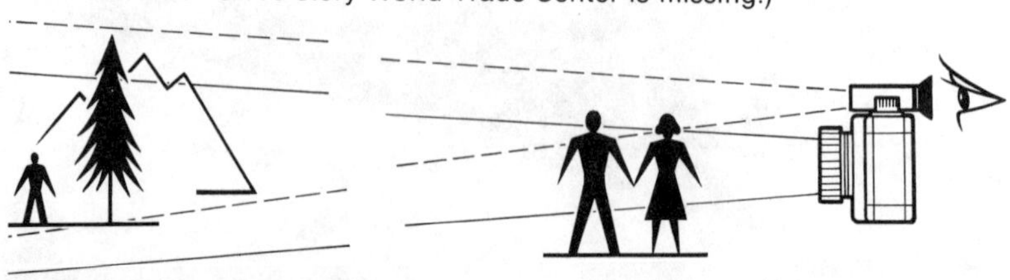

CUT-OFF HEADS come from parallax, the difference between the viewfinder's view and the lens' view of the subject. Parallax can be a big problem with close-ups, but viewfinders almost always warn what will be trimmed off. Otherwise you'll have to remember to leave extra room at the top in close-ups.

tions. And all the good techniques and horrible-example pitfalls shown here apply just as much to Nikons as to Instamatics.

With three exceptions, these photos weren't taken for this article. Among the cameras used were a $30 35-mm camera from a firm you never heard of, a Kodak Pocket Instamatic, a $30 Polaroid Super-Shooter, a folding Kodak from the early Thirties and an old, used Rolleicord. Can you tell which camera shot which?

Here are some favorites we had to leave out of our picture layout:

Bad backgrounds. These range from the merely distracting to the classic telephone pole or tree growing out of someone's head. These problems are usually visible in the viewfinder if you look for them.

Bad shadows. Shoot with the sun over your shoulder, as so many photo books have recommended, and you not only get subjects squinting at the sun, you may get your own shadow in the picture.

Obstructed lens. Be careful your fingers aren't in front of the lens when you shoot; and keep your lens clean with soft lens tissue.

Bad flash. Read the instructions and find out the range your flash is good for. Try to shoot flash at 50 feet, and you'll just get darkness, while flash from too close can wash out details. If you must flash when a window or mirror is in your field of view, stand at an angle so the glass won't reflect light back in your lens.

NO TRIPOD? If you can't (or didn't) bring one, you can still shoot spectacular pictures, even at night. This picture was taken with the camera resting on brick pavement. Fortunately there was a slight slope down to the waterfront. If you lack a tripod, use any solid base for your camera.

Bring your vacation back on film

There's more to good vacation shots than Grandma in front of the Grand Canyon. Here are some tips on taking photos that won't have your audience stifling yawns

By DAVE SAGARIN

■ OKAY, so you've shot your wife in front of the Grand Canyon, and she's shot you. Now what do you do to make your travel and vacation pictures really recapture your vacation?

The first step is to decide just what photo equipment to take with you. Gather everything you think you'll need. Put it in your bag and lift. Now think of what it would be like to carry all that around with you, day after day, and take out everything you can do without.

what to take

You will want to take your filters (UV or haze and polarizing for color, plus yellow, orange or red filters for black-and-white), a pocket tripod and a real tripod if you're traveling by car. Take a set of jeweler's screwdrivers, too, to tighten up all those little screws that keep vibrating loose on your equipment. And take a lens cleaning kit: a brush unit, fluid and lens tissue.

Take Zip-lock plastic bags, too. They hold small things like flash cords and adapter rings together, keep equipment from getting dirty and protect the camera when you're shooting in the rain. I also keep my film in a Zip-lock bag when flying, so I can take it out of my carry-on bag and pass it over the X-ray machine instead of through it.

If you're going abroad, you may also want to take lots of your favorite film with you, but check with that country's consulate before you go. Some countries have restrictions on how much film you can bring in with you.

SEE ALSO

Boat photography . . . Camera accessories . . . Camera bags . . . Camera care . . . Cameras . . . Candid photography . . . Close-up photos . . . Night photography . . . Outdoor photography . . . Underwater photography

SHOOT WHAT YOU SEE, even if it means shooting beneath the wing of a plane (as here). Use a fast shutter speed to prevent motion blur, and when shooting from a plane use a UV or haze filter to keep the ground in the distance from taking on a decidedly bluish cast.

Don't be afraid to shoot a lot of film, either. Film costs money, but it's still cheaper than flying back to take that shot you now regret not shooting.

And train your family to shoot—that's the only way you'll ever get into your pictures. Let the kids shoot once in a while: It not only keeps them happy—it sometimes even results in good pictures.

When you shoot your family, don't pose them: Catch them doing whatever interests them, and you'll have more interesting pictures. The same goes for people in the places you visit.

Whatever you shoot, vary your approach to it, especially when similar subjects keep coming up again and again. Don't just shoot a church's sunlit facade—if the skyline is clear, stop down and shoot a silhouette of it from the shadowed side.

AN OVERALL VIEW of a scene tells what you *saw*, but a related close-up such as the sign offers a change of pace and may orient the viewer specifically to what you *experienced*.

BUILDINGS THAT are obviously foreign in style add local flavor and serve as built-in titles to tell people where the picture was taken. The same is true of billboards and signs in foreign languages. Also, emphasize local dress, exotic hair styles, unique vehicles—anything that provides a clue as to where the photo was taken.

Don't just shoot from eye level, either. Crouch down to get low-angle shots or look for places you can stand for high-angle views.

Anything really interesting will probably have a crowd around it, so learn the pros' technique of holding the camera above your head to shoot the action. Use a wide-angle lens, grasp the camera strap firmly in one hand as a brace, and pull against it with the hand holding the camera.

Take close-ups, too, of details like shells, jewelry, carving—or even shrimp. Extension tubes or close-up lenses don't weigh much and take up little room.

shoot transition slides

If you're shooting color slides, look for transition shots to carry your slide show over from one subject to the next. The view from the plane, in the train station, or from right behind the bus driver tells the audience quickly that the next slides will be from somewhere else; but since that's all they usually tell, get them on and off the screen fast. They're for flavor, not basic nourishment.

more tips

- If the weather's a bit glum, warm up your color photos with an 81 EF filter.
- Whenever you travel, carry a list of all your photo gear, complete with serial numbers, in case any gets lost or stolen. And if you're going abroad, register the list with U.S. Customs to avoid duty charges when you bring it back.
- Never travel with new or newly repaired equipment you haven't checked out first to make sure it's working. It's not a bad idea to check all your equipment, either.
- Engrave your name or Social Security number on equipment as a safeguard against theft. And insure it.
- Everyone tells you not to put a camera in your car's glove box or trunk. So where should you put it? Wrap it in aluminum foil or a refrigerator bag and put it on a pad under the front seat, in a bag taped to the back of the seat, or in a bag hung from the headrest.
- If all of those technical details about exposure, lenses and the like make you feel lost, stop worrying and use an Instamatic. Even box camera photos are better than no pictures at all.

How to take good flash pictures

By BOB BERGER

SEE ALSO

Bounce-flash photography . . .
Candid photography . . . Cartridges, film . . .
Close-up photos . . . Developing, photo . . .
Night photography . . . Outdoor photography . . .

THE FIRST STEP in improving your pictures is to take the flash off the camera. Hold the flash high, and to the side of your subject. This way, you keep the flash from reflecting in your subject's eyes, and making them appear red in a color photo—or white, in a black-and-white shot. You also minimize distracting background shadows while adding a feeling of depth.

If there is one major problem with flash photos, it's that they always look like *flash* photos. After all, aiming the flash squarely at the subject won't result in natural-looking lighting.

A better approach is bounce lighting. Instead of pointing the flash at the subject, bounce the light off a wall or ceiling. Allow two extra F/stops for light loss. Or measure from flash, to bounce surface, to subject, and divide the distance into the guide number, to determine the F/stop.

In most flash situations, using black-and-white film gives enough latitude to cover fairly large exposure errors.

But color slide shooting is more critical. Exposure has to be correct. And bouncing flash off colored walls or ceiling may result in an unpleasantly tinted subject. Easiest way to shoot bounce flash color photos is to restrict yourself to white ceilings and walls. Or, improvise with a white bedsheet or white paper.

Bouncing your flash from a white photo um-

TYPICAL SUNNY-DAY photo, with deep shadow areas on the subjects' faces, is a likely candidate for fill-in flash technique to brighten shadows.

SHOT WAS IMPROVED considerably by simply combining sunlight with flash-fill lighting to give less contrast and add ample detail in shadow areas.

brella eliminates the variables of colored walls and ceilings, and in effect, transforms any room into an instant studio.

There are times when bounce flash just isn't workable. You may, for instance, want a dramatic effect, with deep shadows and bright highlights. In that case, try multiple flash. One setup that works nicely for portraits is to position one flash at a 45° angle to the subject, and high enough to throw a short nose shadow on the subject's face. On the opposite side of the camera, at subject height, place a second flash. Wire the flashes together, or connect the 45° flash to a slave trigger, an electric-eye device which is tripped instantaneously by light from the camera flash.

Some flash setups can make for exposure problems. The most accurate way to measure exposure is with a flash meter. An alternative is to simply bracket exposures.

One seemingly unlikely place to use flash is outdoors, for portraits on a sunny day. The technique is called fill-in flash, and the idea is to brighten shadows which can ruin an otherwise perfect shot. Set your camera as you normally would for a sunny-day exposure. Divide the guide number for your flash by the F/stop you're using. The result will be the distance in feet at which the flash should be set from the subject—if you want a strong fill. Usually a more subtle fill is

FLASH DIFFUSER softened light for these portraits, but retained its directional quality as well.

preferable, and it's best to move the flash 50 percent farther back.

Finally, some miscellaneous thoughts about the sync cord that joins flash unit and camera. Avoid using coil cords; they invariably short out. One notable exception: the Paramount heavy-duty sync cords.

Having read this far, if you have only a simple camera with a built-in flash, you can improve your photos by: 1. Positioning your subject away from background to eliminate distracting shadows. 2. Turning up room lights, and having your subject look at a bright light just before you snap the picture, to avoid red eye. 3. Remembering to watch out for mirrors, windows and eyeglasses that may reflect your flash.

FLASH ON CAMERA creates a photo that is harsh, unflattering. Shadows behind the subjects are distracting. Foreground is overexposed and washed out.

FLASH THAT'S bounced from a photo umbrella gives soft, natural lighting and an even exposure throughout this entire photograph.

Special effects put punch in your pictures

By BURT MURPHY

Creative, exciting effects are easy to add to your pictures. All it takes is practice and the right accessories, many of which you can make inexpensively yourself

SEE ALSO
Camera care . . . Camera gunstocks . . . Cameras . . . Candid photography . . . Filters, photo . . . Montages, photo . . . Night photography . . . Outdoor photography . . . Panorama photos . . . Prints, photo . . . Slides, photo . . . Used cameras

THE FUN IN photography increased when automatic cameras made good, clear photos easy, but automation took some of the fun away, too. You can recapture some of that fun—and dramatize your pictures—with easy (and mostly inexpensive) special effects.

With the right gadgets, a single-lens reflex, and a little know-how, you can:

- Take startling, 180° fisheye views.
- Shoot prismatic, multiple images.
- Vignette away portrait backgrounds.
- Soften portraits with soft focus or diffusion.
- Emphasize distance in scenic shots.

Fisheye shots are less expensive than you may have thought. True, fisheye *lenses* cost hundreds of dollars, but fisheye *attachments* start around $59.95 (for Spiratone and Prinz units) and can fit in front of virtually any lens on any camera.

Fisheye attachments work best on normal or moderate wide-angle lenses, such as a 50 or 35-mm on a 35-mm camera. With very-wide-angle lenses, the circular image may be too small. And

with long telephoto lenses, the curvature of the image is reduced and the effective f-stop becomes uncomfortably slow. Behind-the-lens meters may work with fisheye attachments; if not, or if you're using another type of meter, a ring on the attachment tells the true effective f-stop.

Fisheyes take in more than you may think possible at first. Until you're used to them, you'll find your pictures showing your feet, your tripod's legs or other things you'd rather not have in the picture. Fisheyes distort, but selectively: objects at the picture edge are always curved, but central objects aren't very distorted unless they're very close.

The diaphragm of the prime lens should be wide open when a fisheye attachment is used, and the control ring of the fish-eye should be set to the desired f-stop. For best definition, close down about two to three stops from maximum aperture.

Multiple images require even simpler, less expensive attachments: filter-like prisms designed to produce three, five or six simultaneous images on one frame. Spiratone offers three models: the 3P, which produces three parallel images; the 3C, producing three concentric images, and the 5C that surrounds its central image with four secondary images. Prinz's Mirage is similar, with five secondary images surrounding its central one. Prices, depending on the size and model chosen, range between $9 and $20.

Though these prisms can attach to the front of almost any camera lens, reflex or view cameras are by far the best to use, since they let you place the secondary images exactly where you want them. The prisms also rotate in their mounts, to help you place images precisely; the concentric models may even be rotated during exposure, producing deliberately blurred images surrounding a sharp one.

For more clear-cut images, mount the prism in front of the lens. A paper cup, its inside sprayed with flat black paint, can be used to mount the prism this way.

FILTER-SIZED prisms mounted in front of your camera lens give multiple images (right). You can pick from several prism types. Some give five concentric images as in this example; others give fewer. Some give three parallel images. Multiple-image prisms are made to mount like filters, but they can be held an inch or two ahead of the lens. A paper cup can become a mount (below), but should be painted black first. And you must focus and set the lens before you cover it with the cup.

FISHEYE shots (left) take in an ultrawide, 180° angle. But, unlike true wide-angle lenses, these curve the scene before them with the effect increasing toward the edges. (The face here, since it's in the picture's center, is less curved by the fisheye than it is distorted by proximity to the lens.) Fisheye attachments (right) fit nearly any lens, start at about $60. Used on wide-angle lenses, they produce full circles; used with normal-length lenses, their circles' outer edges may go beyond the edges of the film and be lost.

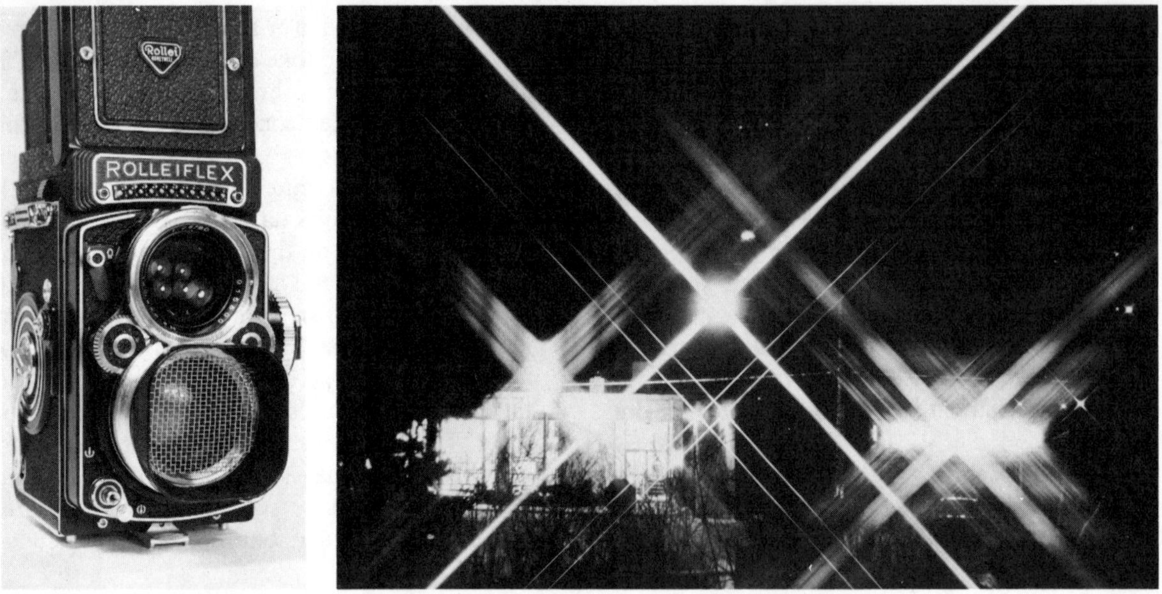

SPARKLING STARS SPREAD out from lights in night scenes or from sharp highlights in daytime photos when you use commercial or homemade star filters. To make one, simply cut a piece of screen to fit your lens hood or filter holder. For eight-pointed stars, use a second layer of screen. This simplified method may reduce contrast.

Multi-image prisms don't affect exposure, but they may cut off the corners of the picture at small apertures. Check this by previewing your pictures with the lens stopped down to the f-stop you're actually shooting at.

Star effects—long streaks or crosses of light surrounding strong highlights in daylight pictures, or light sources in night scenes—can add glitter and sparkle to your shots. You can buy filters to produce these effects, or make your own.

Spiratone has three models available: the Crostar 2P, which extends highlights along a single line, and the 1SQ and 2SQ, which produce crossed highlights. Prinz markets the Cross-Screen, producing an effect like that of the 2SQ. Prices are around $5 to $10, about the same as other filters.

To make your own, use aluminum screen patches (or scraps from discarded screens), either cut to fit your filter holder or simply crimped inside a lens hood. These homemade attachments diffuse the image more than commercial ones do, reduce contrast; and they can't be rotated as easily to orient the starlines where you want them.

If you combine two star attachments at right angles, you'll get eight-pointed stars. The angle between the points will vary if you vary the angle between the grids of the attachments.

Vignetting, or gradually blanking out the edges of a picture, is a time-honored technique to focus attention on a subject by separating it from its background. It's usually done in the darkroom, but it's even easier to do it in your camera—and that way, you can vignette your color slides as well.

For maximum control of your vignetting effects, you can use Spiratone's Vignetar attachment (about $16.00), which is adjustable for sharply or softly defined vignettes. Prinz has a spot filter that is not adjustable, but—at around $6.00—is even less expensive. Or you can make your own by rubbing petroleum jelly around the outer portions of a haze filter; here, the effect will vary with the thickness of the coating and

SOFT-FOCUS effect (right) makes antique-looking portraits and hides blemishes. This shot was made with Spiratone's Portragon soft-focus 100-mm f/4 lens.

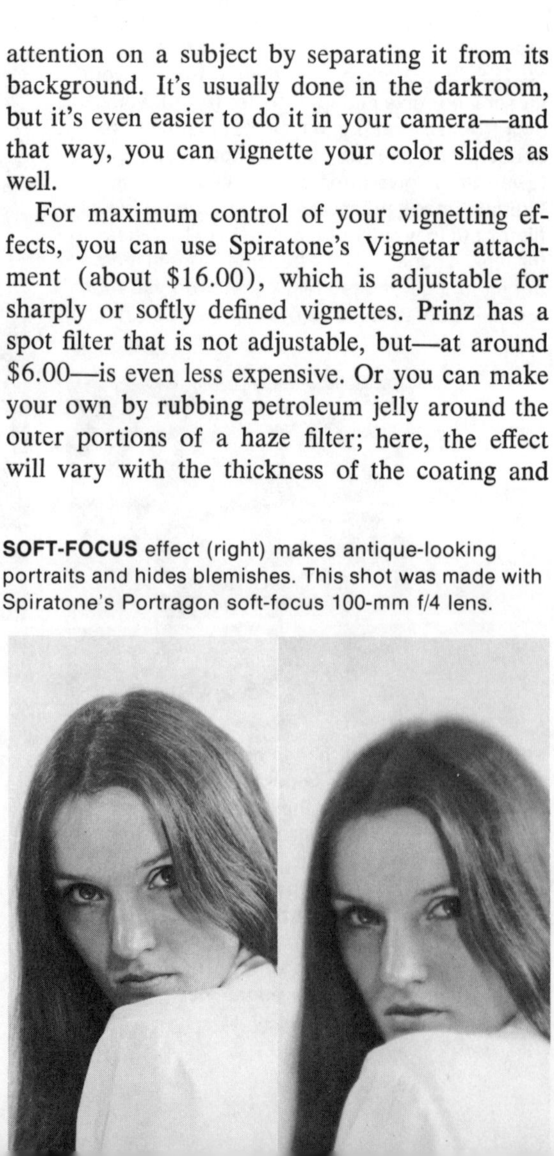

VIGNETTING SOFTENS photos' appearance and hides distracting backgrounds for another touch of the old-fashioned. Effects vary with the lens (135-mm, top left; 50-mm, top right) and type of attachment. Nonadjustable, homemade types include frosted cellophane tape (right) and a clear filter, its edges smeared with petroleum jelly as at the far right.

the size of the clear central spot. (You can get a similar effect by applying Scotch Magic cellophane tape to a lens hood.)

Longer lenses will enlarge the center spot and soften the edge of the vignette (too long a lens will integrate the spot and vignette into an overall haze). But smaller f-stops sharpen the edge, so you can juggle focal length and f-stop to get precisely the effect you want.

Diffusion and soft focus are also interesting portrait techniques, which soften the image for a more romantic effect and simultaneously minimize skin blemishes.

Diffusion is the milder of the two effects, gently lowering overall contrast by spreading light from the highlights into the shadows. Diffusion filters are available from Prinz, Spiratone and others for about the cost of ordinary filters. You can also make your own by stretching one or more layers of nylon stocking over a filter holder (use black or black-dyed nylon stockings in your color shots).

In cool weather, you can fog the lens by breathing on it, then shoot at the instant the lens has cleared enough to give you the exact effect you want.

Soft-focus, a stronger effect than diffusion, is usually associated with professional portraiture. It's not the same as incorrect focus, but rather a combination of a sharply focused image with an unsharp image that is formed by the lens's aberrations.

Spiratone's Portragon (about $25) is a 100-mm lens (a good focal length for portraiture) with such aberrations deliberately designed in. Its aperture is fixed at f/4; you control exposure by your choice of shutter speed.

Similar products are widely available. If your store doesn't have what you want, get Spiratone products from Spiratone, Inc., 135—6 Northern Blvd., Flushing, NY 11354; Prinz from Bass Camera Co., 179 West Madison St., Chicago, IL 60602. The prices in this article are, of course, subject to change.

Frame movies with a matte box

Here's a Hollywood-style special-effects device that you can adapt to almost any home-movie camera. It gives your movies that professional look

By JAMES R. OSWALD

USING SOME NEARBY OBJECTS to put a frame around your movie shots can make a good shot even better, by adding depth and atmosphere to a pretty scene that might otherwise look flat and dull on your screen. Look carefully, and you'll find suitable objects all around you—overhanging trees, picturesque archways, portholes, windows—the list is limited only by your imagination, by what the subject of your particular shot calls for, and by the location of these natural frames.

SEE ALSO

Boat photography . . . Cartridges, film . . . Dryers, photo . . . Night photography . . . Outdoor photography . . . Panorama photos . . . Theaters, home . . . Used cameras

But often the right object to silhouette in your foreground isn't quite in the right place to frame your subject. And sometimes you may want to spice a shot with a frame not naturally on the scene—a keyhole, perhaps, or the overlapping circles of movie "binoculars" (real binoculars, of course, show more of a fuzzy oval than the sharp figure-8 pattern the movies show you).

Professional filmmakers always have the frames they need, though, whenever they need them. Their frames are small cutouts called "mattes," attached to their cameras with simple devices called "matte boxes." The effect is quite professional—but the construction of a matte box is so simple that you can easily build your own.

It's basically just a tapered, light-tight box painted black inside, with a round hole at its small end to admit the camera lens, and provision for mounting interchangeable framing masks over the other end. Dimensions vary from camera to camera. The small end of the box should be just large enough to admit the front of your lens.

The dimensions of the other end will depend upon the type of lens you have: With a zoom lens, you should be able to see the edges of any mask in your finder when the lens is set to its shortest focal length, yet be unable to see the mask when the lens is zoomed to its telephoto position. With a nonzoom lens, you want the edges of the mask to be visible when the mask is mounted, but for the edges of the mattebox to be out of the frame

CONSTRUCTION IS SIMPLE, but the dimensions must be adapted to the particular lens and camera model.

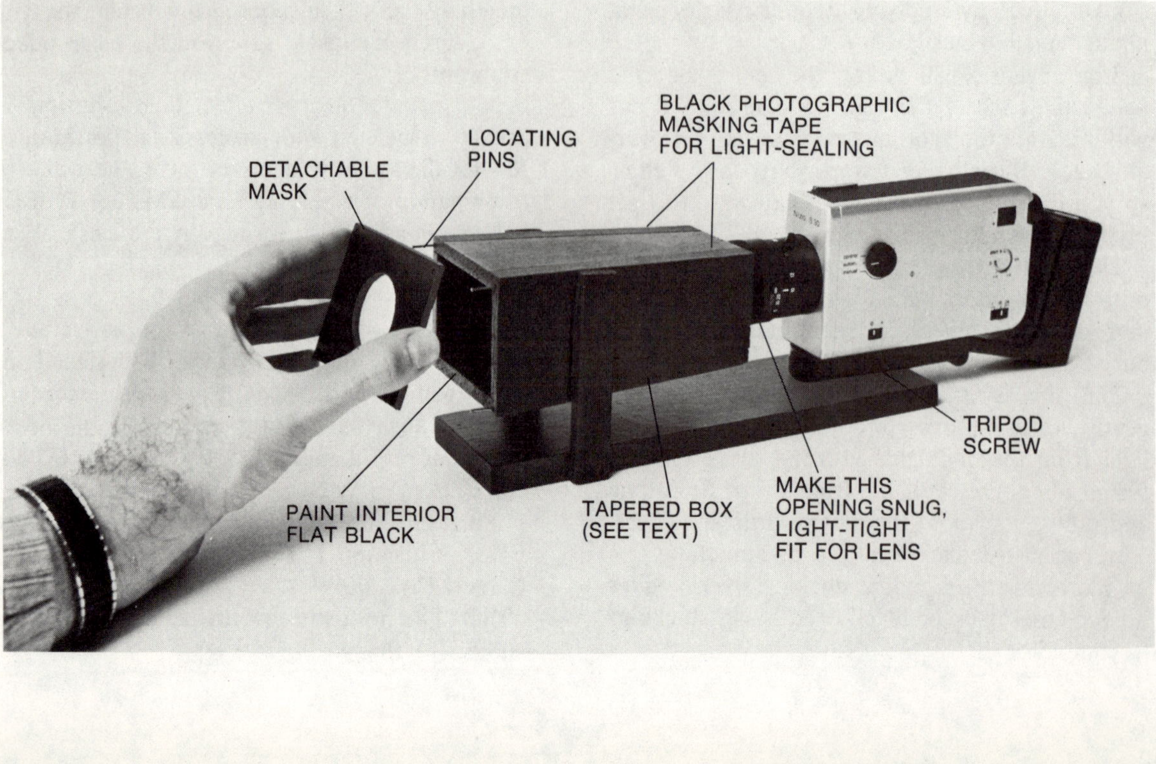

THE VARIETY OF MATTES is unlimited. Besides these, others could be cut from photos of trees or other subjects.

when the mask is off. The mask size also depends on the length of the box—and the length must be a compromise; the longer you make it, the more sharply outlined your matte frame will be—but the more ungainly and harder to handle the box will be, too.

Both the top and sides of the box should taper evenly and symmetrically, and the box's cross section should be a rectangle, approximately three quarters as high as it is wide.

With most cameras, the box will have to sit on struts above the baseboard, as mine does; again, the height of the struts depends on the camera. You can make your box from ¼-inch hardboard, plywood, opaque plastic, or what have you. Suitable scraps of wood can usually be picked up from lumberyards for a song. For the base, use ½-inch lumber. Drill the base below the tripod-screw socket, and let your tripod's screw hold both the camera and the matte box assembly.

The mattes themselves can be cut from ⅛-inch hardboard, wood, cardboard, or similar material. Four ¾-inch brads in the corners of the box's "window" end mate with small holes in the matte's corners to hold them in place.

To finish, tape the corners of the box with black photographic tape to prevent light leaks, and kill interior reflections by painting the inside of the box with flat black paint.

A few of the possible effects are shown above.

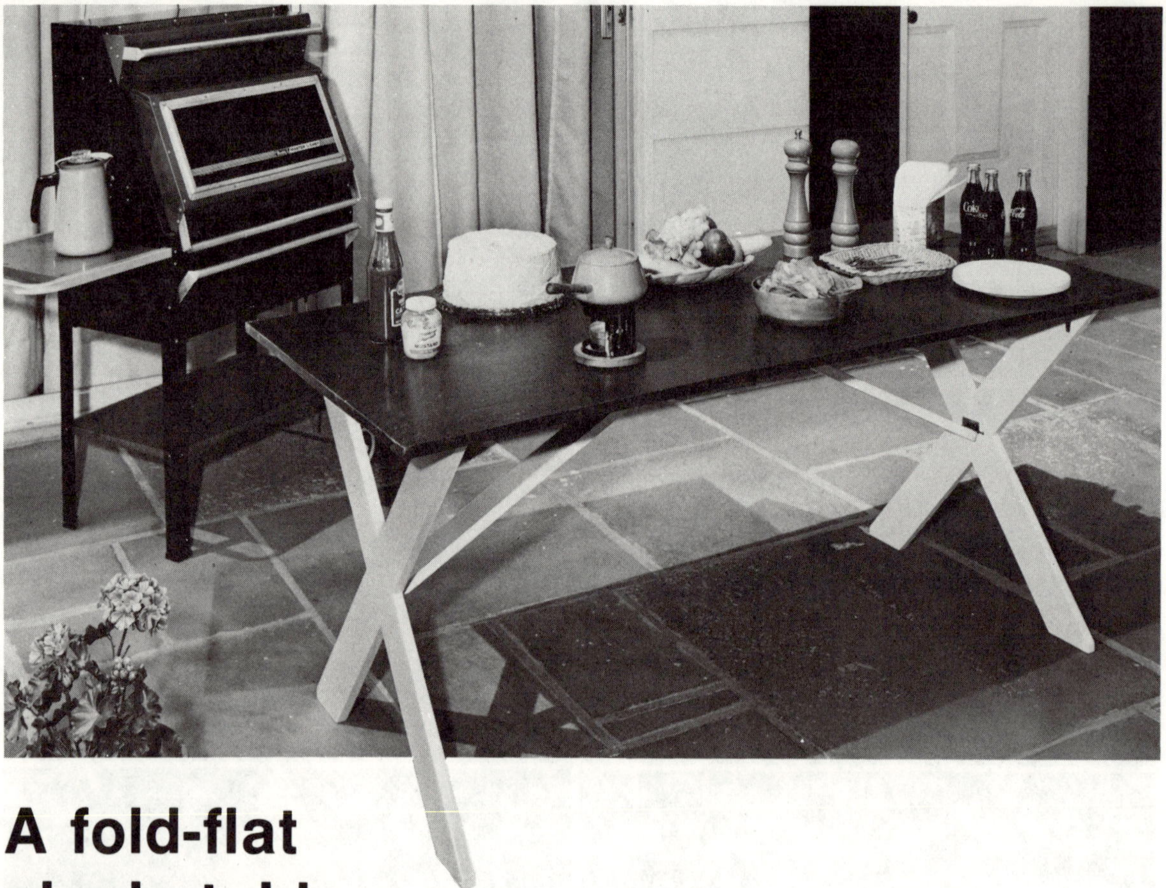

A fold-flat picnic table

By PAUL BELL

THE BIG PROBLEM with a conventional back-yard picnic table is that you can't put it away between cookouts. It's just too big to store—which means it's in the way when you mow the lawn, and it takes a beating from the weather. The latter means you'll have an annual paint or stain job.

You don't have such problems with this patio table. When the party's over, it can be stored in a minimum of space in your garage. With legs folded, it takes only 2¼ in. of space.

The table is sturdy when it's set up; the sawbuck-type legs are braced by their hinged supports. The braces not only lock the legs in the open position; they also lock them when folded—by using a pair of regular loose-pin hinges and substituting pull pins made from coathanger wire for the original hinge pins.

You can increase the size of the top, but if you maintain the 5½-in. dimension at the ends, you'll have to increase the length of the braces accordingly.

Block B is glued and screwed to the underside of the plywood top at its exact center. Although the braces are hinged to this block with plain butt hinges, you'll see in the enlarged detail that the braces are on the top of the hinge leaf and the screws are turned in from the rear side of the leaf.

The 1x4s, which are used to make the legs should lap flush at the point where the members cross. To cut the dadoes at the correct angle, set your saw miter gauge at 11°.

Use three loose-pin hinges (six leaves). One leaf is screwed to each end of the braces. Another is screwed to each block A and the other two are screwed to the inside of each leg assembly. Thus, single leaves at ends of the braces engage the single leaves screwed to the legs as well as to those screwed to blocks A. To set up the table you pull the hinge pin at blocks A, swing up the legs to engage the hinge leaf of the brace with the one on the legs and replace the wire pull pin.

SEE ALSO
Barbecues . . . Cookout bars . . . Firepits . . . Grills . . . Insect traps . . . Patios

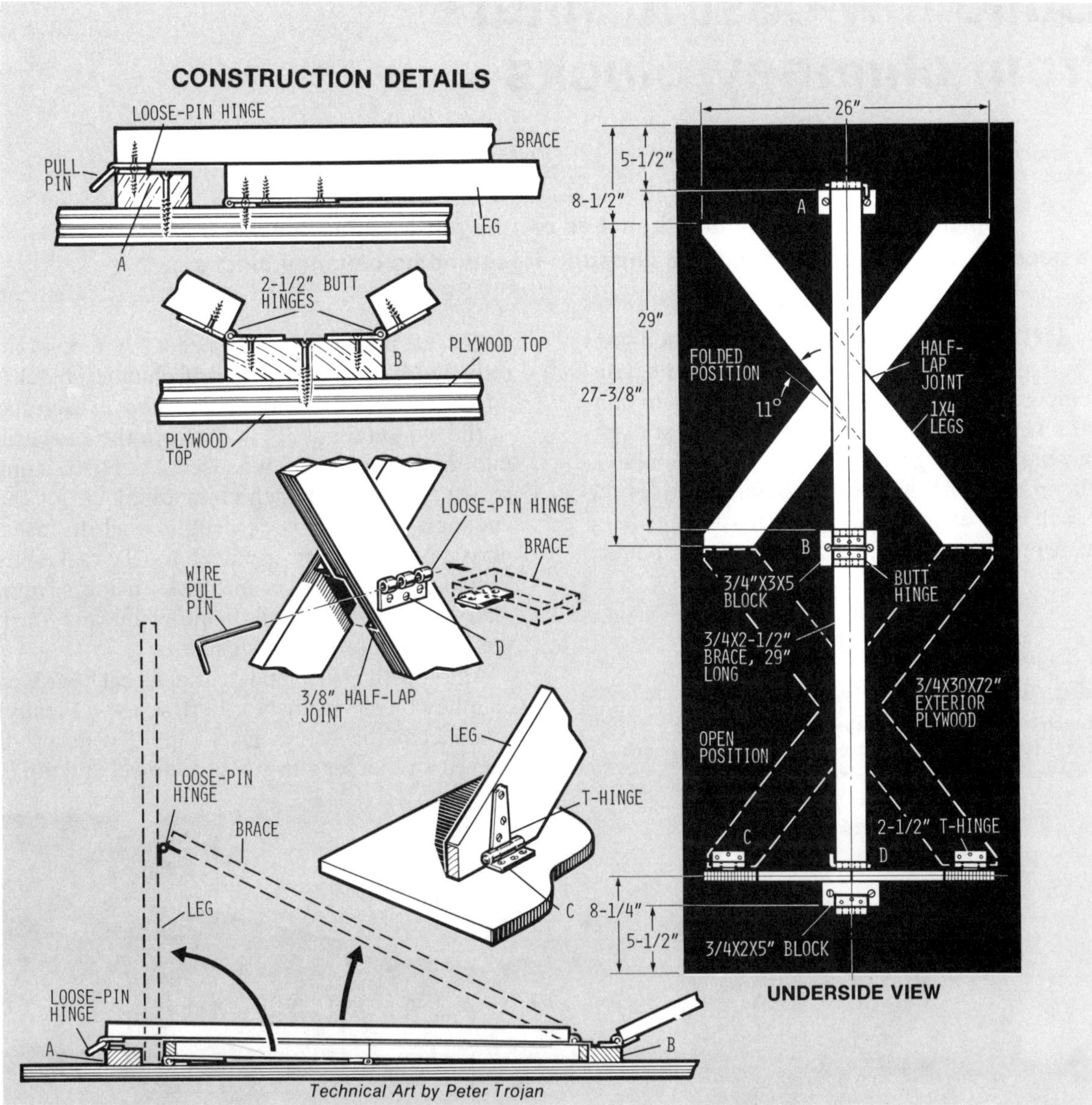

Technical Art by Peter Trojan

LEG IS BRACED in open position by engaging mating hinge leaves and replacing the L-shape hinge pin.

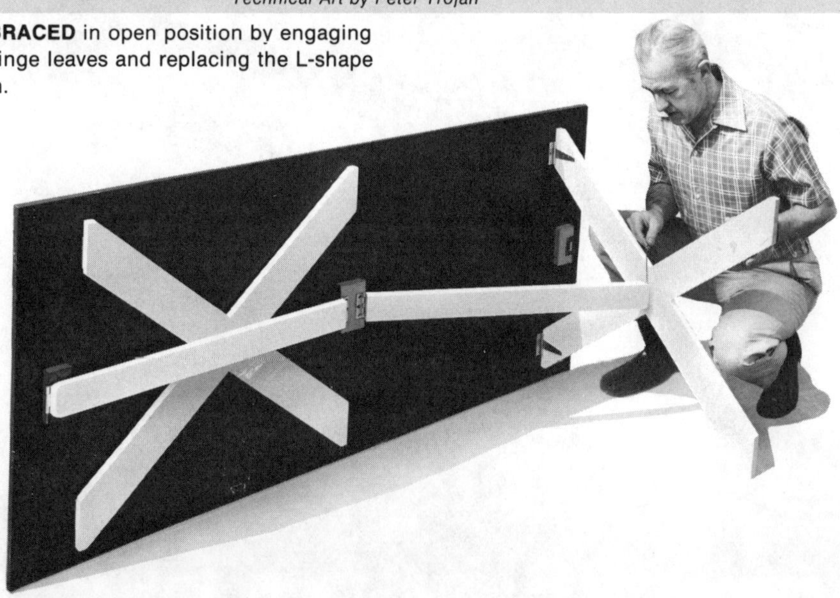

Build low-cost furniture from chimney blocks

By GARY GERBER

A picnic table and matching benches can be put together quickly using few tools because the redwood is simply fastened to freestanding chimney blocks

THIS SUMMER you'll enjoy your back-yard patio even more if you add this handsome, contemporary furniture to the scene. Easy to construct, these sturdy pieces have low-cost chimney blocks for legs; a lot of high-priced lumber is eliminated from the project. Blocks used for the bench and seats cost around $1.00 apiece. They were purchased at a local mason's supply outlet.

SEE ALSO
Benches, deck . . . Concrete blocks . . . Decks . . . Gazebos . . . Patios . . . Screened summer rooms

For each bench, you'll need 2 x 6 x 48-in. redwood boards and a pair of chimney blocks. After drilling a ¾-in. hole ½-in. deep, in each end of the wood (about 3¼ in. in from the end) drill pilot holes for No. 12 woodscrews. Next, using masonry bits, drill each chimney block for the anchors. Drill the block deep enough to insert plastic or metal masonry anchors. To make bits last longer, drill holes in blocks using several bits. Start with a small-diameter bit and work your way up to the finish size.

After pushing in anchors, attach seat boards to chimney blocks using No. 12 fh screws. Finally, to conceal the screwheads, apply waterproof glue to a ½-in. lengths of ¾-in. dowel and tap in

SLATTED COFFEE table is a slight variation of the furniture shown on the facing page. The ¾-in. redwood stock is separated by spacers, and the seat assembly is fastened to the blocks with galvanized screws and masonry anchors.

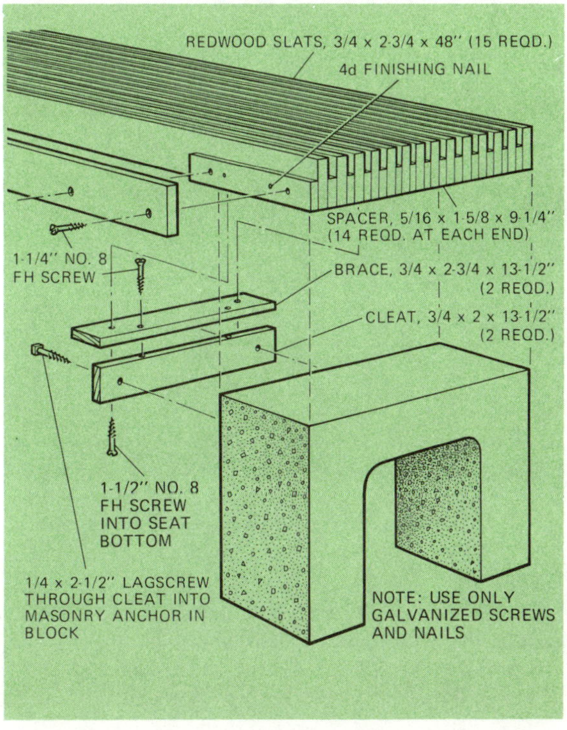

dowels. To make the table, place two benches back-to-back atop two pairs of chimney blocks as shown in the photo on page 2152. I've found the table is sturdy enough without tying the two benches together, and you retain the flexibility of being able to take apart the table to create two benches.

To build the coffee table with slatted top, use 14 spacers at each end of the table to separate the 15 redwood boards. Fasten the spacers to each board with 4d finishing nails, and tie them all together with an L-shaped brace on the bottom which, in turn, is fastened to each chimney block.

For eye-appeal, give the blocks one coat of pastel-shade masonry paint.

1 **BENCH SEAT BOARDS** are cut to length, positioned on blocks, and ¾-in. holes are drilled through. Tip of bit marks spot where you drill.

2 **HOLES IN MASONRY** should be bored in stages to make bits last longer. Start with a small bit and work your way up to the desired diameter.

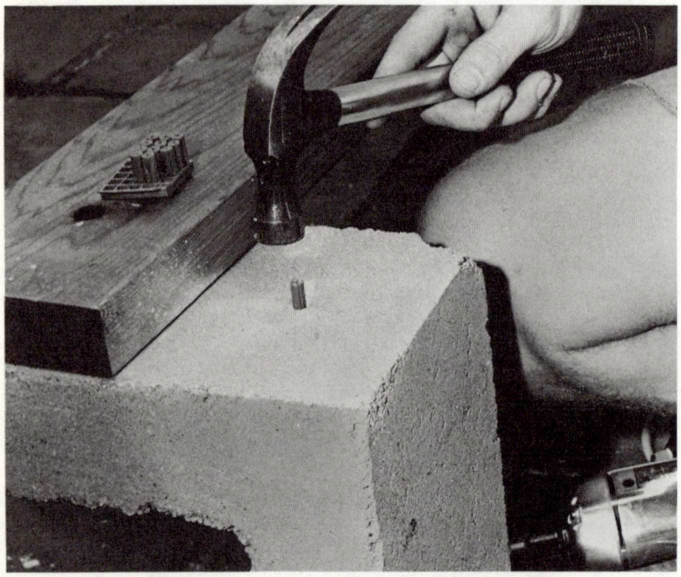

3 **MASONRY ANCHORS** are then tapped into the predrilled holes. The author used one at each end. Two per board at each end would be even better.

4 **FLATHEAD SCREW** is turned home in counterbored hole; ¾-in.-dia. dowel plug hides screwhead. Use waterproof glue to assure dowel stays put.

PLASTIC ELECTRICAL CONNECTORS of the Mars type make large pull grips for pull-chain light fixtures. Drill a small hole in the end of the connector and slip the chain through; then replace the end clip on the chain.—*Ken Patterson, Regina, Sask.*

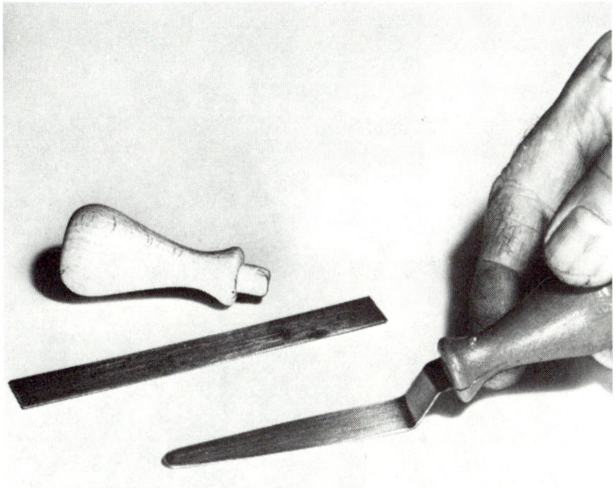

A SPATULA for shop use can be made from a bit of springy $1/64 \times 1/2 \times 4$-in. steel strapping and a handle from a rubber stamp. A slot about ½ in. deep is cut in the handle and the blade inserted, with household cement to fill the space. Two holes are drilled through the blade and handle, and brass escutcheon pins are used as rivets. The blade is rough-shaped before the handle is attached, then finished by grinding and polishing.—*Walter E. Burton, Akron, OH.*

LACKING DRUM SANDERS of the correct size for some inside curves, we found that sections of dowel could be used to serve the purpose. A slot was cut in the end of the dowel and a strip of sandpaper inserted and wrapped around the dowel. We have used these sanders in the drill press and on portable electric drills. When the ends of the paper become worn, pieces are torn off and the "sanders" are like new again.—*M. K. Cox and D. L. Palmer, Cambridge, IL.*

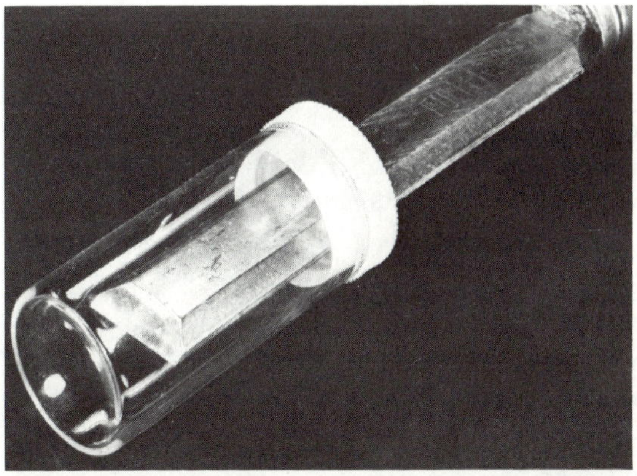

TO PROTECT the edge of a chisel kept in your toolbox, use a plastic prescription bottle just larger than the chisel's width. Use the chisel to cut a snug slot in the cap, then push the capped bottle over it.—*David L. Wiest, Cloudcroft, NM.*

You can stow away this picnic table

By WAYNE C. LECKEY

It looks complex, but this handsome picnic table is easy to build. It's designed to fold up to a compact 2 x 5 feet for convenient storage

IT'S GREAT TO HAVE a big table out on your deck or patio for those pleasant summer-evening meals. But finding a place to store it is something else. Often it simply stays outdoors all year.

We tossed the storage problem at designer Tom Fung, well known for his unique designs, who came up with the ingenious folding table you see here. Eighteen pivot points make it possible to fold the table into an incredibly small space of 2x5 feet, which means you can park it in a garage or basement with room to spare.

END VIEW

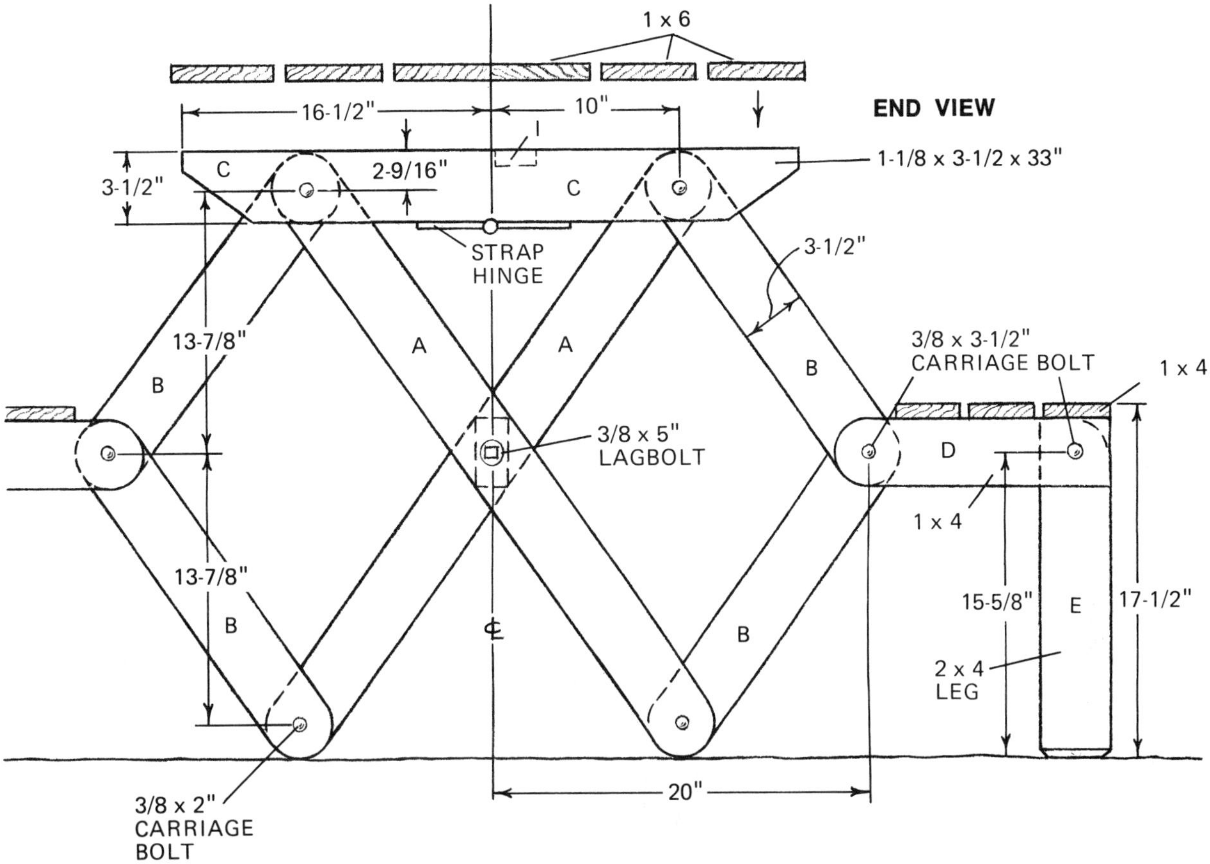

HINGE JOINT

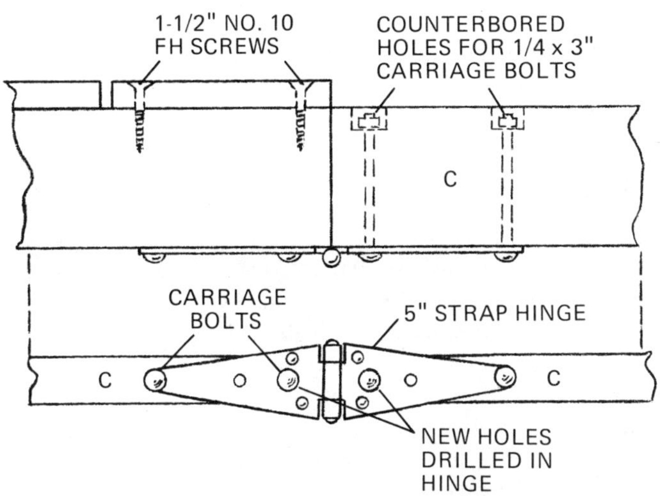

SEE ALSO

Benches, deck . . . Bolts . . . Cookout bars . . . Dining tables . . . Garden shelters . . . Gazebos . . . Grills . . . Hinges . . . Patios . . . Privacy screens . . . Yard lighting

TURNBUTTON DETAIL

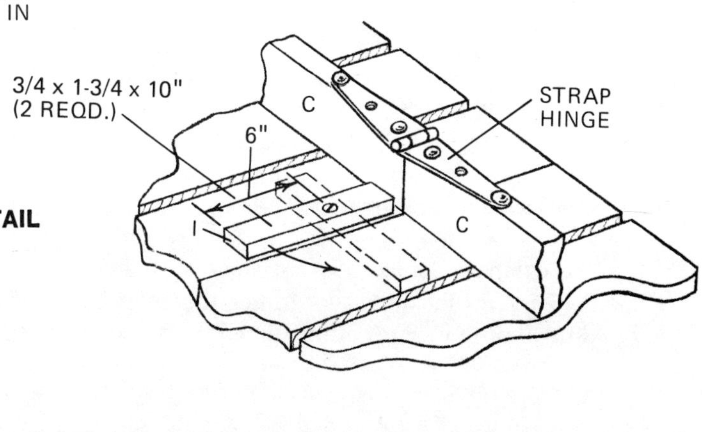

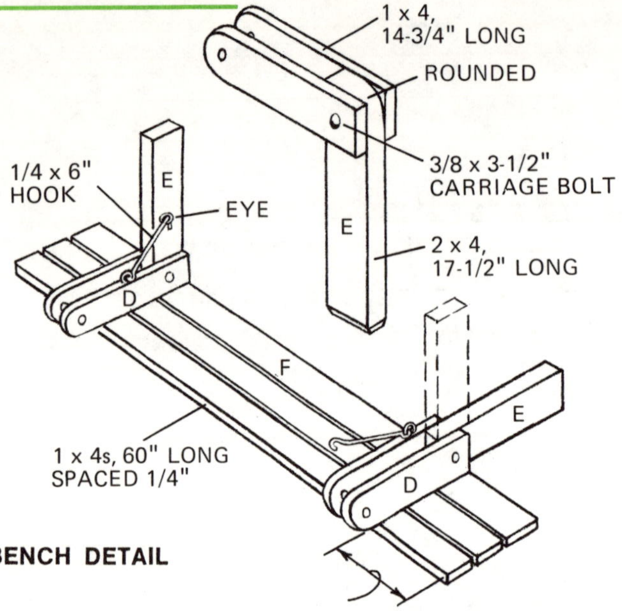

BENCH DETAIL

MATERIALS NEEDED (Redwood)

Key	Size	Amt.
A	¾ x 3½ x 38″	4
B	¾ x 3½ x 20¾″	8
C	1⅛ x 3½ x 16½″	4
D	¾ x 3½ x 14¾″	8
E	1½ x 3½ x 17½″	4
F	¾ x 3½ x 60″	6
G	¾ x 5½ x 60″	6
H	1½ x 3½ x 34¾″	1
I	¾ x 1¾ x 10″	2
	Hardware	
	¼ x 3″ carriage bolts	8
	¼ x 3½″ carriage bolts	4
	¼ x 2″ carriage bolts	4
	1¼″ No. 10 FH wood screws	2
	1½″ No. 10 FH wood screws	48
	¼ x 6″ hooks and eyes	4
	5″ strap hinges	2
	Cadmium-plated washers	34

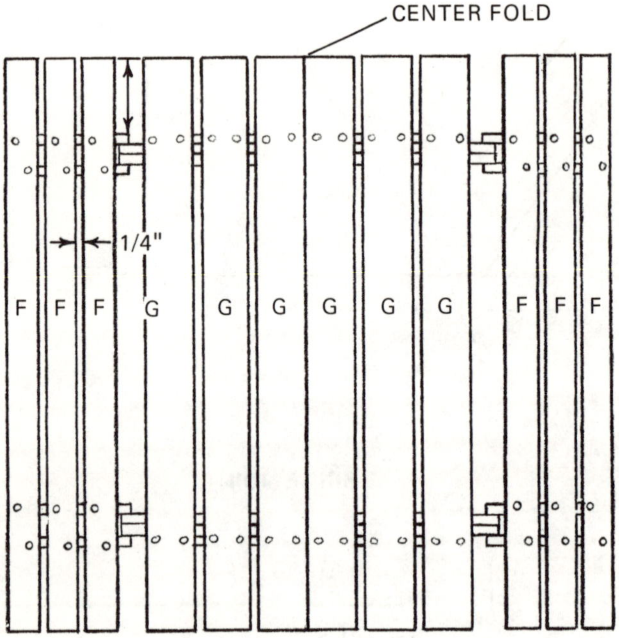

TABLETOP

We built the prototype, from long-lasting redwood, for a material cost well under $100. If you use No. 2 pine and paint it, you can make it for less. While it may look difficult, it's actually an easy table to build, mainly because all the parts are of lumberyard size. You just cut them to length.

The table is identical each side of a centerline. Each bench is alike, as is each scissor-folding leg. Spotting the seven pivot holes for each leg is done best by marking their locations on a sheet of plywood or wrapping paper and drilling the holes in the leg members to correspond. Round the ends of the members to a 1¾-in. radius and drill holes at the compass points. A good stunt to follow when rounding the ends and drilling the holes is to do two or more ends at one time by clamping the members together. This assures perfect alignment of the holes and makes for a neater job.

Cut parts C, to which the six tabletop members are attached, from 1⅛-in.-thick stock and join them endwise with 5-in. strap hinges. Drill an additional hole in each hinge leaf for a second carriage bolt. Use wood turnbuttons to lock the tabletop in the open position; place them on the underside near the hinges, on opposite sides of the centerline. You can keep the bench legs from being kicked outward accidentally by use of king-size hooks and eyes, and drawing up the carriage bolts holding the legs snugly so the legs do not swing freely. Place three large washers between leg members at each point where the benches attach, elsewhere, just one washer. Place washers under all nuts, of course.

Two unique picnic-table plans

continued

■ PLENTY OF ELBOW ROOM and attached benches are two of the most obvious advantages offered by the two king-sized redwood tables shown here and detailed on the following pages.

The hexagon design can be framed with 1¼-in. tubing, 1-in. standard pipe or 1¼-in. square tubing. If you don't have access to bending equipment, use square tubing and cut V-notches at the bending points, then bend and weld each joint.

The octagon model is a simple, straight-forward carpentry project with no metal-working involved.

Since redwood has its own natural preservative, the only finishing required is a thorough sanding and a coat of redwood stain to ensure uniform color. Finish other woods with exterior enamel.

SEE ALSO

Barbecues . . . Benches, deck . . .
Cookout bars . . . Garden shelters . . . Gazebos . . .
Insect traps . . . Patios . . .
Screened summer rooms . . . Tubing, metal

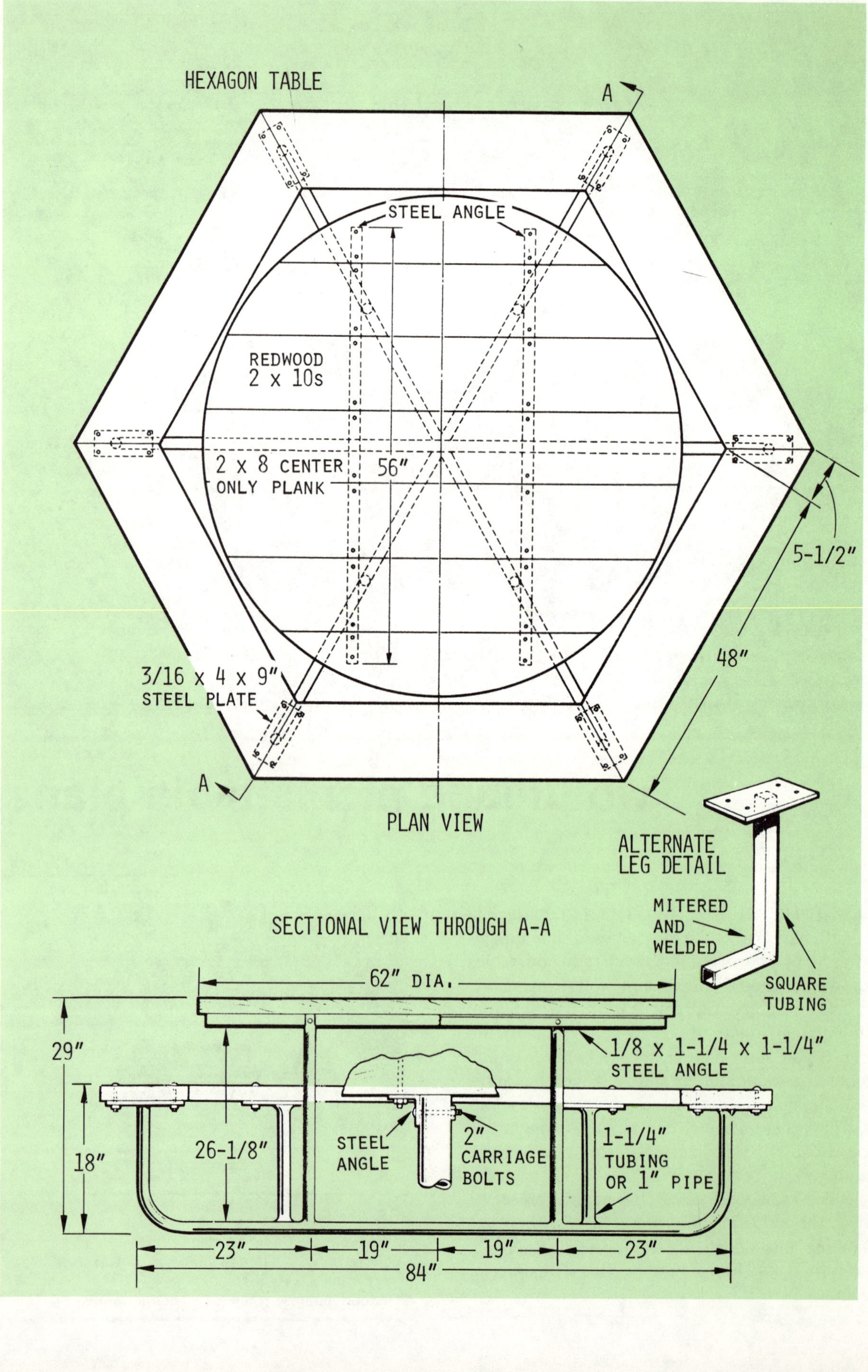
HEXAGON TABLE
A
STEEL ANGLE
REDWOOD
2 x 10s
2 x 8 CENTER
ONLY PLANK
56"
5-1/2"
48"
3/16 x 4 x 9"
STEEL PLATE
A
PLAN VIEW
ALTERNATE
LEG DETAIL
MITERED
AND
WELDED
SQUARE
TUBING
SECTIONAL VIEW THROUGH A-A
62" DIA.
29"
1/8 x 1-1/4 x 1-1/4"
STEEL ANGLE
18"
26-1/8"
STEEL
ANGLE
2"
CARRIAGE
BOLTS
1-1/4"
TUBING
OR 1" PIPE
23"
19"
19"
23"
84"

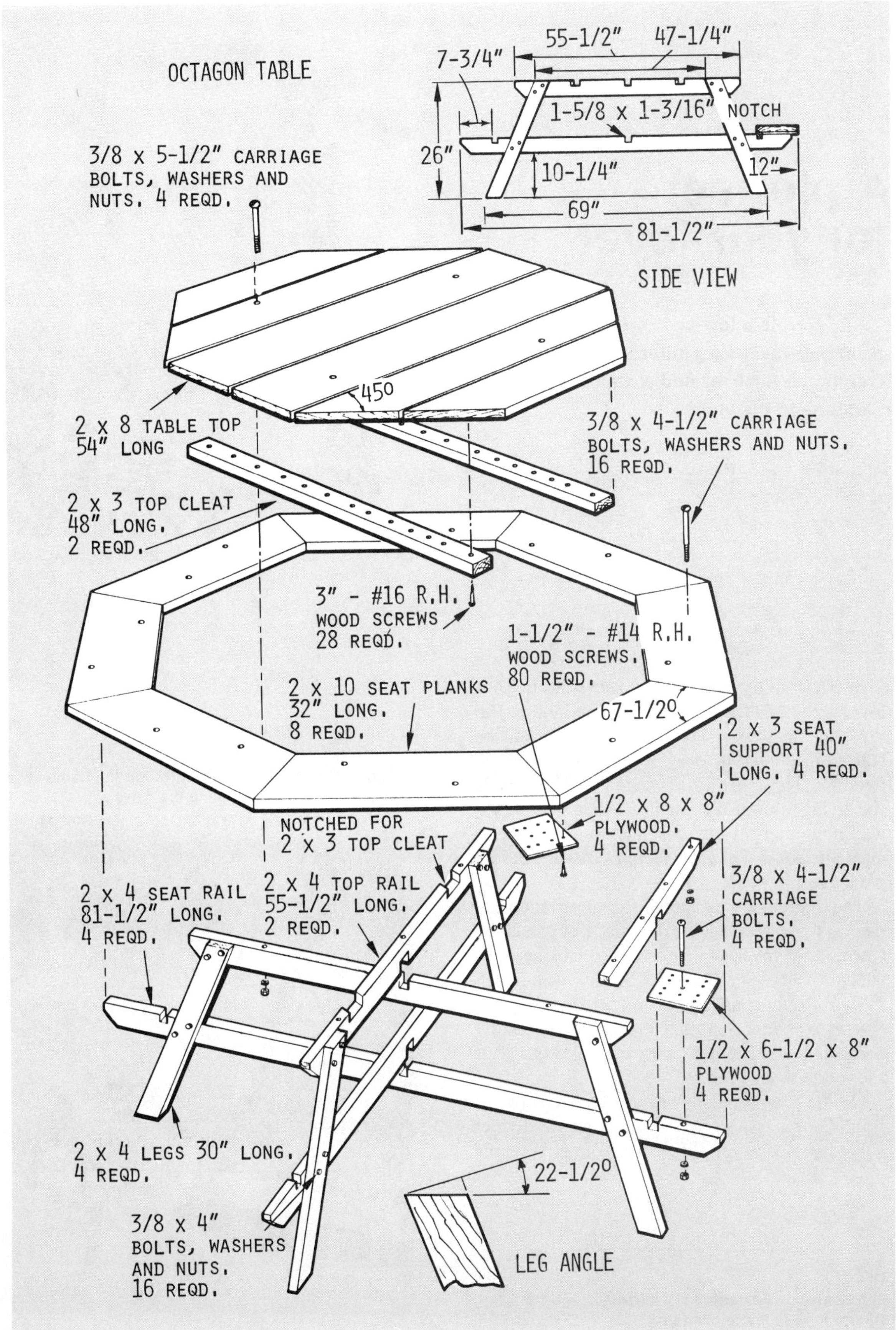
OCTAGON TABLE
55-1/2"
47-1/4"
7-3/4"
1-5/8 x 1-3/16" NOTCH
26"
10-1/4"
12"
69"
81-1/2"
SIDE VIEW
3/8 x 5-1/2" CARRIAGE BOLTS, WASHERS AND NUTS. 4 REQD.
45°
2 x 8 TABLE TOP 54" LONG
3/8 x 4-1/2" CARRIAGE BOLTS, WASHERS AND NUTS. 16 REQD.
2 x 3 TOP CLEAT 48" LONG. 2 REQD.
3" - #16 R.H. WOOD SCREWS 28 REQD.
1-1/2" - #14 R.H. WOOD SCREWS. 80 REQD.
2 x 10 SEAT PLANKS 32" LONG. 8 REQD.
67-1/2°
2 x 3 SEAT SUPPORT 40" LONG. 4 REQD.
1/2 x 8 x 8" PLYWOOD. 4 REQD.
NOTCHED FOR 2 x 3 TOP CLEAT
2 x 4 SEAT RAIL 81-1/2" LONG. 4 REQD.
2 x 4 TOP RAIL 55-1/2" LONG. 2 REQD.
3/8 x 4-1/2" CARRIAGE BOLTS. 4 REQD.
1/2 x 6-1/2 x 8" PLYWOOD 4 REQD.
2 x 4 LEGS 30" LONG. 4 REQD.
22-1/2°
3/8 x 4" BOLTS, WASHERS AND NUTS. 16 REQD.
LEG ANGLE

A pier set for your foyer

Here's a low-cost way to finish up your front hallway, using mitered filigree to enhance a mirror and a small table that fastens to the wall

By ROSARIO CAPOTOSTO

LAY A THIN BEAD of glue in mirror-frame grooves and insert mitered filigree.

WHEN WE FINISHED dressing up our foyer, I thought the project would end there. But my wife was so pleased with the results that she started dreaming up ways of utilizing what, at that time, was a stretch of wasted wall just inside the living room. We finally decided to add a wall-hung pier set for those last-minute appearance checks that always seem necessary before we leave the house.

The filigree of the frame is the same material I used in the entry divider. (It's made by Masonite Corp., 29 North Wacker Drive, Chicago, IL 60606.) And a piece of scrap Marlite wall paneling was used to back up the mirror. Total cost of the set was less than half the price of a ready-made unit. But I haven't seen any I like as well as the modern set I made.

On the prototype shown, the same hardwood framing that was used for the room divider served perfectly for the mirror frame. I simply

STURDY EYEBOLTS installed through the frame edge, joined with picture wire, hang the mirror.

SEE ALSO

Entryways . . . Fasteners . . . Mirrors . . . Quarry tile . . . Room dividers

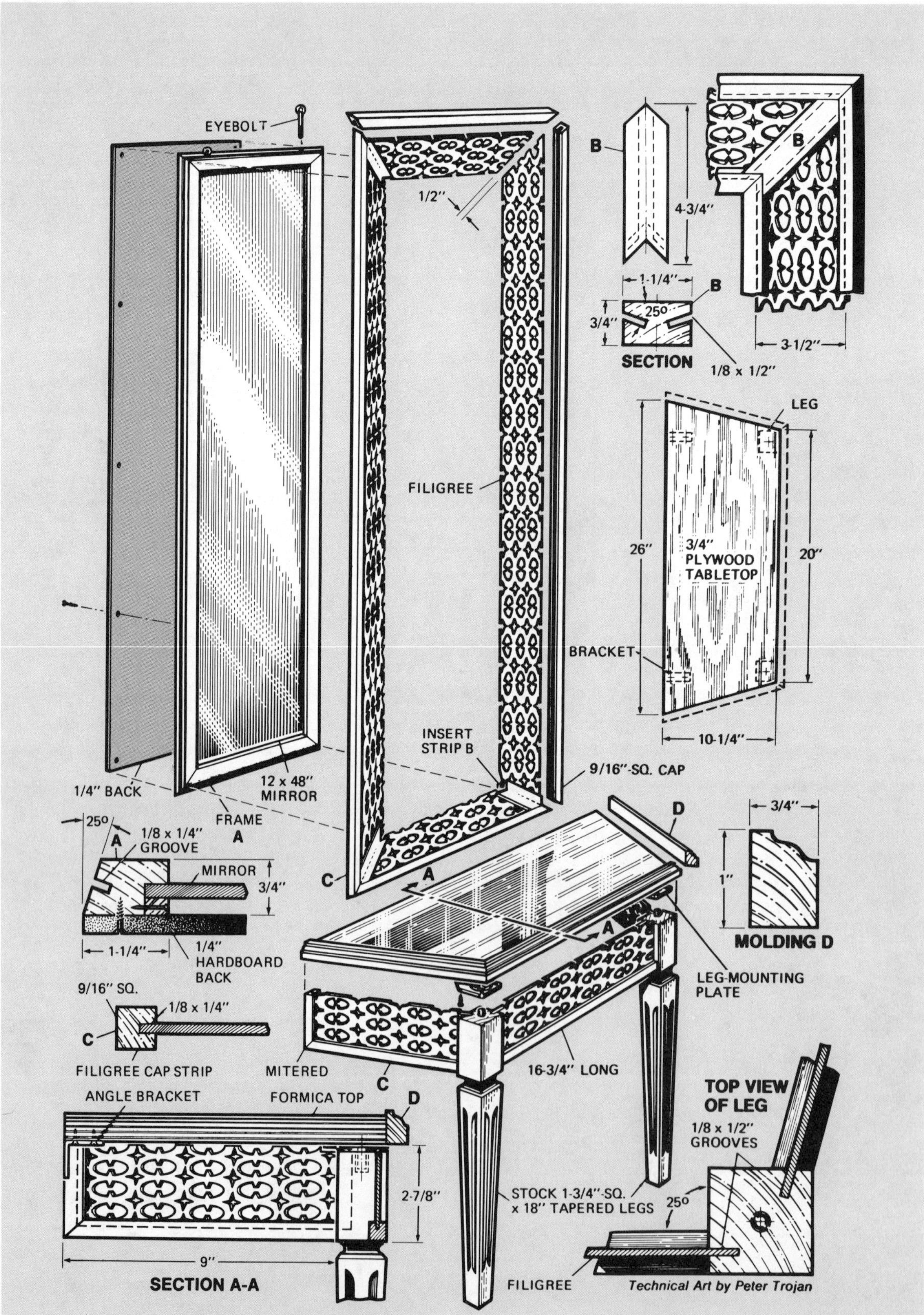
EYEBOLT
1/2"
B
4-3/4"
B
1-1/4"
B
3/4"
25°
SECTION
1/8 x 1/2"
3-1/2"
LEG
FILIGREE
26"
3/4" PLYWOOD TABLETOP
20"
BRACKET
10-1/4"
INSERT STRIP B
9/16"-SQ. CAP
1/4" BACK
12 x 48" MIRROR
FRAME A
25°
1/8 x 1/4" GROOVE
A
MIRROR
3/4"
1-1/4"
1/4" HARDBOARD BACK
C
A
D
3/4"
1"
MOLDING D
A
LEG-MOUNTING PLATE
9/16" SQ.
1/8 x 1/4"
C
FILIGREE CAP STRIP
MITERED
C
16-3/4" LONG
ANGLE BRACKET
FORMICA TOP
D
2-7/8"
9"
SECTION A-A
STOCK 1-3/4"-SQ. x 18" TAPERED LEGS
TOP VIEW OF LEG
1/8 x 1/2" GROOVES
25°
FILIGREE
Technical Art by Peter Trojan

enlarged factory grooves in the wood frame to accept a 1x4-ft. mirror that I bought. (If you wish, you can run a rabbet in the framing strips and use a cleat to hold the mirror.) Next, make a 25° bevel cut to remove some of the excess width along the solid edge, leaving about 1 in. across the face. Then plow a ⅛-in. groove about ¼ in. deep perpendicular to the beveled edge. This groove receives the filigree.

Miter the corners of the strips to form a frame around the mirror, and for rigidity, back up the mirror with a piece of Marlite or hardboard as mentioned above.

Glue and screw three sides of the frame only to this backing. The bottom frame is joined with screws only so that the mirror can be inserted after most of the carpentry is completed. And, if your mirror should ever become cracked, this makes replacement a simple task.

To hang the frame, two eyebolts are installed on the back and fitted with an appropriate length of picture wire. Make certain that these bolts do not enter the groove that is intended to receive the mirror, and install them before inserting the mirror.

To attach the mitered filigree sections, squirt a bead of white glue into each outside groove. Notice in the photo at the right that the mitered filigree ends do not meet. This is to insure room for the reinforcing corners. Here you should allow about a ½-in. space which will be bridged by the insert.

figure the angles

Cutting these inserts is truly an exercise in angle cutting. The lead end is an inside miter while the tail end is the reverse. The tail end also slants back 25° toward the bottom to assure a good fit at the frame corner. Finally, two angled grooves along the sides permit it to slide over the mitered filigree. Since the face of the insert is left flat it won't fit flush with the 9/16-in.-sq. strip which surrounds the outer edge of the filigree and is not intended to. Glue the inserts in place first and add the square strips last.

The table is made using a pair of factory-made legs purchased at a lumberyard and a ¾-in. plywood top. Grooved slots cut into the leg tops secure the filigree. A piece of molding (D) was used to enclose the table top which I first covered with white paneling. You could use decorative laminate here.

The console can be stained or painted. I sprayed mine all white to contrast nicely with a green wall in back.

INSTALL MIRROR before the final section of the frame is placed. This last piece goes in without glue for easy replacement, should the mirror crack.

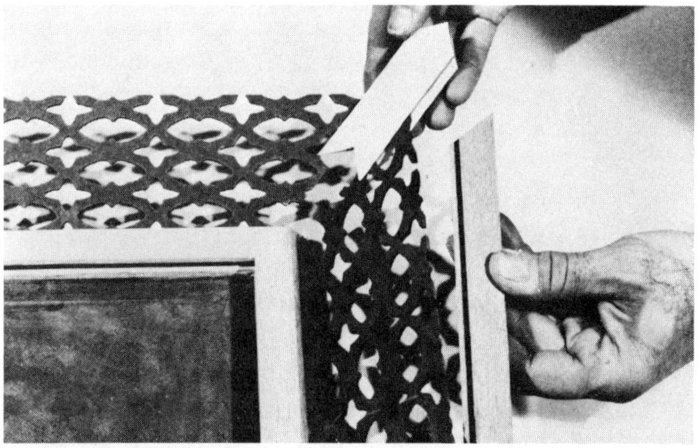

ARROW-SHAPED reinforcing corners provide an exercise in angle cutting (see text for details). Glue is used in groove here; edge cap goes on next.

FACTORY-MADE TAPERED LEGS must have grooves cut in at top to receive filigree—which is cut a bit long, then bowed and sprung into place.

How to figure your planing speed

This "slideless slide rule" will reveal your boat's potential speed

By JIM MARTENHOFF

KNOWING the fully loaded gross weight of a planing boat, and the horsepower, allows you to compute the probable optimum speed—assuming the engine is tuned and delivering its rated hp, a correct propeller is fitted, and the boat is properly trimmed.

Here is a nomograph, or slideless slide rule, that tells you what top speed you can expect from your boat. If you know the hp, all you have to do is figure the gross weight, *fully loaded.*

Using a straightedge, connect the gross weight with the hp. Read optimum top speed at the point where the straightedge intersects the speed scale in the center.

The hp scale, you'll note, is in two parts: conventional planing hull hp on the right side; deep-vee and tri-hull hp on the left. (Boats with complex bottom configurations are not ordinarily as efficient as hulls with flat bottoms aft, and require slightly more power to attain the same top speed.) Timing your boat over a measured distance and comparing true speed with that obtained from the nomograph does two things:

First, if you fall badly below what you expected, you may have an engine not putting out its rated power, a poor propeller—you may need more pitch—or your boat may be poorly trimmed for peak performance with, perhaps, too much weight forward.

Second, the nomograph serves as a "rating" of powerboat efficiency, including hull design. If actual speed on a measured mile equals the speed obtained from the scale, then the boat rates at 100 percent, or par. Most boats will reach top speeds at 90 percent of that obtained from the scale, or better.

Boats rating much less than 90 may have performance or even design problems. A rare boat will exceed 100 on the scale.

The nomograph can be used when buying a boat, providing a clue to what hp you need for the top speed you want. Connect weight with the top speed required, and read minimum necessary hp where the straightedge intersects the hp line.

For heavier inboards with weight and hp above those on the scales, take 10 percent to use table. Example: 9000-pound boat, 420 hp; use 900 pounds and 42 hp. The answer from the nomograph is the optimum speed for that boat.

Forty miles per hour is a sort of "barrier." Efficiency tends to improve sharply above 40 mph, as the boat's bottom "breaks out," gets air under it, and has less wetted surface and therefore less drag. It would not be unusual for boats exceeding 40 mph to rate above 100 in performance efficiency.

Give your boat a try on this handy chart. The result may be a surprise and give you some new insights into your boat's performance.

EXAMPLE: A 100-hp engine mounted on a 2000 pound (gross weight) deep-V boat should give 35-mph speed.

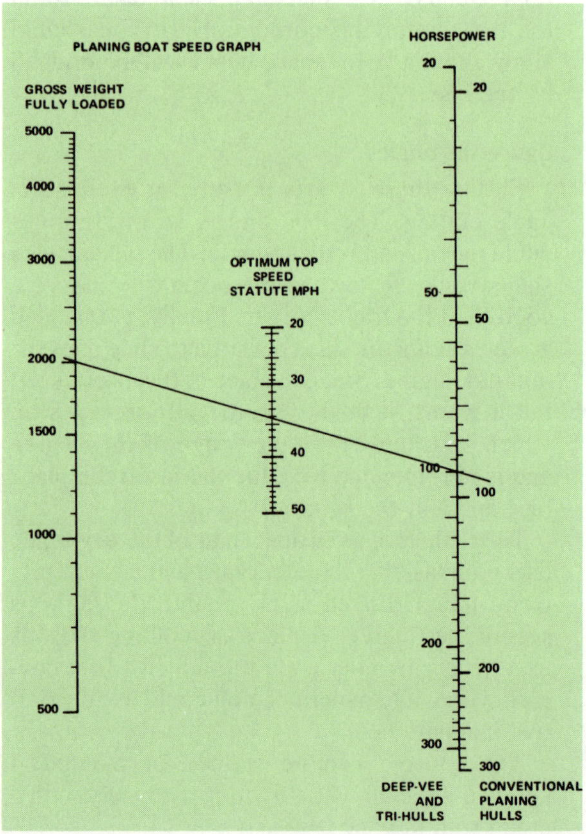

SEE ALSO
Boats . . . Boating safety . . . Boat testing . . . Outboard motors

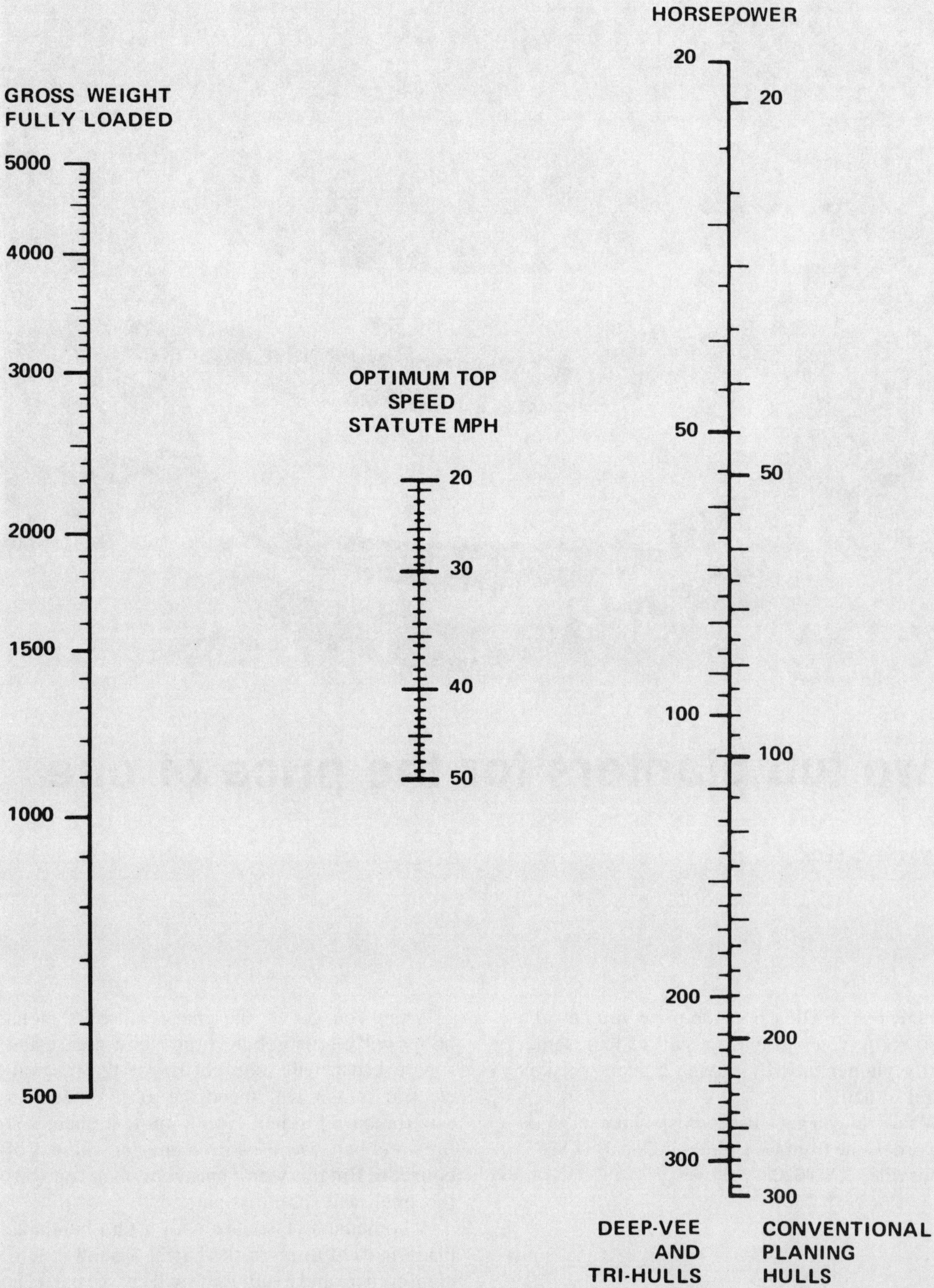
GROSS WEIGHT
FULLY LOADED
5000
4000
3000
2000
1500
1000
500
OPTIMUM TOP
SPEED
STATUTE MPH
20
30
40
50
HORSEPOWER
20
20
50
50
100
100
200
200
300
300
DEEP-VEE
AND
TRI-HULLS
CONVENTIONAL
PLANING
HULLS

Two tub planters for the price of one

By WAYNE C. LECKEY

FOR HALF OR LESS the price you pay at a patio shop, you can make a pair of handsome, sturdy planter tubs by sawing a used whiskey barrel in half.

Where do you get a used whiskey barrel? You can order one from G. I. Frazier Co., Box 8275, Louisville, KY 40208.

SEE ALSO
Bars . . . Decks . . . Garden shelters . . . Gazebos . . . Patios . . . Strawberry barrels

When you get it, the chances are its metal hoops will be rusty, but a little elbow grease and a wire brush will soon get rid of the rust (an electric sander will speed the job). When you saw the barrel in half, you'll know it once held firewater because its charred interior will reek of bourbon. But this won't hurt your plants one bit; the smell will soon dissipate.

A homemade T-square with a thin bendable blade is used to mark the barrel around its circumference, and a sabre saw will cut the barrel in half quickly. Drain holes are required in the bottom of each tub, and you have a choice of painting the oak staves or sanding and varnishing them.

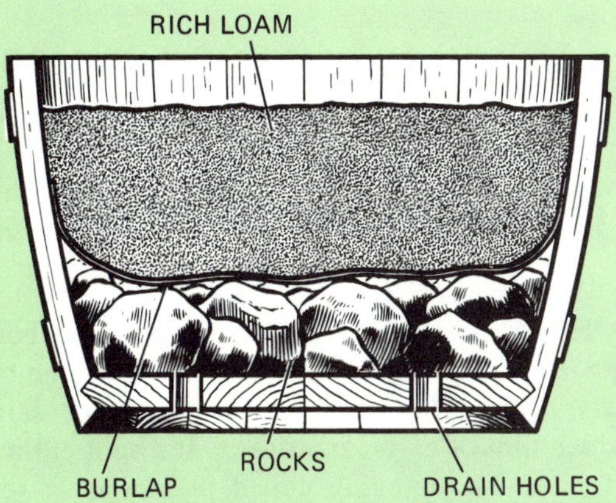

ELECTRIC SANDER and coarse abrasive paper will derust the hoops in a hurry; or do it by hand with a wire brush. For a varnish finish, sand the staves for a new-wood look.

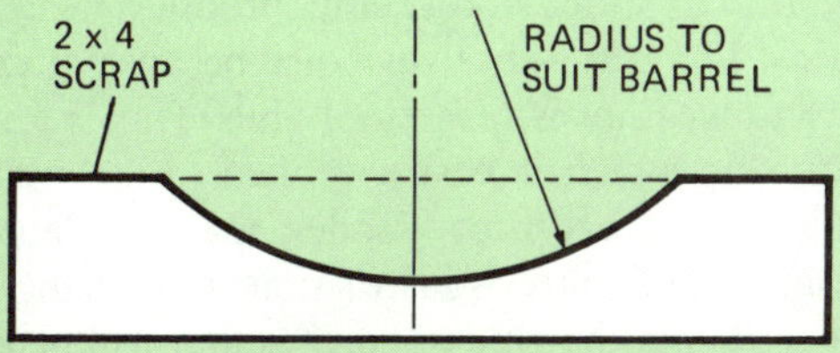

BARREL STAYS PUT for sawing when cradled with wood blocks at each end. Mark cutting line around circumference, plunge cut with a sabre saw, then rotate barrel.

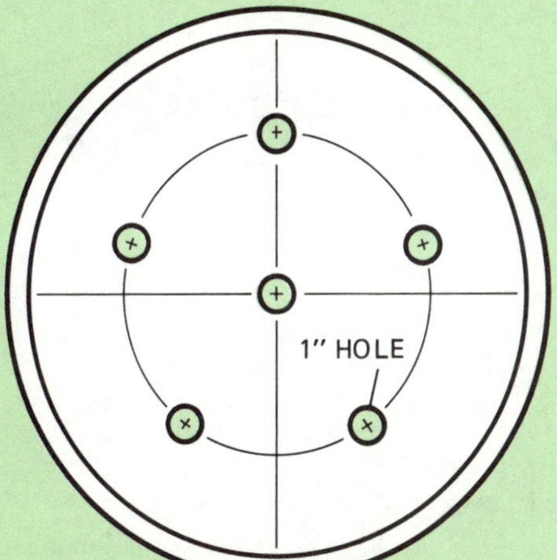

DRILL SIX DRAIN HOLES in the bottom of each tub; when you're ready to add plants, place rocks in the bottom, cover them with burlap and fill tub with potting soil.

Planters you can use indoors or out

HERE ARE TWO handsome pieces for showing off your prized potted plants. The contemporary bench-type stand features scalloped skirts which hint of early Americana. It's built entirely of pine. The hanging cubed planter is of redwood, and ordinary window sash chain is used to hang it.

Both of these plant containers can be used on the patio during the summer and simply moved indoors when cool weather arrives.

Use only hot-dipped galvanized or aluminum nails and screws for fastening. Ordinary steel fasteners will quickly rust and produce unsightly stains. The best adhesive choice because of exposure to weather is resorcinol glue. This is a two-part glue which is easily applied (after mixing) with a clean brush or wooden spatula. Caution: Read manufacturer's instructions for mixing and use, and mix the glue in batches that will be used in your work session—leftovers cannot be saved.

SEE ALSO
Benches, potting . . .
Decks . . . House plants . . .
Outdoor tables . . . Patios . . .
Strawberry barrels . . .
Terrariums

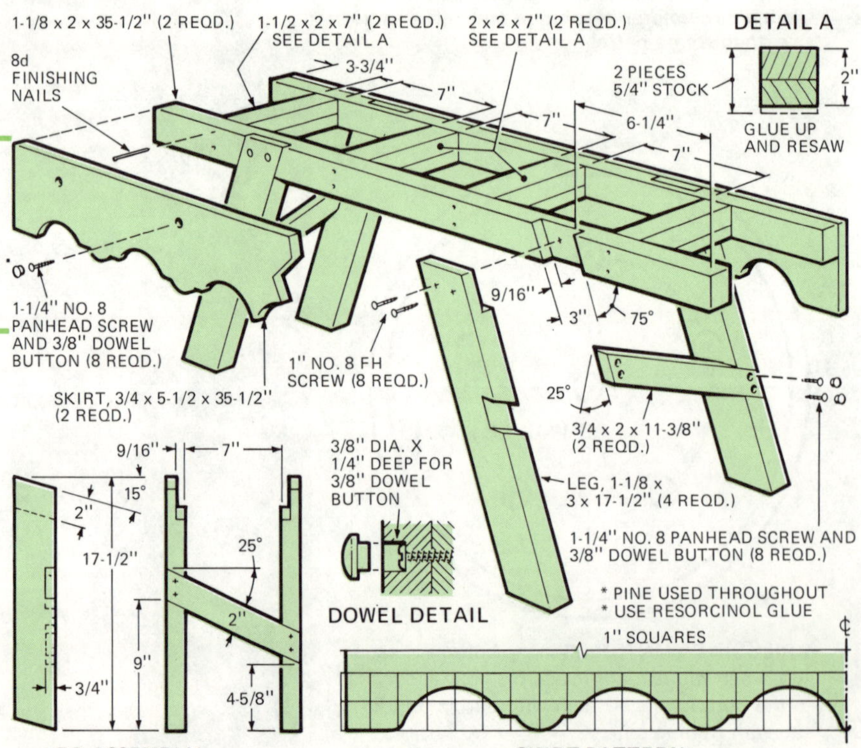

The bench was finished with an exterior stain and two coats of Man O'War spar varnish. The hanging planter was left natural, because it is of redwood, and treated with clear wood preservative.

bench-type planter

To save cutting problems through and around knots, use clear pine for the skirts. Other parts can be of No. 1 or 2 common pine.

Start by cutting parts to size. To make notches in the legs, use either a handsaw and chisel, table saw or radial-arm saw. Note that the crosspieces are created by gluing up two thicknesses of 5/4-in. stock and then resawing them to desired size. When all parts are cut, test-assemble using 4d finishing nails only. When satisfied, permanently assemble with glue and fasteners.

hanging planter

A quickie project that actually is fun to make, this hanging plant container is sized to suit a good-size flowerpot. The design can be used for smaller flowerpots, but the blocks must then be reduced in length and width.

Cut the required number of blocks on a table saw or radial saw. Notice that each course of blocks is a slightly smaller size than the one above it. This gives the proper taper to hold the pot. Refer to the drawing for exact dimensions. Sand and dust off all parts. Assemble the planter upside down using glue and nails. Note: Lay out each course on the preceding layer, arrange blocks until satisfied, mark their positions, and permanently fasten them with glue. Insert screw eyes, attach sash chain and suspend planter from a stout S-hook. Install flowerpot.

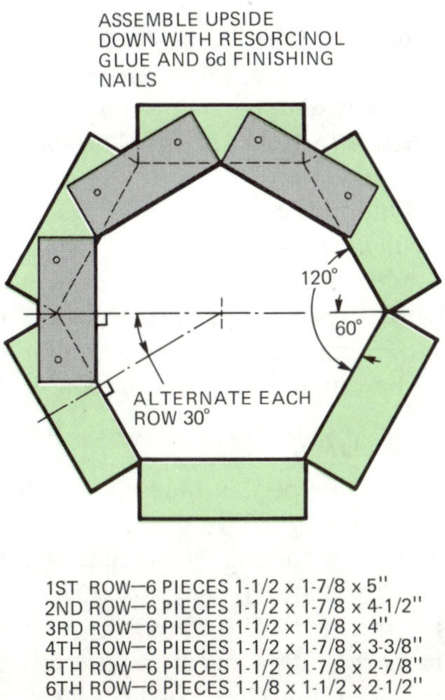

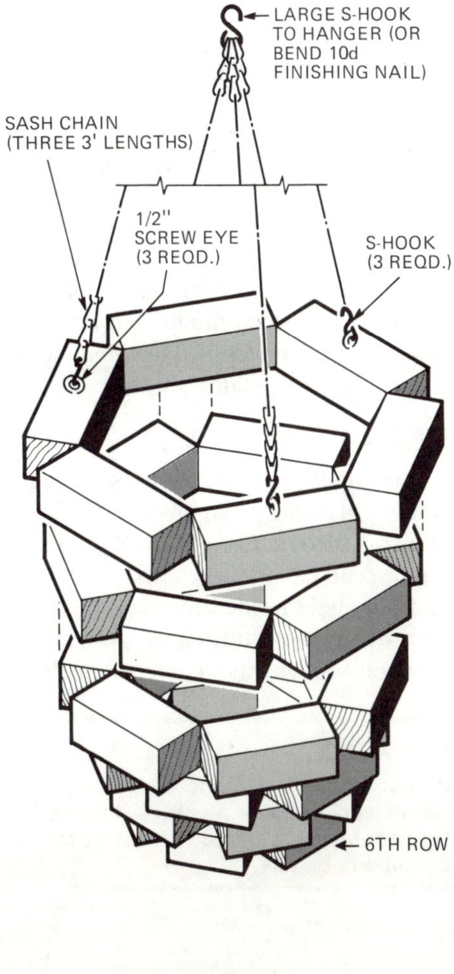

Lighted planters—the way to grow

Plants thrive indoors when the lighting conditions are optimal. These beautiful pieces of furniture serve double-duty as indoor planters

By MICHAEL RAY AUGUST

BUILT-IN FLUORESCENT lamp, housed in an adjustable light-box shelf, adds supplemental light in a most dramatic way to potted plants displayed in waterproofed base of this handsome table/planter.

GROWING PLANTS indoors is a fascinating hobby. Attractive flowering, trailing and foliage plants can be nurtured successfully inside the house with the aid of fluorescent and incandescent lamps. Plants can add beauty and color to your house all year long.

Plants need light to grow. Daylight in your home is neither uniform nor abundant. Fluorescent or incandescent lamps can be used alone or to supplement daylight. They make growing and showing healthy plants possible at all times.

balance of red and green

The dual-purpose planters shown here—a lamp table and room divider designed by the General Electric Co.—use GE's "Gro and Sho" fluorescent lamps to get perfect balance of red and blue light needed for plant propagation and reproductive growth.

Mounting heights of fluorescent lamps above plants vary depending on the number of plants used and their light requirements. Lamps are normally 6 to 8 in. above plants, and most plants need 14 to 16 hours of light a day to grow satisfactorily.

Fluorescent lamps are the best and most popular light sources for growing plants. However, incandescent lamps can supplement natural light or be used where fluorescents are not practical. Flowering or foliage plants needing no high light, do best under incandescent lamps.

SEE ALSO
Barbecue tables . . . Benches, potting . . . Gardening . . . House plants . . . Lighting . . . Outdoor tables . . . Patios . . . Picnic tables . . . Strawberry barrels

table planter

Movable pegs in the table-planter legs let you place the light box in three locations to adjust growth-promoting light and warmth for the plants, whatever their size. Overall sizes of adjustable and fixed "boxes" are identical, so all parts should be cut in duplicate. The top of the light-box unit has notched-out corners cut by

HANDSOME three-shelf room divider with its built-in growing lamps provides your indoor plants with their own grow-and-show display case. Plants on top shelf get their turn under the lights as part of a weekly rotation.

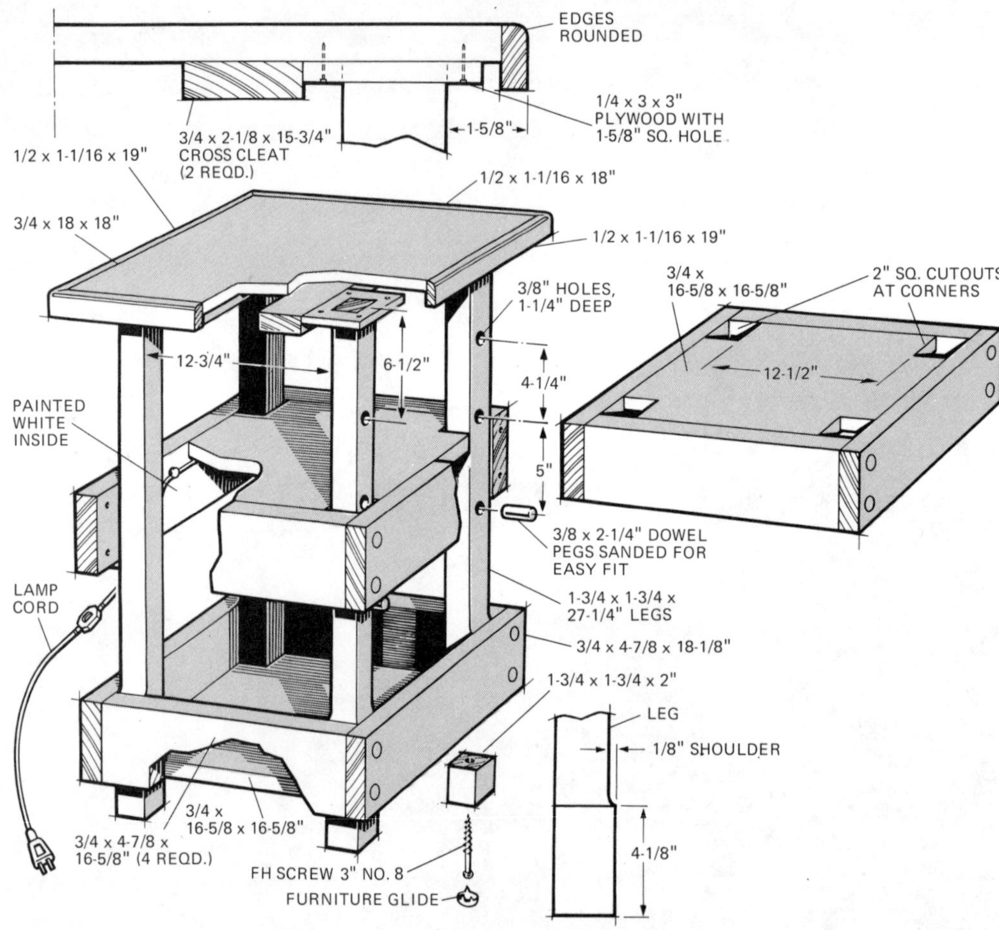

SET BLADE high and make two right-angle cuts to notch corners. Make such cuts so waste falls free to outside.

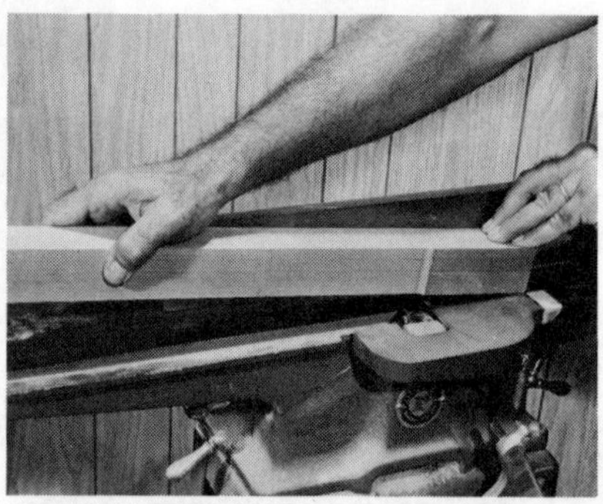

FORM CLEARANCE shoulders on two leg faces by making partial passes on jointer. Tape shows when to stop cut.

USE ⅜-IN. spur bit in a drill press to obtain clean-cut holes in legs for pegs. Dowels are lightly sanded for slip fit.

USE A PAIR of notched blocks and a C-clamp to hold leg for gluing. Apply waterproof glue such as resorcinol.

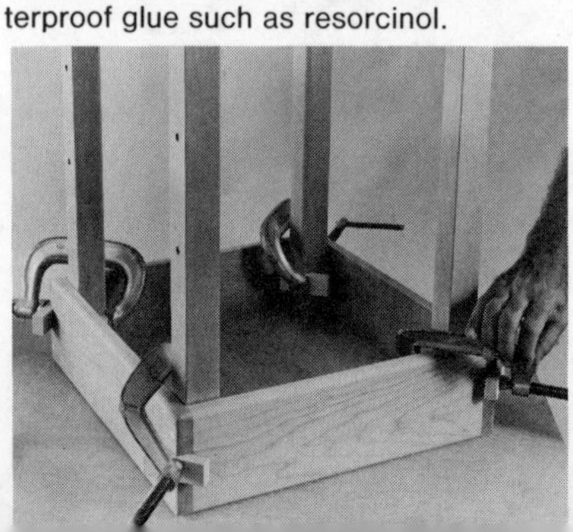

INSERT LAMP cord in bushed hole of fixture shell and connect the black and white leads in the lamp.

ATTACH fixture to center of light box with threaded nipple and nut. For safety, knot cord.

making two intersecting saw cuts on the table saw. Set the blade high to limit the amount of overkerf on the underside.

use nails and glue

Assemble the lamp and plant boxes with No. 2 common nails and glue; use waterproof glue for the plant box, white glue for the light box. Drill pilot holes for nails and counterbore for wood plugs. *Special note on gluing:* Waterproof resorcinol glue leaves a dark stain, so you must scrape away any excess with a sharp chisel and wipe the area clean with a damp cloth before the glue sets. Use white glue for all plugs.

Round all outside corners and edges—most easily done with a router and ½-in.-radius bit. Sand all inside surfaces smooth before assembly.

forming clearance shoulders

To allow ample clearance for free movement of the light box, plane the four 1¾-in.-square legs on two adjacent faces to make them 1⅝-in. square from a point 4⅛ in. from the bottom. Do this on a jointer and stick a piece of masking tape to the rear table to tell you when to stop planing. If you have no jointer, take a 1⅝-in.-square leg and add ⅛-in. thick pieces to the two outer faces at the bottom to form shoulders.

Bore holes for the pegs before gluing and clamping to the plant box. One C-clamp at each

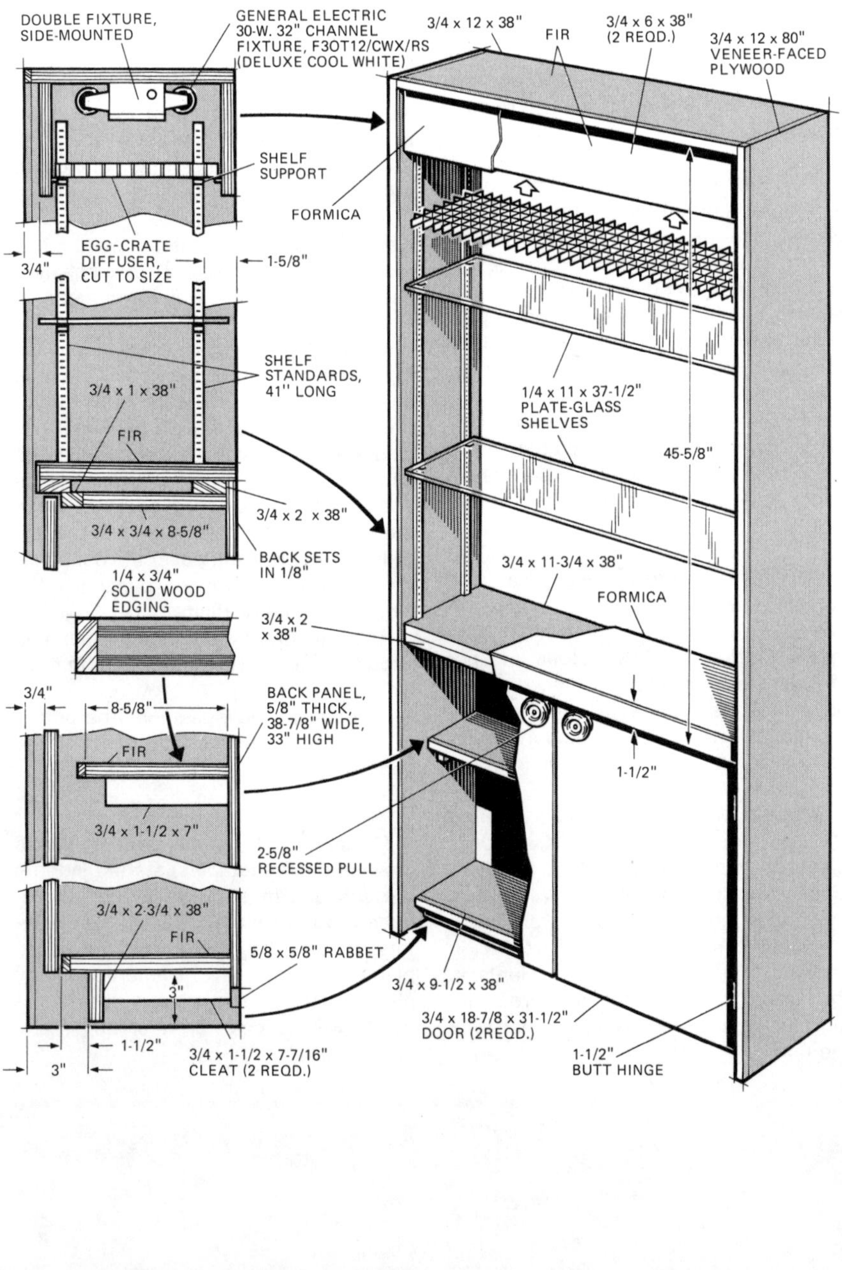

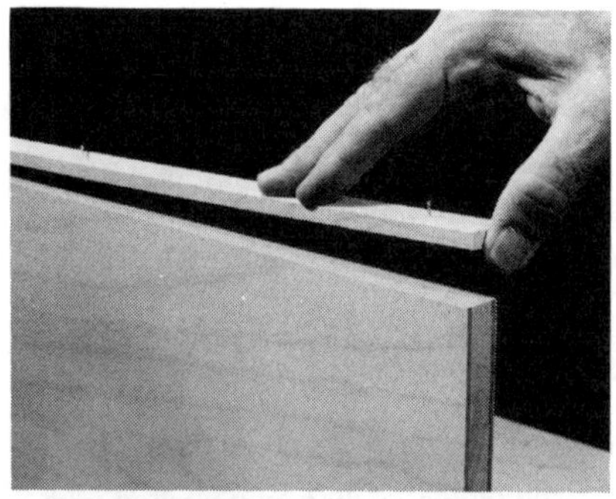

FACE EXPOSED edges of plywood with ¼-in. strips of solid wood. Use glue only, and clamp with masking tape.

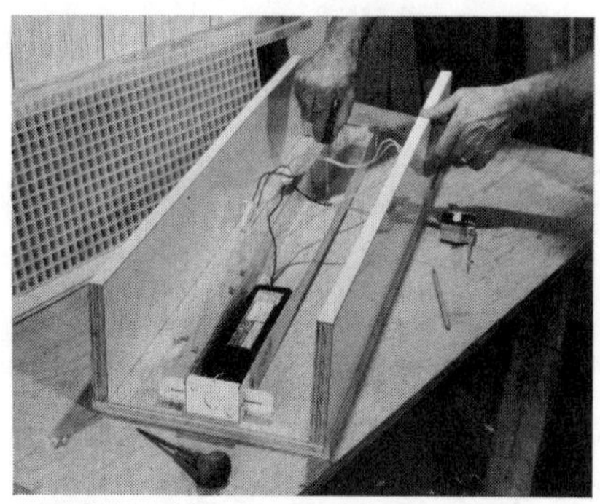

INSTALL side-mounted fluorescent lamp fixture as shown; bottom-mounted type can also be used if you wish.

USE FINE-TOOTH plywood blade to cut "egg-crate" lamp-diffusing grid. Material comes in 24 x 48-in. panels.

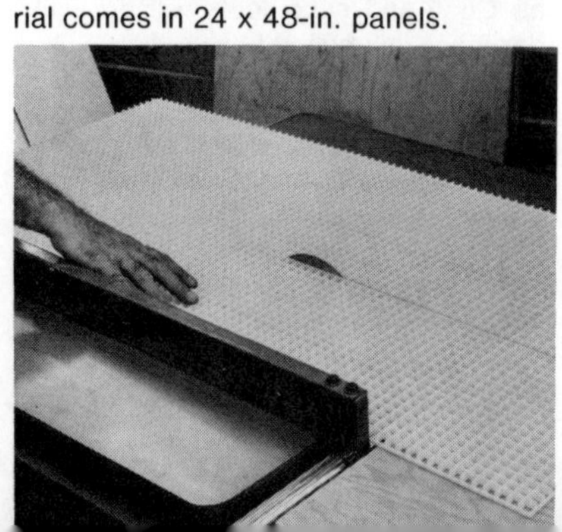

corner will do. Use waterproof glue and a pair of notched clamp blocks. Attach the 2-in.-long leg extensions with glue and fh screws in counterbored holes.

top is built up

Two or more boards are glued together to build up the 18-in.-square top which is cleated (across grain) on the underside to prevent warp-

GROWING TIPS

Light intensity. Most beginners do not give plants enough light. As a result, their plants often grow and bloom poorly or have pale-colored foliage and leggy new growth. For more light, you merely bring the fluorescent tubes closer to the plants or add more lamps.

A good plant-lighting rule of thumb is to "provide 15 to 20 watts of fluorescent light for each square foot of plant-growing area." When growing seedlings, cactus or orchids, keep fluorescent tubes 6 to 8 in. above the foliage for strong light exposure.

Medium-intensity-light plants—African violets, gloxinias and begonias—should have tubes 8 to 12 in. above the foliage. Ferns and cuttings, the low-light-requirement plants, can be lighted 12 to 18 in. from above.

Duration of light. Flowering of many plants is controlled by the length of the daily light and dark periods. In general, short-day plants, such as poinsettias, chrysanthemums and Christmas begonias, need 10 to 12 hours of light a day. Long-day plants, such as the China aster, dahlias and annuals, need 14 to 18 hours of light to flower.

The indeterminate plants (12 to 18 hours) will produce flowers at all seasons. This group includes most household plants such as African violets, gloxinias, coleus, roses and carnations.

Temperature. A daytime-temperature range of 70 to 75° F. (nighttime, 60° to 65°F.) is recommended for development of quality plants. The cooler night temperature is important because plants gather their food during the day, but digest it during the night.

Humidity. The recommended humidity for most plants is 45 to 50 percent or higher. Often, in winter, homes have a relative humidity of only 10 to 15 percent. Cacti and succulents will do well under these low-humidity conditions, but other plant types will suffer.

You may increase the humidity by misting the plants twice daily with a water-spray atomizer, by setting the pots on trays of water-saturated gravel, or by using a portable room humidifier.

Ventilation. Plants lose water vapor through small pores on the underside of the leaves. Poor ventilation causes this to condense in a film on the leaf surface encouraging disease-producing organisms. To limit this, use a small fan or humidifier with its own fan to circulate air around the plants.

Plant spacing. Crowded plants result in long weak stems and encourage development of foliage diseases due to lack of air.

Soil. Since heavy clay and some other natural soils are not desirable for indoor plants, many hobbyists use commercial soils that are well aerated, provide excellent drainage and are sterilized before packaging. They contain shredded peat moss, vermiculite and perlite with added nutrients. You can purchase them under trade names such as Jiffy-Mix and Redi-Earth. Expandable containers for starting seeds and cuttings are alternatives to loose soil pots and can be purchased under the trade name Jiffy-7 Peat Pellets.

Fertilizing. There are many kinds of complete fertilizers on the market. A complete fertilizer has three major elements—nitrogen, phosphorous and potassium—and comes in dry powder, liquid or tablets. Follow the directions of the manufacturer, but remember, too little fertilizer is better than too much.

Watering. Many automatic watering systems are now available for indoor plantings, but the best method is still to inspect your plants daily and water them by hand when needed. Over-watering is the most common cause of trouble in growing house plants. Water plants in the morning when the temperature is rising. Use tepid water, not cold water from the tap.

From experience you will learn how much water each plant needs. Differences of size and leaf area, plant type, conditions of soil, and temperature of growing area will affect your decision.

Cuttings. A common way to start new house plants is with cuttings. A cutting is any part cut from a plant capable of producing roots and continuing growth, thus developing into a new individual plant. The cutting allows plants to mature rapidly and closely resemble the parent plant.

Cuttings of 4 to 5 inches can be removed from a parent plant with a sharp knife. Cut the stem just below the joint. As soon as it is cut, insert the cutting into a moist rooting medium such as vermiculite, perlite or a fine grade of peat moss. Keep medium moist until the cutting has rooted. Cuttings should be transplanted as soon as roots are well developed.

Seeds. Sow seeds as evenly as possible in a container having good drainage; then cover with a fine soil. Or use compressed peat pots, following the maker's instructions. Small seeds should be lightly covered, while larger seeds should be covered to a depth of twice their greatest diameter. Dampen the soil with a fine spray and cover the container with clear plastic or glass to maintain the moisture of the medium.

The temperature for seed germination should be about 10° higher than that required for normal plant growth.

The small seedlings should be potted or reset as soon as they are large enough to handle.

Hardening off plants. Bedding plants (flowers and vegetables) started indoors are soft and must gradually get accustomed to the wind and sun. A week before transplanting the garden, move the plants outdoors to a sheltered, shady place. After a couple of days outside, the plants will become stronger and ready for the sun.

age. Facing strips, ½x1⅟₁₆-in., are mitered and applied to the four edges, then the top corners are rounded with block plane or router.

The legs are glued to the top in ¼-in.-deep wells formed by gluing and nailing 3-in. squares of plywood to each corner. Wait until later to glue the legs to the top.

Mount a standard circular fixture to the center of the light box with a pipe nipple and a fixture crossbar. You'll have to drill a hole in the side of the fixture for a rubber grommet, lamp cord and switch.

finishing the table

Finish table with a coat of sanding sealer and two coats of satin-drying varnish. Apply two coats of bartop varnish to the inside of the plant box, and paint the inside of the light box matte white to help reflect the maximum amount of light onto the plants.

Now you can glue on the top. Place it upside down on your bench, apply glue to ends of the legs and wells and stand legs in the wells. Weight of the table will hold it until the glue dries.

room divider planter

As a hutch or freestanding room divider, this planter makes a handsome display case for plants. Birch-faced, lumber-core plywood is used for exposed surfaces; common fir plywood and pine for the rest. The plywood will prevent warp, which might affect the fit of the doors. Use your portable saw with a smooth-cutting blade to cut the pieces from your 4x8-ft. panel. Remember to cut with the good side face down when using a portable saw. Guide it with a straightedge clamped in place.

All exposed plywood edges are faced with strips of solid wood, so allow for them when ripping your pieces for width. If you're planning a room divider with both front and back exposed, cut the sides 11 in. wide instead of 11¼ in. Cut all cross and shelf members 38 in. long, then butt, glue, nail and cleat them to the sides. Since solid wood generally measures 13/16 in. thick and plywood 12/16 in. thick, the slight extra thickness helps in gluing and adding strips. After the glue dries, you plane the strips flush on both sides with a sharp block plane, being careful not to cut into the veneer. A brad or two can keep the strips from shifting, and masking tape will hold them in the absence of enough clamps.

use plastic laminate

Before assembly, cover the 6-in. fascia board at the top (both boards if the unit is to be a room divider) and the double-thick counter with plastic laminate such as Formica. The Formica counter surface will be easy to clean in case you spill when watering. Do the edges first, then surfaces.

Make a ⅝-in.-square rabbet along the rear edge of the counter and rear edges of the sides at a point from the counter down to hold a ½-in.-plywood back panel. Guide a straight-shank bit in your router with a straightedge clamped to the work.

assembling the unit

To assemble, nail the top member first to the two 6-in. fascia boards and the bottom board to the 2¾-in. kickboard. Paint the inside of the top matte white. Next, start two nails through one side member at each of the four cross-member locations. Apply glue, drive home the nails within ⅟₁₆ in. of the surface, set the heads and fill. Now, with help, turn the assembly over onto protective wood strips on the floor and nail and glue the other side member the same way.

Check for squareness, then hold the assembly square with a diagonal brace across the back. Install the back panel that will help hold the unit square once it is in place. Finally cut, fit and hinge the doors with 1½-in. butts.

rubbed finish

For a rubbed-effect finish, brush on a wash coat of sanding sealer diluted 50 percent with lacquer thinner. Sand lightly when dry and follow with a coat of Beverlee's natural-teak satin stain. Even out the coat and lighten by wiping with a soft cloth. Work fairly fast, one section at a time. For a darker accent on front edges, brush on stain and omit the wiping. Then add two coats of Fabulon's polyurethane satin-luster finish. A polyurethane finish is durable and will stand up to water spills better than traditional lacquer or varnish.

attach the fixtures

If you can't find a side-mounted fluorescent fixture, there's space for a conventional 36-in. two-lamp channel-type fixture with a T8 ballast. Fit it with two GE 30-w. Gro & Sho fluorescent F30T8/PL lamps. Run the lamp cord through a hole in the cabinet top, knot the cord, insert a grommet in the fixture and connect wires. The plastic "egg-crate" diffuser is available at lighting and building-supply centers.

Planters for your garden

■ SOMETHING DIFFERENT in the way of planters are these niches that are framed as part of the fence. Besides being a novel feature that serves to break up a long expanse of plain fence, the enclosures actually afford protection to a plant from strong winds and at the same time provide extra bracing to the fence itself.

A small bridge, such as the one below with its built-in planter boxes, will add charm to a fish pond and rock garden. When building both these projects from long-lasting California redwood, use noncorroding nails (hot-dipped galvanized, aluminum alloy or stainless steel) so the nails won't discolor the wood.

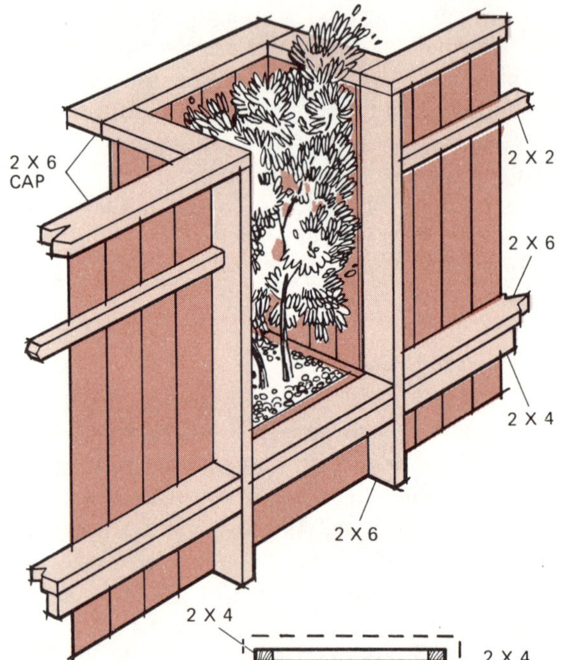

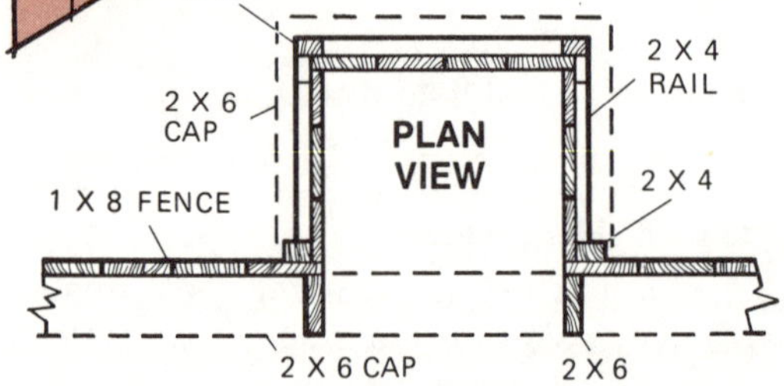

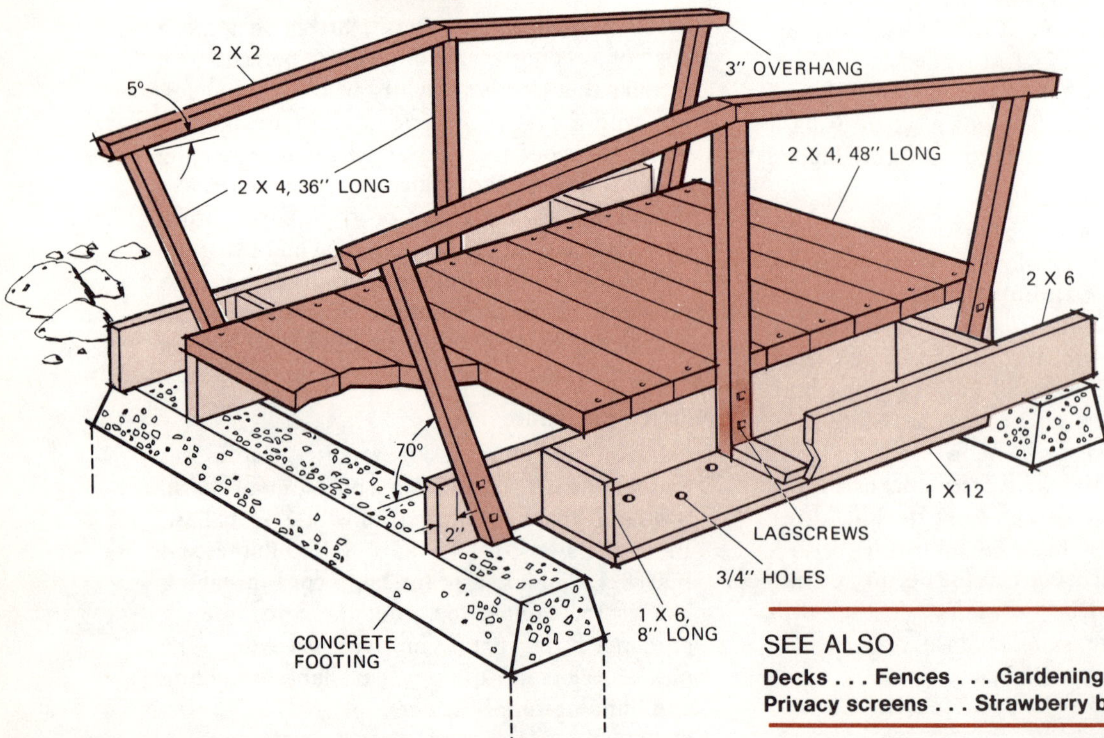

SEE ALSO
Decks . . . Fences . . . Gardening . . . Patios . . . Privacy screens . . . Strawberry barrels

A wheelbarrow planter

■ THIS LITTLE patio planter is fun to build whether you are a dyed-in-the-wool wood-worker or a guy taking his first whack at a project. Douglas fir was used here but other material can be used. To start, lay out and make all straight cuts for the bottom, side panels and the two end pieces that make up the wheelbarrow bucket. Next, set the saw blade at a 30° angle and make the bevel cuts in the two end pieces. To keep construction simple, use butt joints for all assembly. Make certain that edges to be joined are perfectly square. Finally, cut the handles and the wheels. The plans call for all parts to be cut from ¾-in. (actual) stock. The wheel axles are 3-in. lengths of ½-in. dowel.

By BOB CORLEY

SEE ALSO
Decks . . . House plants . . . Patios . . . Strawberry barrels . . . Weekend projects

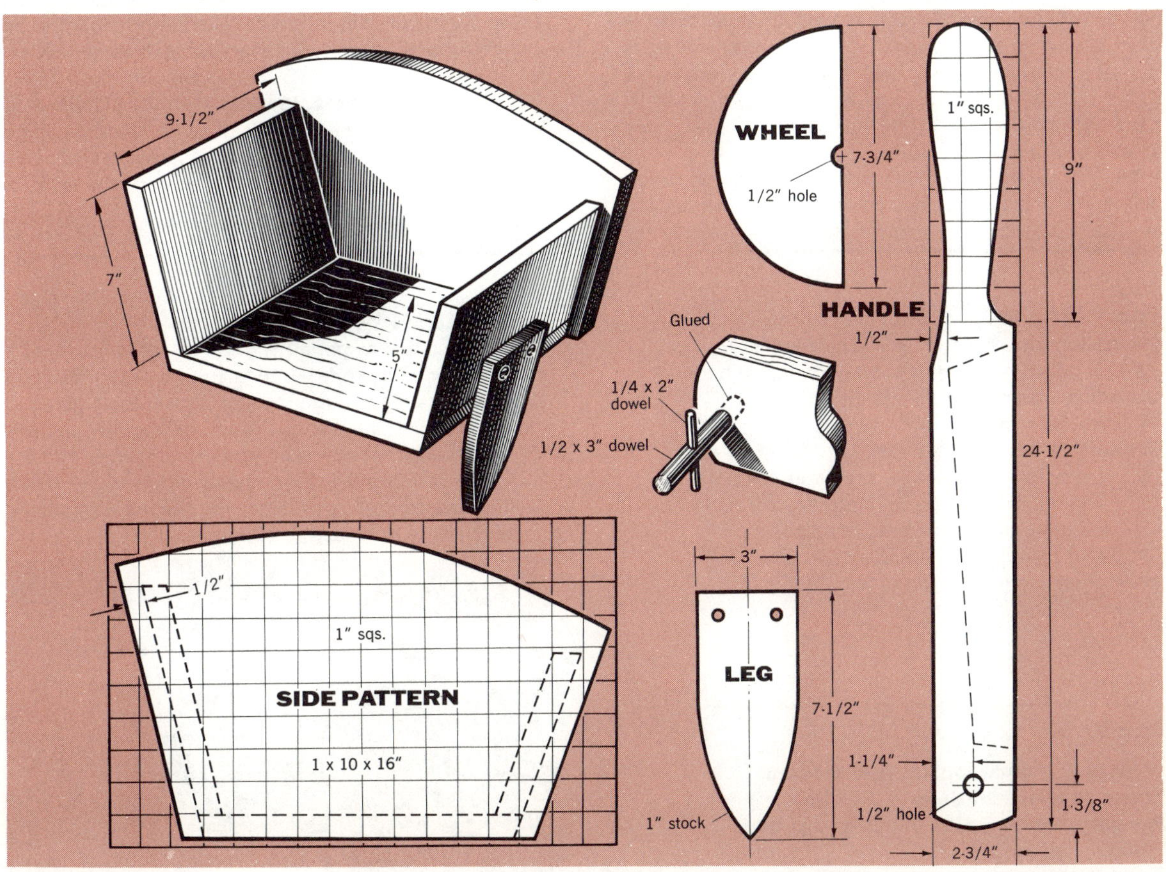

How to work with plasterboard

■ GYPSUM-CORE plasterboard provides a low-cost interior-finish wall that is an ideal surface for both paint and wall coverings. When it is installed properly, your walls can have the smooth look of plaster. Plasterboard is available in fire-resistant grades that meet most building codes too. Most codes require this type on walls between house and attached garage.

Many of the techniques for repair of plasterboard surfaces are the same as for new installation, and professionals frequently use plasterboard to replace large areas of damaged plaster.

When joints, nailheads and corners in an installation are finished, allowed to dry thoroughly and sanded, the entire surface should receive a coat of vinyl or oil-base primer-sealer to assure uniform absorption of paint or wall-covering adhesive.

Estimating materials
NAILS

Wallboard thickness	Nail type	Per 1000 sq. ft. of wallboard
3/8", 1/2"	1¼" annular-threaded wallboard nail	6 lbs.
5/8"	1⅜" annular-threaded wallboard nail	6 lbs.

PREMIXED JOINT COMPOUND AND TAPE

Plasterboard (sq. ft.)	Ready-mix joint compound (gals.)	Wallboard tape (rolls)
100-200	1	2/60′
300-400	2	3/60′
500-600	3	1/250′
700-800	4	1/250′, 1/60′
900-1000	5	1/250′, 2/60′

Start by making a drawing of the surfaces to be covered with plasterboard and planning the arrangement of panels. Use the longest panels you can to reduce the number of end joints. Horizontal application to a wall is often preferred for this reason. Vertical application is desirable where the ceiling height of a wall is more than 8 ft. 2 in. or the wall space to be surfaced is 4 ft. wide or narrower. Where end joints cannot be avoided, they should be staggered.

The installation method that uses both an adhesive and nails is not only quicker, because there are fewer nails to drive and conceal, but also means a better-quality installation than nails alone. With this method, you will require about half as many nails as indicated in the chart at left above; for a professional-grade installation, you will need a quart tube of adhesive for every two 4x8 panels (64 sq. ft.).

Use the chart above to estimate the quantities of wallboard tape and ready-mix joint compound (spackling compound) you will need. Joint compound is also available in dry powder form; allow 60 lbs. per 1000 sq. ft. of surface.

Tools required

1. Wallboard cutting knife or utility knife
2. Wallboard hammer or crown-head claw hammer
3. 4-ft. T-square or steel straightedge
4. Steel tape measure
5. Keyhole saw or sabre saw
6. Joint-finishing knives, 4- and 10-in. blades
7. Pan for joint compound (mortarboard)
8. Medium-grade sandpaper and block
9. Cartridge-type caulking gun (for adhesive)
10. Corner-taping tool (optional)

SEE ALSO

Ceilings . . . Family rooms . . . Hardboard . . . House additions . . . Nails . . . Painting, interior . . . Paneling, hardboard . . . Paneling, plywood . . . Paneling, wood

Cutting plasterboard

Using a T-square to get an aligned straightedge, hold a wallboard or utility knife perpendicular to the surface and score completely through the face paper. The board can then be snapped with a firm, even pressure. Folding back the snapped-off section, cut through back paper with the knife. Use sandpaper to smooth any rough edges. Use a keyhole saw or sabre saw to cut any needed openings in panel; be sure to measure them carefully.

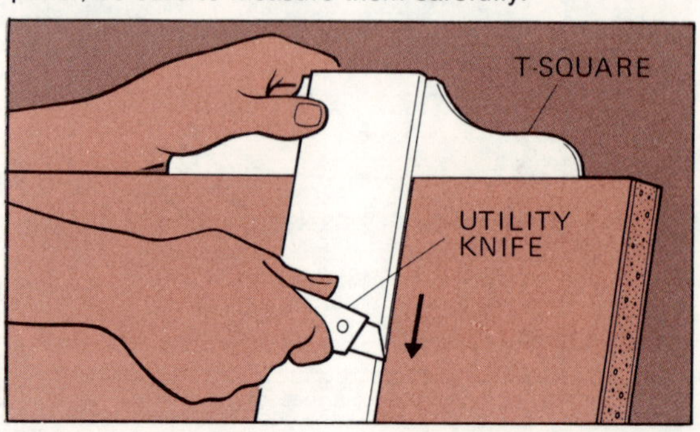

Ceiling installation

Ceilings should be covered before walls. Panels are held in place for nailing with support tees; make them about 1 in. longer than floor-to-ceiling height. Place nails 7 in. apart. If the adhesive-and-nails method is used, all edges should still be nailed, but only one nail per ceiling joist will be required in the "field" of the board. Drive nails to bring the panel tight to framing, then strike each nail one more time to "dimple" (set) the head, taking care not to break face paper.

Wall application and corners

In horizontal application, bottom panels are installed first; the second row can then be rested on the first. Nails are spaced 7 in. apart and dimpled. No nail in the top course should be less than 7 in. from the ceiling. If adhesive is used, no nails in the field are required unless a panel is bowed—then it may be nailed temporarily while adhesive sets. In a vertical corner, the panel edge that is lapped over need not be nailed.

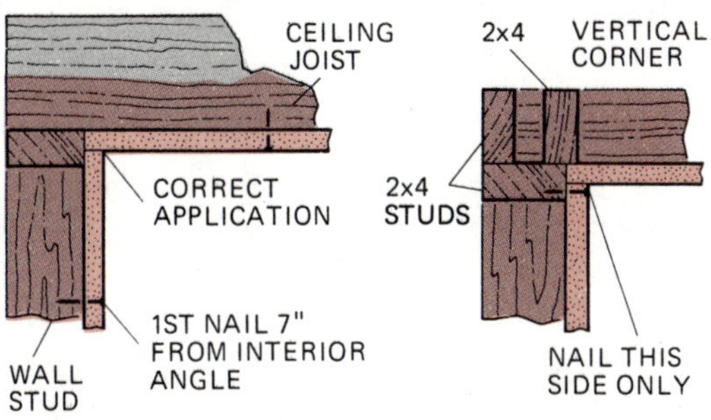

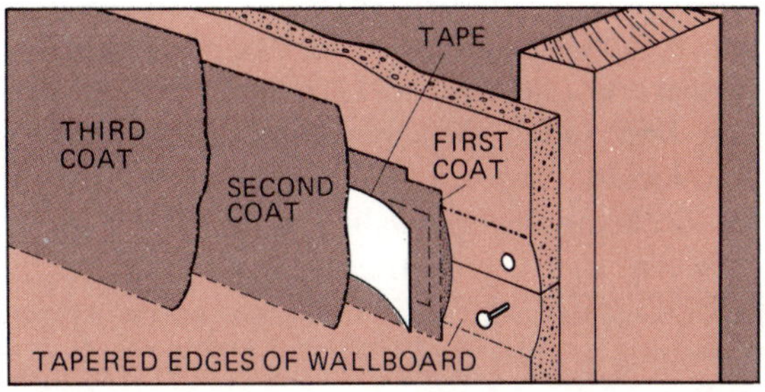

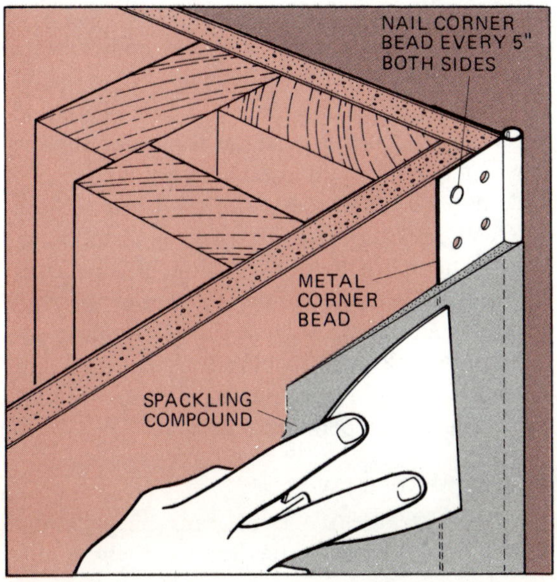

Finishing joints

Joints are filled, reinforced and finished as shown. First coat of joint compound is applied with 4-in. joint knife and tape pressed into it with knife held at 45° angle. Allow at least 24 hours for each coat to dry. Second and third coats are sanded and third feathered-out with 10-in. joint knife to a total width of 12 to 14 in. Treat end and butt joints the same way, with final coat 14 to 18 in. wide. Nailheads get three sanded coats of compound, no tape unless paper is broken.

Finishing corners

Two coats of compound may do for an outside corner. Final coat should extend 7 to 9 in. back from nose of corner. Tape creased lengthwise is embedded in inside corners, topped with one or two feathered coats of compound. To halt cracking, use the least possible compound in crease line.

How to work with plastic pipe

By JIM MCINTOSH

■ SOME YEARS AGO, when copper tubing was the only smart choice for home water pipes, do-it-yourself plumbers enjoyed a complete system comprised of hard-temper (rigid) and soft-temper (flexible) copper. They could use the one that best suited their purpose—rigid pipe for neat-looking, exposed plumbing and flexible pipe for threading through walls and floors.

When rigid chlorinated polyvinyl chloride (CPVC) pipe was introduced, it made home plumbing a great deal easier, but didn't offer a system. Now, with the advent of flexible polybutylene (PB) pipe, plumbers again have the choice they had with copper, but at less cost and with far less effort. CPVC serves as the "hard-temper" and PB as the "soft-temper" thermoplastic pipe. Where one isn't best for a specific task, the other is.

Plastic pipe materials, usually beige in color are sold at hardware stores, home centers and wholesale plumbing outlets. Both CPVC and PB service hot and cold water and have a complete line of fittings. CPVC joins via simple solvent-welding. PB can't be solvent-welded, but joins with even greater ease using mechanical adapters, which solvent-weld to all standard CPVC fittings.

Both CPVC and PB can be cut with any fine-toothed saw. CPVC is usually sold in rigid, 10-ft. lengths with ½ and ¾-in. outside diameters. PB comes in 25 and 100-ft. coils with ⅜, ½ and ¾-in. outside diameters. According to Genova, a large manufacturer of thermoplastic piping, CPVC and PB pipes and fittings in these sizes are common.

Neither CPVC nor PB should be compared to lesser quality black polyethylene (PE) or polyvinyl chloride (PVC) pipe. PVC and PE should never be used inside a house for water supply; they can't stand up to household hot water.

Perhaps the chief reason for do-it-yourself use of CPVC/PB piping is its ease of installation. There's no more hand-tightening of pipe ends and no more sweat-soldering flames playing around your pipes. Solvent CPVC welding requires only a clean cloth, plus cans of cleaner and solvent. Joining PB requires even less—sandpaper and a little petroleum jelly.

deciding which to use

CPVC, because it's rigid, runs off with the honors for appearance. It's best used where pip-

SEE ALSO
Bathrooms . . . Drains . . . Heaters, water . . . Kitchens . . . Plumbing . . . Sewage systems

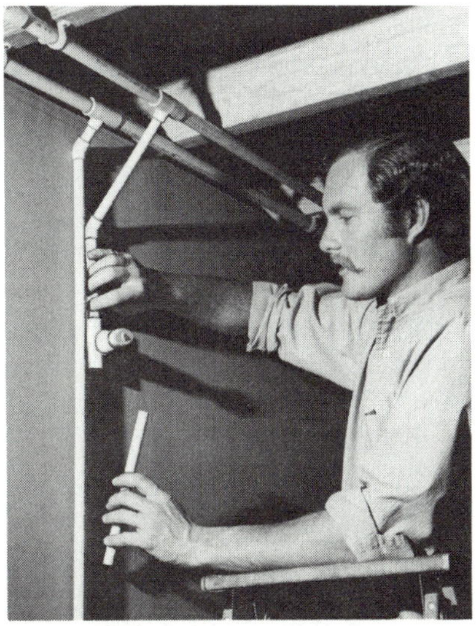

FOR A NEAT, craftsmanlike look where plumbing shows—as in this basement—use rigid CPVC piping.

WHEN PIPING must be fitted behind walls or fished through openings, use flexible PB to save time and effort.

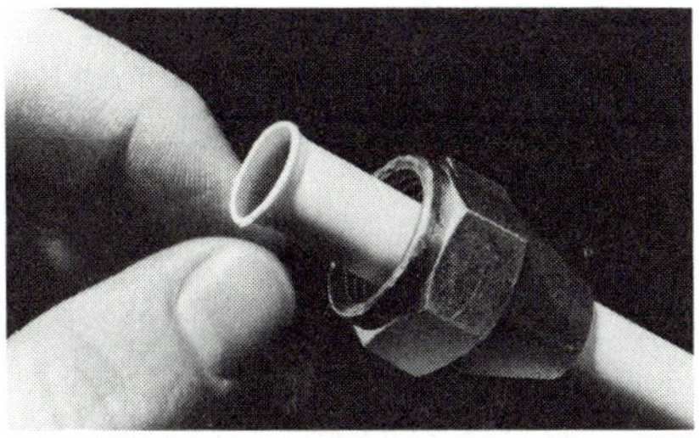

PB AND CPVC can be joined by using the same flaring tool as for copper. Fittings like this, on a flared riser tube, join PB to uncommon fixtures.

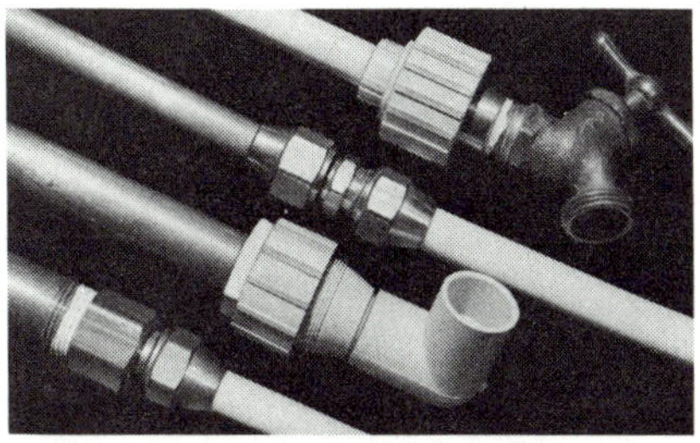

CPVC AND PB adapt to other pipes. From top, CPVC/FIP (female thread) transition union joins CPVC to male-threaded bibb; a compression union joins copper to the PB tubing; a special adapter connects the solderless joint with copper tubing; CPVC connects to the threaded brass pipe via a flare-reducing adapter.

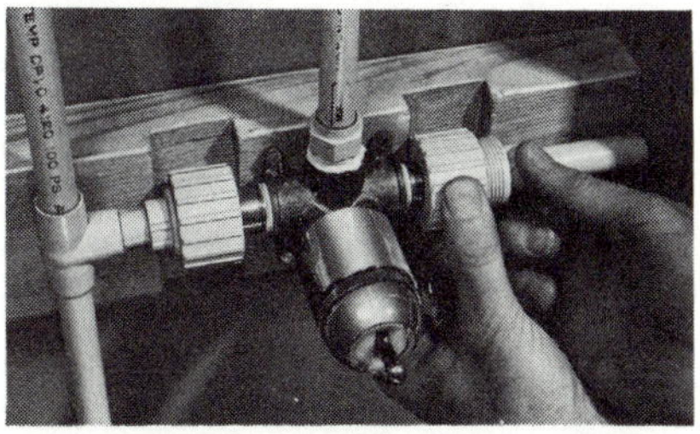

TRANSITION UNIONS connect CPVC to tub/shower mixing valve. Unions solvent-weld to CPVC or to push-in adapters, preventing leaks from thermal expansion.

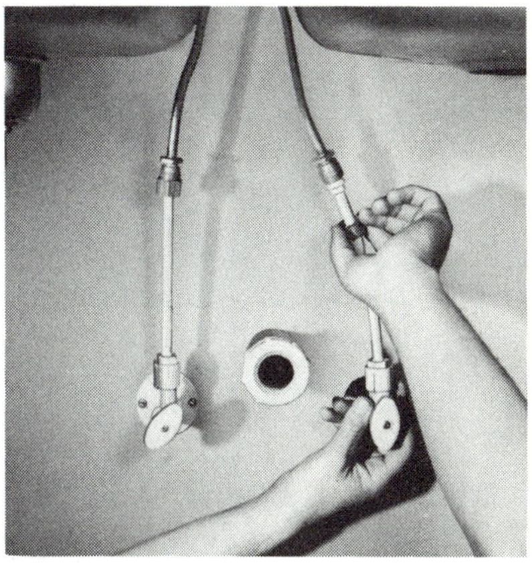

USE superflexible PB riser tubes between all types of fixture shutoff valves and faucet tailpipes. Tubes seal the inside threaded fittings.

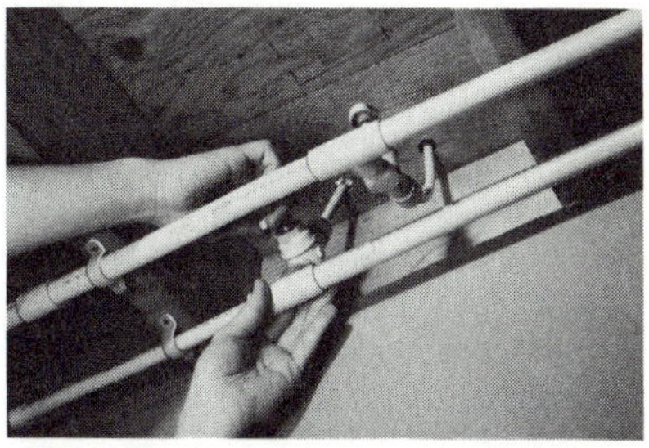

IDEAL combination: rigid CPVC pipes look tidy in basement while flexible PB riser tubes simplify runs to fixtures. Combination saves much cutting and fitting.

PB CAN BE used beneath a concrete slab. Install joint-free runs. Then attach any fixtures to the exposed pipe ends located above the slab.

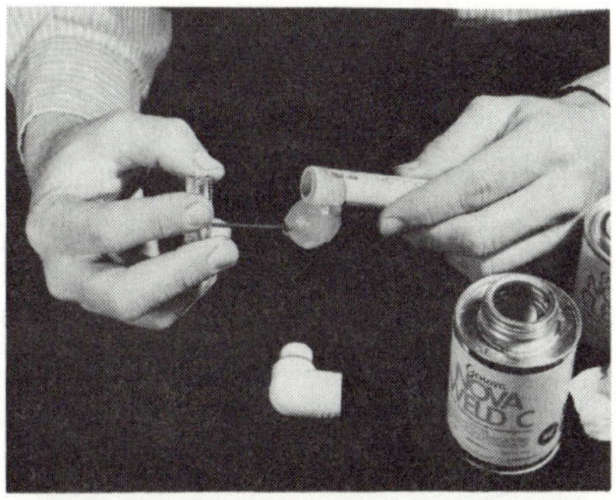

TO JOIN plastic pipe to fitting, remove burrs from cut end with knife and apply the cleaner-primer. Apply solvent cement using swab from can.

IMMEDIATELY after applying the cement, join the pieces with a twisting motion. Quickly orient fitting because solvent dries rapidly. Wipe off excess.

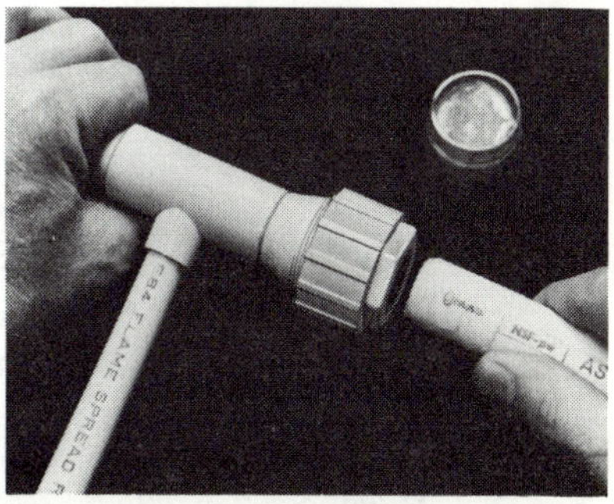

TO JOIN PB to PB, CPVC or metal pipe, use an adapter that hand-tightens. Cut tube end even (use miterbox), round corners and coat with petroleum jelly.

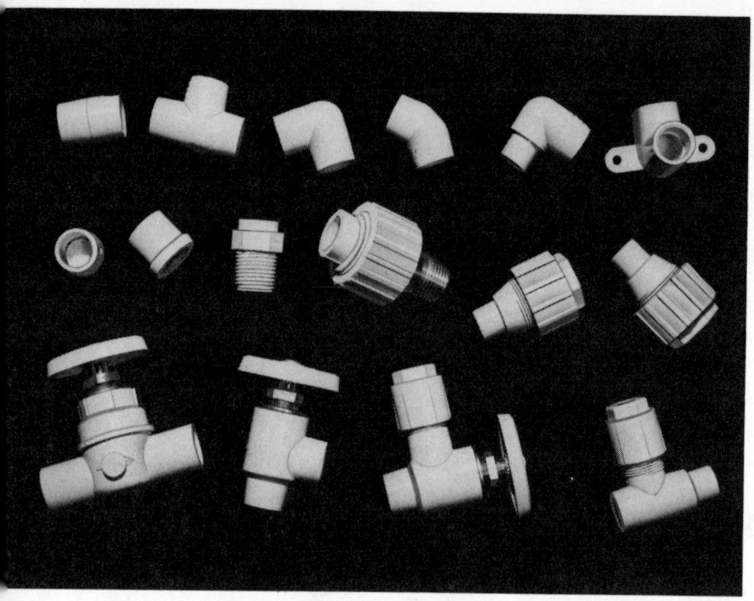

FITTINGS FOR CPVC AND PB pipe, top row from left: coupling, tee, 90° and 45° elbows, 90° street elbow, wing elbow. Center row: cap, reducing bushing, male thread adapter, transition union, two copper adapters. Bottom: line-shutoff valve, angle-shutoff valve, fixture shutoff valve and stackable tee.

ing will be seen: in basements, unfinished utility rooms and garages. It's also useful where pipe must support a faucet, such as an outdoor hose bibb. Use CPVC for pipe sections requiring lots of fittings. CPVC fittings—like those for sweat-soldered rigid copper—are less costly than those for PB. Also, use CPVC elbows for within-wall turns in a run of PB where the PB can't bend as sharply as needed.

PB, because it's flexible, takes the cake for runs where pipe must be fed through bored holes. It's also ideal for long runs with gentle bends that are free of joints and fittings. This not only saves money, but cuts down on flow restrictions. It also reduces or eliminates measuring and cutting to fit complex runs around obstructions. A single, joint-free PB pipe can go through floors, around corners and wherever needed—in the ground, without joints. It's great beneath concrete slabs, too. Use PB to make runs you'll want to take apart easily at a later date. Adapters can be removed and reassembled as often as desired.

You can, but probably won't, use PB in exposed locations. Being flexible, it sags and doesn't look very neat. Also, for shorter runs, PB requires more fittings than are economical.

Another PB use is for flexible riser tubes. These reach from a water supply outlet on the wall or floor behind a fixture up to the faucet connections. PB riser tubes come as ⅜-in.-outside-diameter parts which you cut to length. They have factory-shaped ends. Riser tubes for sinks and lavatories are made with bullet-nosed ends to fit directly into most faucet tailpipes. They're held in place by a faucet nut, also called a jam nut. Riser tubes for toilets are flange-ended to connect into the toilet's inlet valve with a jam nut. PB risers are so flexible they reach from outlet to faucet easily without kinking. Cut them to length with a pocket knife.

advantages of plastic pipe

Both CPVC and PB are also energy savers. Their walls pass heat much less rapidly than metal. Hot water stays hot longer and cold water pipes sweat less. The smooth walls of CPVC and PB offer less resistance to water flow, enabling smaller sizes to do the same job as larger steel pipes.

A CPVC/PB system won't corrode and won't conduct electricity, making it free from electrolysis that eats away at metal pipes. One disadvantage here is that your water system can't be used as an electrical ground.

Both CPVC and PB meet practically all building codes. CPVC conforms to ASTM Standard D-2846; PB to ASTM Standard D-3309. Both are accepted by the Federal Housing Administration and meet all requirements for potable water by the National Sanitation Foundation. They both take 100 lbs. p.s.i. continuous pressure at 180° F. However, before undertaking any plumbing project, you should verify that all procedures and materials meet local codes.

tips for an expert installation

CPVC pipes and fittings join together by solvent-welding (see photos). Besides using a liberal amount, it's important to use a high-quality solvent containing lots of tetra hydrofuran, a high-cost but effective ingredient of good solvent cements. PB pipe can't be solvent-welded, so don't try. To join PB to CPVC, solvent-weld the CPVC to one end of an adapter, and, after applying petroleum jelly, simply hand-tighten the PB to the other end.

CPVC or PB can be joined directly to threaded metal pipe and fittings or to unthreaded copper pipe. This is also a simple task, but requires special adapters, called transition unions. You'll need them for appliance outlets and inlets, at threaded faucets and when using plastic to ex-

WHERE TO USE CPVC AND PB

LOCATION	CPVC	PB	SIZE OF PIPE ¾″	½″	⅜″
Service entrance		1	•		
House mains:			•		
Basement	1				
Crawlspace		1			
Beneath slab		1			
Fixture branches	3	2		•	
Riser tubes		1			•
Below ground to outbuildings		1	•	•	
To outdoor hose bibbs	2	3		•	
Water softener	3	2	•		
Water heater	2	2	•		
T & P valve relief tube	2	3		•	
Air chambers	1		•	•	
Automatic washer hose bibbs	2	3		•	
Showerhead riser pipe	1			•	
Furnace humidifier		1			•
Boiler inlet connection*	2	3			
Evaporative cooler		1		•	•
Lawn sprinkler supply*	3	2	•		
Piping of manifolds		1	•	•	•
Behind finished walls		1	•	•	•
Sharp turns within walls	1			•	•
Gentle turns		1	•	•	•
Around obstructions		1	•	•	•
Long, joint-free runs		1		•	•
Short runs, many connections	1			•	•

* With approved backflow preventer 1—Best 2—Better 3—Good

THERMOPLASTIC PIPE CONNECTIONS AT WATER HEATER

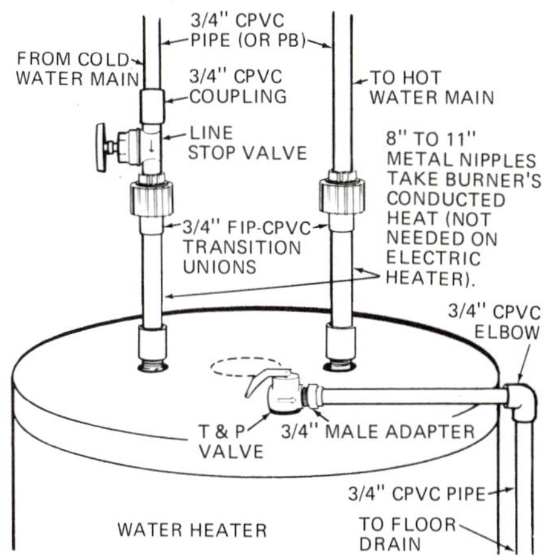

tend an existing system of metal pipe.

Transition unions mate up metal and thermoplastic piping across an elastomeric rubber gasket. They permit differential thermal movement between the two materials without straining the parts. They also prevent the leaking associated with ordinary threaded adapters.

Transition unions come in male and female threads for metal pipes and fittings and can also be sweat-soldered to unthreaded copper. CPVC solvent-welds directly to transition unions, but a transition union *and* an adapter are needed to join PB to metal, because PB can't be solvent-welded.

Use transition unions at every pressurized hot water connection between threaded metal and solvent-welded plastic piping. At nonpressurized hot water and at cold water connections, use simple male thread adapters, if possible. Transition unions can be taken apart and reassembled without cutting pipes.

With all water supply piping, but especially with thermoplastic, you must allow for pipe expansion and guard against overpressure or excessive temperatures. When installing CPVC pipe, always use special hangers that let the pipe slide back and forth without binding, yet hold it securely to the framing. Leave room for expansion at the ends of long runs of CPVC, generally allowing ¼ in. for each 10 ft. of pipe. Install dog-legs—offsets—in CPVC runs of more than 35-ft., and where risers reach up from water mains through the floor. Make sure offsets are at least 8 in. long to permit slight end-wise movement. With PB risers, forget this precaution. Use PB wherever possible on long runs; it's so flexible, it's not harmed by expansion or contraction.

To control high temperature in the system, install 8 to 11-in. threaded nipples atop the tank of your gas or oil-fired water heater before putting in transition unions to connect piping. Nipples keep conducted heat from the plastic piping. They aren't necessary on an electric heater.

To control excessive pressure caused by water action within the piping system, put an air chamber at each fixture. You can make one by simply adding a capped 12-in. length of ½-in.-outside-diameter CPVC pipe to a tee behind the wall at the fixture. If the pipe serves an automatic-shut-off appliance like a washer, use a ¾-in.-outside-diameter pipe 18 in. long.

Locate a stop-and-drain valve so the whole system can be turned off and drained to prevent freeze-up. While PB isn't damaged even by repeated freezing and CPVC can take a number of freeze-ups, their fittings cannot. Of course, the cold water inlet to the water heater should contain a valve. A line stop (shutoff) valve is handy for this. One type solvent-welds either to ½-in. pipe *inside* the hubs or to ¾-in. pipe fittings *outside* the hubs. A pair of ¾-in. couplings make it serve a run of ¾-in. pipe.

Waiting game

Why do I have so much trouble taking off old finishes with a remover? I put the stuff on, but can't get the old finish off. After several applications, I still have to do a lot of scraping.—I.L., Ore.

Perhaps you don't wait long enough for the remover to "work," or you may be using a liquid remover on a vertical surface, where a paste-type should be used. Give it time—10, 15, 20 minutes or even more—to cut through the old finish. You'll find the washoff-type less messy.

Rare 'find' in attic

While cleaning the attic of an old home I recently occupied, I found an odd-looking hook, apparently a brass casting shaped like a dolphin with the tail and part of the body turned up to form the hook. What looks like a lagscrew extends about 3½ in. from the mouth. Can you tell what it is, and what it's for?—P.N., Me.

Judging from your description, you've made a rather rare find. I'm guessing it's what was known as a "jamb hook." The lagscrew end was turned into a hole in the mortar between bricks of a huge colonial fireplace to hold fire-tending tools.

Bugs in fireplace wood

I've been told that if I bring fireplace wood into the house I'll populate the place with bugs, that in time they'll eat up the furniture, and maybe the house itself. True, or false?—R.E., Mo.

Mostly false, if you're referring to the several pieces of wood you bring into the house in a carrier for the evening fire and not to the storing of a winter's supply of wood somewhere inside the house. True, you might bring in an occasional spider, a wood roach and even some wood borers. The latter won't riddle the furniture—they'll be done to a turn by the time the fire becomes ashes—and the spiders and roaches are objectionable only when they become sufficiently warmed to race for cover. Usually these stay put until you replenish the fire.

The bug to worry about is the carpenter ant. If he gets inside the house via the wood carrier there's almost sure to be trouble. Some homeowners spray their woodpile, piece by piece with a spray containing chlordane in a recommended mix, paying special attention to any cracks or crevices. It's wise to stack the winter supply some distance from the house. Lay down two "stringers," stack the wood on these over a piece of heavy plastic and then wrap the plastic up over the stack to keep the wood dry. Remove only what you'll need for one evening.

Old red paint

How do you mix the old red paints that were so often used on colonial furnishings? What are the ingredients? I want to finish a reproduction of an old blanket chest I've made.—A.F., Vt.

I've had fair success simply by thinning red paints of the color desired and using them as a stain, rather than a paint. The trick is to get the paint thinned to just the right consistency—not too watery. If it's too thin you generally get a splotchy coloring; if too thick you get an ordinary paint job. You'll have to determine the consistency by tests on small pieces of the same wood.

You can also use artist's reds, thinned so that they act as a stain, rather than a paint. At best it's a tricky business and I can't go along with the procedure all the way. Neither do I recommend that you try the old "recipes" as some of the materials are difficult, if not impossible to obtain. There are several old recipes and, just for the fun of it, here's one: It calls for 3 pounds of red oxide of iron, 2 quarts of skim milk, 8 ounces of fresh-slaked lime, 6 ounces of linseed oil, 2 ounces of white Burgundy pitch, all mixed with whiskey to a fairly thick liquid. The lime is slaked in water, exposed to the air for a time and then thinned with one-fourth of the skimmed milk. The pitch is dissolved in the oil before adding to the original mix a little at a time, then the rest of the milk and finally the iron oxide, stirring in the ingredients as you go. Presumably this makes a paint, not a stain, but according to the record such mixtures were used before ready-mixed paint was available.

Checking for termites

A neighbor and myself have reason to suspect the presence of termites in our houses. How can we check for sure?—George Desmond, Indianapolis.

Termites usually indicate their presence by tiny mud tunnels on masonry foundations, these tunnels extending from ground level or below up the walls to the wood framing. Tunnels can appear on masonry walls, inside or outside, in a crawl-space or on a basement wall. To discover them, one must make a foot-by-foot search, inside and out. There are other wood-boring insects—often mistaken for termites—that attack buildings. Powderpost beetles and carpenter ants are those most often found. They make small entry holes in exposed ends of rafters and especially in floor joists and the wood posts that support center beams in basements. Look for holes in the beams and wood dust below them, as an indication of their presence.

A stilt-house slide

YOUR KIDS will get your money's worth of fun and then some from this combined stilt house, playground slide and monkey bars. It's inexpensive to build, and remember, it's an item you'll be able to sell when your moppets outgrow it. With this in mind I made it in sections and bolted them together for easy dismantling. Other than the pipe bars, you'll find all materials at your lumberyard. The drawings give you all the construction data you need. Set it on bricks so the legs don't sink in the ground. Coat the slide with a clear sealer and then paint the rest of the structure in bright colors.

By R.S. HEDIN

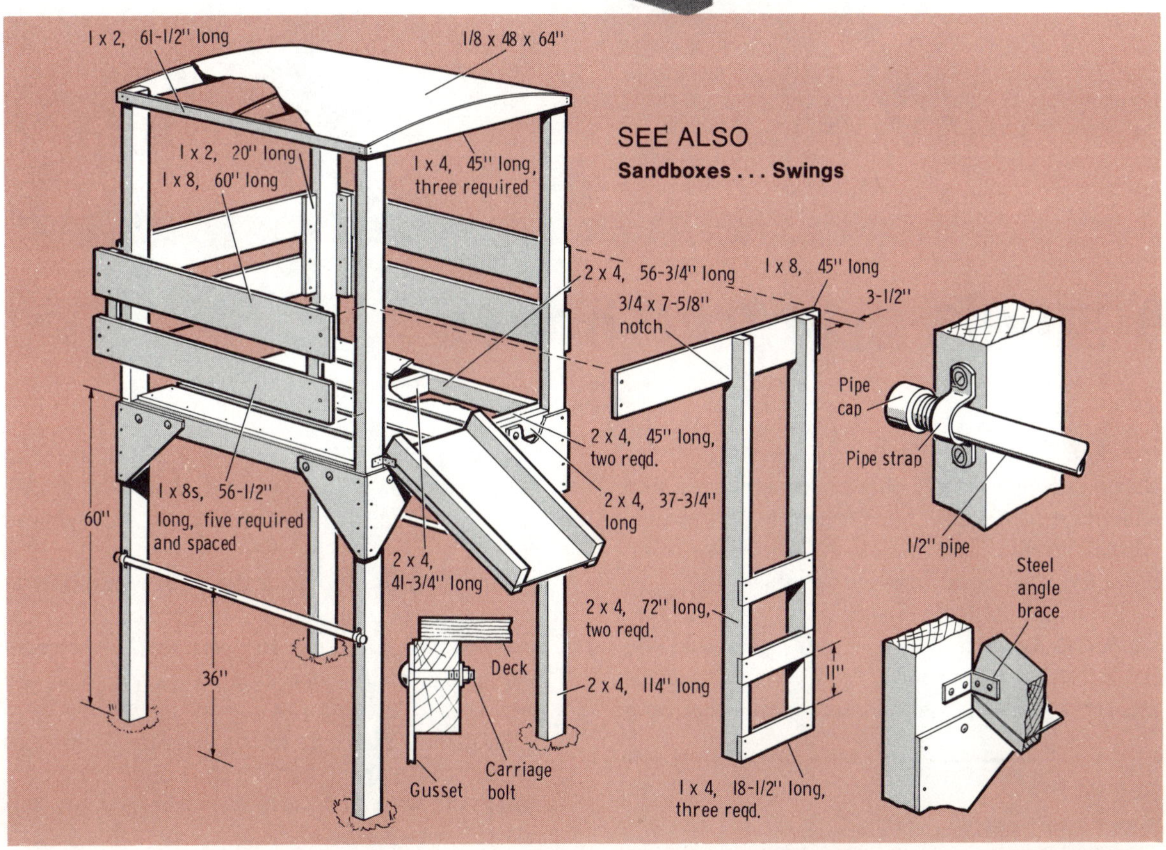

SEE ALSO
Sandboxes . . . Swings

A jungle-gym tree house

■ A COMBINATION JUNGLE GYM and tree house such as this can be constructed for about $65. The whole thing is designed to take advantage of standard lumber lengths and widths, which simplify construction. All you have to do is cut the various members to length.

The main platform is 6 ft. off the ground and supported by four 4 x 4 corner posts that are buried in 2 ft. of concrete. Each of the two levels measures 4 x 4 ft. square which means that both platforms can be cut from one 4 x 8-ft. sheet of ½-in. exterior-grade plywood. A 24-in. square hole is made in the lower platform for a fireman's pole. The pole is 1¼-in. galvanized pipe and is anchored at the top in a 2 x 4 crossrail and at the bottom in a hole filled with concrete. A seesaw uses the same pipe to pivot on. Two vertical ladders and a third one at approximately 60° are used here.

Designing different levels, ladders, poles and trapeze bars can be half the fun of construction. After all, your kids and their interests are different from all others!

SEE ALSO
A-frame swing sets . . . Swings

Playground fun

BOUNCING TEETER BOARD

IT'S POSSIBLE to add playground equipment to your back-yard "family-fun center" without spending a great deal of money. With a little imagination, you can convert everyday items that no longer serve their original purpose into games for your youngsters. The teeter board, for example, is simply four coil springs from a car attached to an old wheel hub. Use a heavy truck tire for a base and a 2x10 plank for the board. Paint in bright colors.

MERRY-GO-ROUND SWING

WHEN YOU LAY out the location for this toy, allow plenty of room so the kids can swing and twist on it in all directions. For a base, cut a 3-ft. disc from ¾-in. exterior plywood. Bore four holes equidistant around the circumference 2 in. from the edge. Secure with short hemp ropes knotted below and fasten to a length of rope attached to an overhead horizontal crosspiece between two trees.

SEE ALSO
A-frame swing sets . . . Swings

■ YOU CAN BRING a touch of old Coney Island into your back yard by building this simple roller coaster. The wood rail sections can be propped up with boxes or, for a more permanent arrangement, secured to posts planted in the ground. Notice that sections are pivoted together with bolts so that the entire set-up can be quickly disassembled for relocation or storage. There's no limit as to how long the coaster track can be.

Wheels fit between the guides to keep the cart on the rails. Here is where accuracy is a must. Build the roller assembly first, and then measure for wheel placement so there can be no side wobble. An old rug around the last rail tie makes a good brake for stopping.

Back-yard roller coaster

By R. S. HEDIN

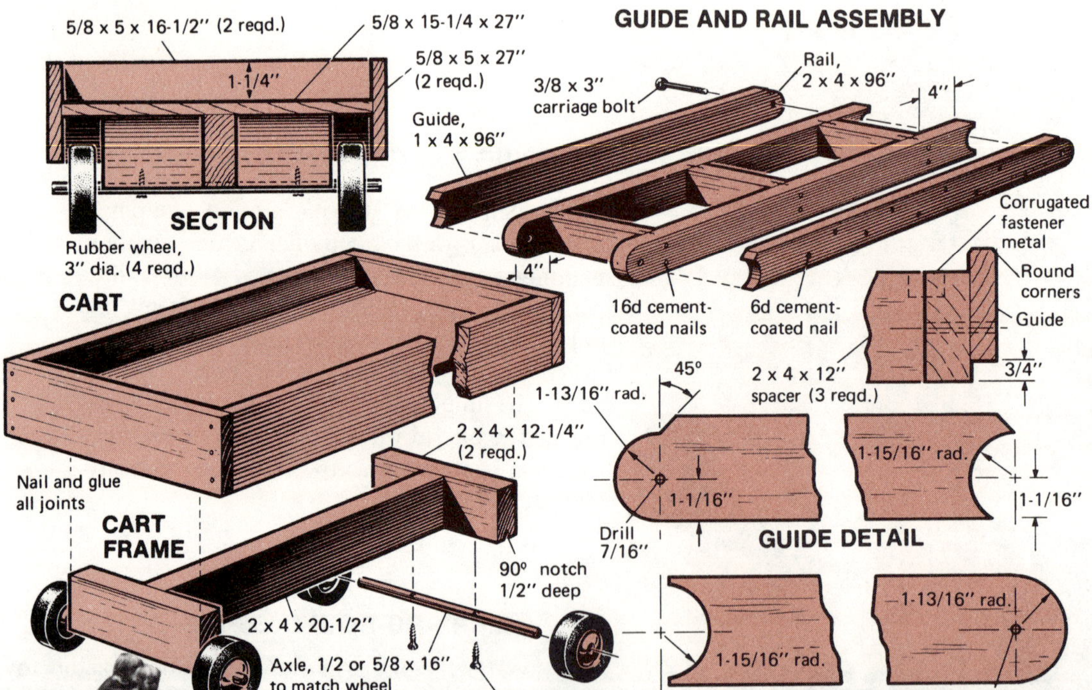

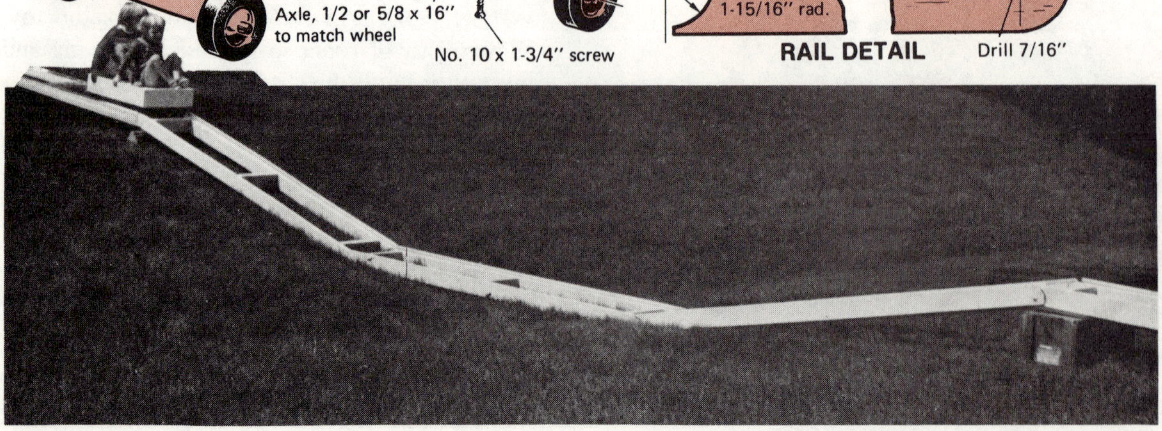

For summer fun—a water hoop

This project serves two purposes—the kids have a ball jumping "rope" while you sit back and watch as your lawn gets well watered

■ THIS ROLLICKING water hoop enables you to water the lawn at the same time the kids are having a ball jumping "rope" and getting drenched as the hoop turns. Strong jets of water escaping from pinholes drilled in opposite ends of the hoop cause the hoop to turn Ferris-wheel fashion when it's connected to a hose.

The toy was invented by Frank Reed and Marty Trent of Palos Verdes Peninsula, Calif., and you can make one like it from ½-in. PVC pipe and standard plumbing fittings. The hoop turns on two supporting posts anchored in the ground, and a double female hose coupling prevents the garden hose from twisting into a pretzel as the hoop turns. PVC pipe tees, plus short pipe nipples, provide axles at the center point of the hoop. The hoop is easily assembled with regular PVC cement.

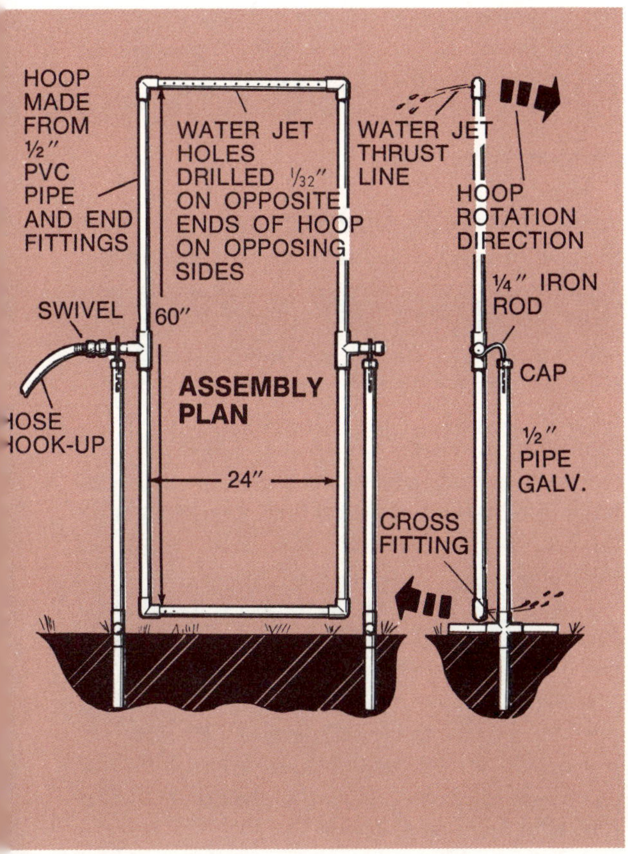

HOSE HOOKUP is assembled from standard brass fittings. Adapter threads take PVC nipple.

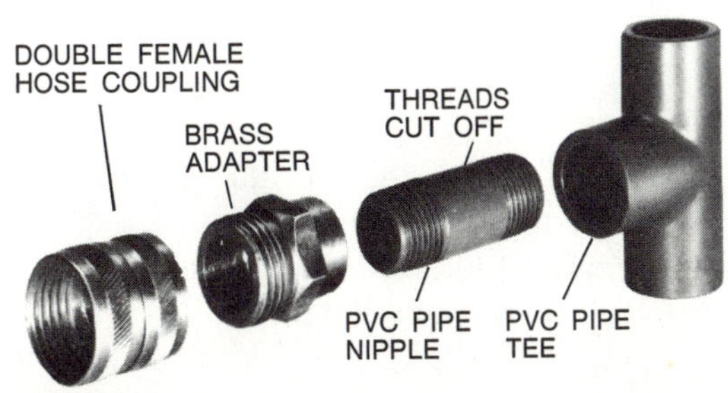

SEE ALSO
A-frame swing sets . . . Swings

Build a super sandbox

By STEPHEN MENKE

■ YOUNGSTERS WILL PLAY by the hour in this inviting sandbox. When the kids are grown, it can be closed in to serve as a utility shed.

The sandbox is made using 2x4 framing covered with weather-resistant cedar siding. It features a redwood seat and hip-roof construction. Use pressure-treated wood for the framing, rails and posts.

Prepare the ground for the sandbox. First mark out the 4x4-ft. sandbox area using stakes and a mason's line and check each corner of the rectangle to be sure it is square.

SEE ALSO
A-frame swing sets . . . Swings

Level the area to a 6-in. depth. Then set the corner posts below the frost line and chamfer the inside edges.

Add a 4-in.-deep gravel layer and top it with 1 or 2 in. of mason's sand. Rake the sand level and tamp. Lay the brick floor.

Begin work on the sandbox section. Corner members Y are 2x4s notched to receive the rails.

The framing of the sandbox entry is somewhat tricky. To avoid having to drive nails through a full 2x4 width, notch the bottom plate to receive the filler strip.

Next, cut a 1½x1¾x19-in. strip from a scrap 2x4. Secure the notched legs X by spiking with nails. Then nail-fasten the strip into the notch cut in the bottom plate. Use 10d common nails and drill pilot holes to avoid splitting. Assemble the other three sides using resorcinol glue and nails. Attach the sides to the corner posts.

Before installing the cedar siding, bevel all edges using either a router or table saw. The flat next to the bevel should be at least ⅝-in. wide to assure adequate material meeting at the joints.

Install the siding, one board at a time, in this fashion:

1 Make a 45° miter cut on one end; hold the board in position on the frame, mitered end at the bottom of the sandbox.

2 Mark the miter cut at the upper end, remove board and make cut.

3 Install the siding using resorcinol glue and 6d galvanized nails. Sink nails and fill holes.

constructing the seat

For durability, build the sandbox seat of either redwood or pressure-treated wood. Use miter cuts at the corner joints to give a professional look to the job. Notch the corners where they meet the posts.

Center the seat on the 2x4 frame and attach it with resorcinol glue and 6d galvanized finishing nails. Set the nails and cover them with a weatherproof wood filler.

The roof is a square hip roof with a 6½-in. pitch (6½-in. rise in a 12-in. run). Construction is of 2x4 framing skinned with ½-in. plywood sheathing.

Cut the 2x4 frame parts and 1x2 ceiling cleats. Predrill holes and attach frame to posts using. No. 18 3½-in. lagscrews.

Cut the ceiling, make corner notches for the posts, and attach to the ceiling cleats. Roof rafters rest on the corner posts. Install rafters with No. 18 3½-in. lagscrews. Nail the sheathing to the roof with 8d common nails.

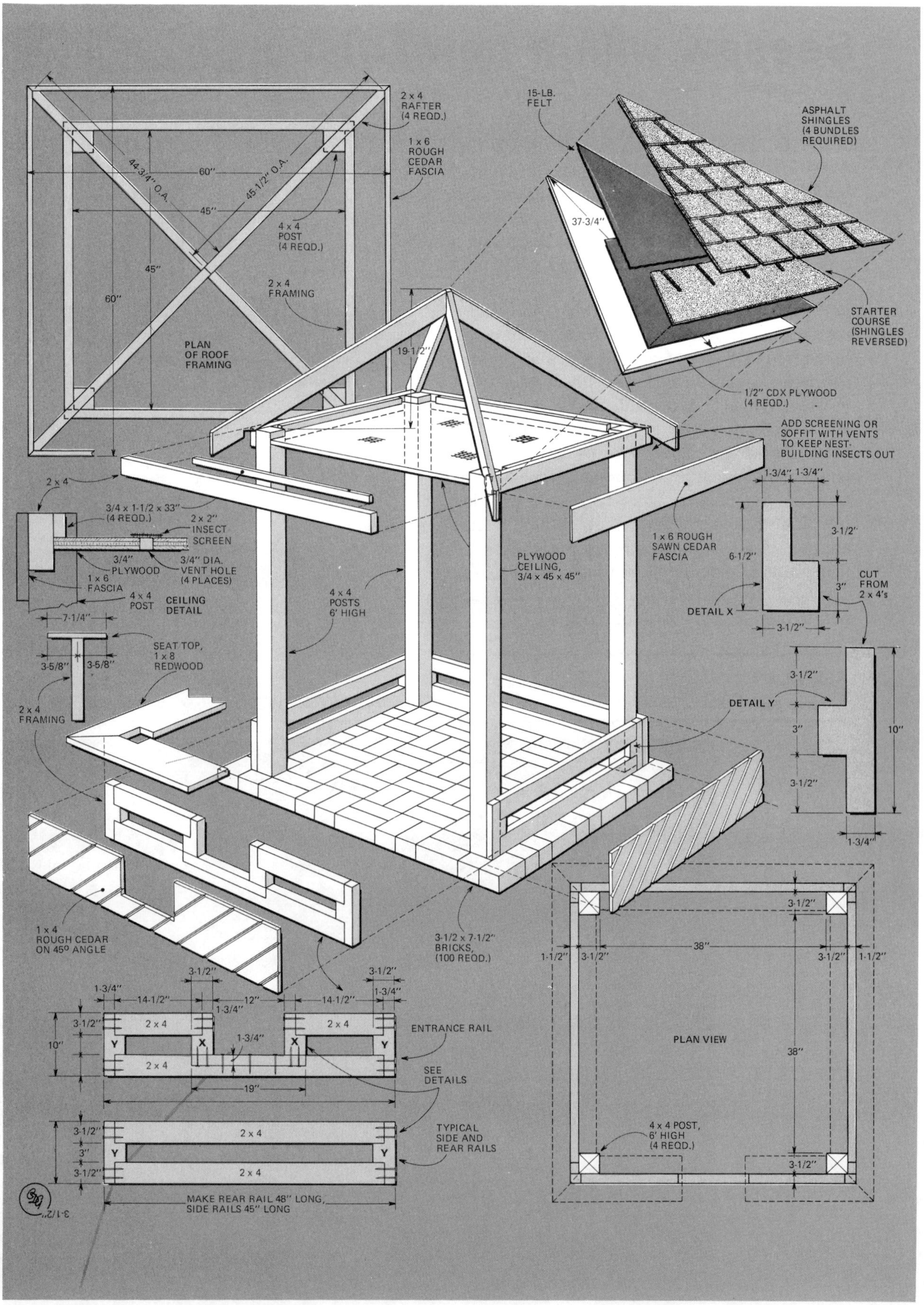
2 x 4
RAFTER
(4 REQD.)
1 x 6
ROUGH
CEDAR
FASCIA
44-3/4" O.A.
45-1/2" O.A.
60"
45"
4 x 4
POST
(4 REQD.)
2 x 4
FRAMING
PLAN
OF ROOF
FRAMING
15-LB.
FELT
ASPHALT
SHINGLES
(4 BUNDLES
REQUIRED)
37-3/4"
STARTER
COURSE
(SHINGLES
REVERSED)
1/2" CDX PLYWOOD
(4 REQD.)
19-1/2"
ADD SCREENING OR
SOFFIT WITH VENTS
TO KEEP NEST-
BUILDING INSECTS OUT
2 x 4
3/4 x 1-1/2 x 33"
(4 REQD.)
2 x 2"
INSECT
SCREEN
3/4"
PLYWOOD
3/4" DIA.
VENT HOLE
(4 PLACES)
1 x 6
FASCIA
4 x 4
POST
CEILING
DETAIL
1 x 6 ROUGH
SAWN CEDAR
FASCIA
PLYWOOD
CEILING,
3/4 x 45 x 45"
4 x 4
POSTS
6' HIGH
1-3/4"
3-1/2"
6-1/2"
3"
CUT
FROM
2 x 4's
DETAIL X
7-1/4"
3-5/8"
SEAT TOP,
1 x 8
REDWOOD
2 x 4
FRAMING
DETAIL Y
10"
1 x 4
ROUGH CEDAR
ON 45° ANGLE
3-1/2 x 7-1/2"
BRICKS,
(100 REQD.)
38"
1-1/2"
PLAN VIEW
4 x 4 POST,
6' HIGH
(4 REQD.)
14-1/2"
12"
ENTRANCE RAIL
SEE
DETAILS
19"
TYPICAL
SIDE AND
REAR RAILS
MAKE REAR RAIL 48" LONG,
SIDE RAILS 45" LONG

Seesaw with a new twist

By R. S. HEDIN

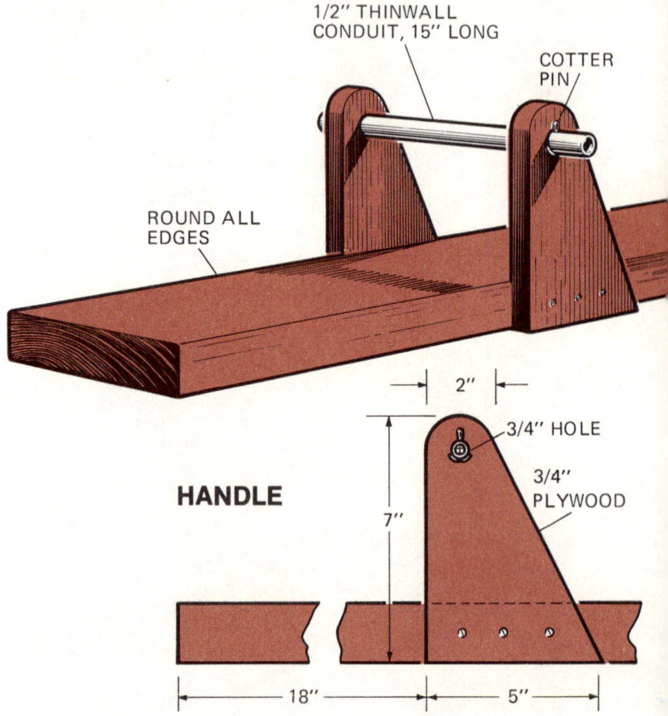

■ THIS SEESAW has a new twist and is sure to be irresistible to kids of all ages. In addition to the usual up-and-down movement, the seat board rotates on a vertical shaft that's fitted with a thrust bearing. The shaft in turn fits inside a pipe post that's anchored and braced solidly to a nontipping base of 2 x 4s. For safety, you would be wise to rope off the area in which the seesaw rotates and provide only one entrance to eliminate any possibility of a child who's among the spectators getting bowled over and injured.

Use a sound 2 x 8 plank for the seat board and round all edges to prevent splinters. To finish the seesaw, apply two coats of exterior house paint. You'll probably want to use a lubricant on the moving parts to assure a quiet, trouble-free action. Notice that conduit clamps are used to attach the seat board to the steel rod that pivots in pipe-nipple bearings. A ⅜ x 5-in. carriage bolt is used to secure the seat board support to the 1-in. pipe used for the pivot.

SEE ALSO
A-frame swing sets . . . Swings

YOUNGSTERS GET lots of exercise on this seesaw that takes them around as well as up and down.

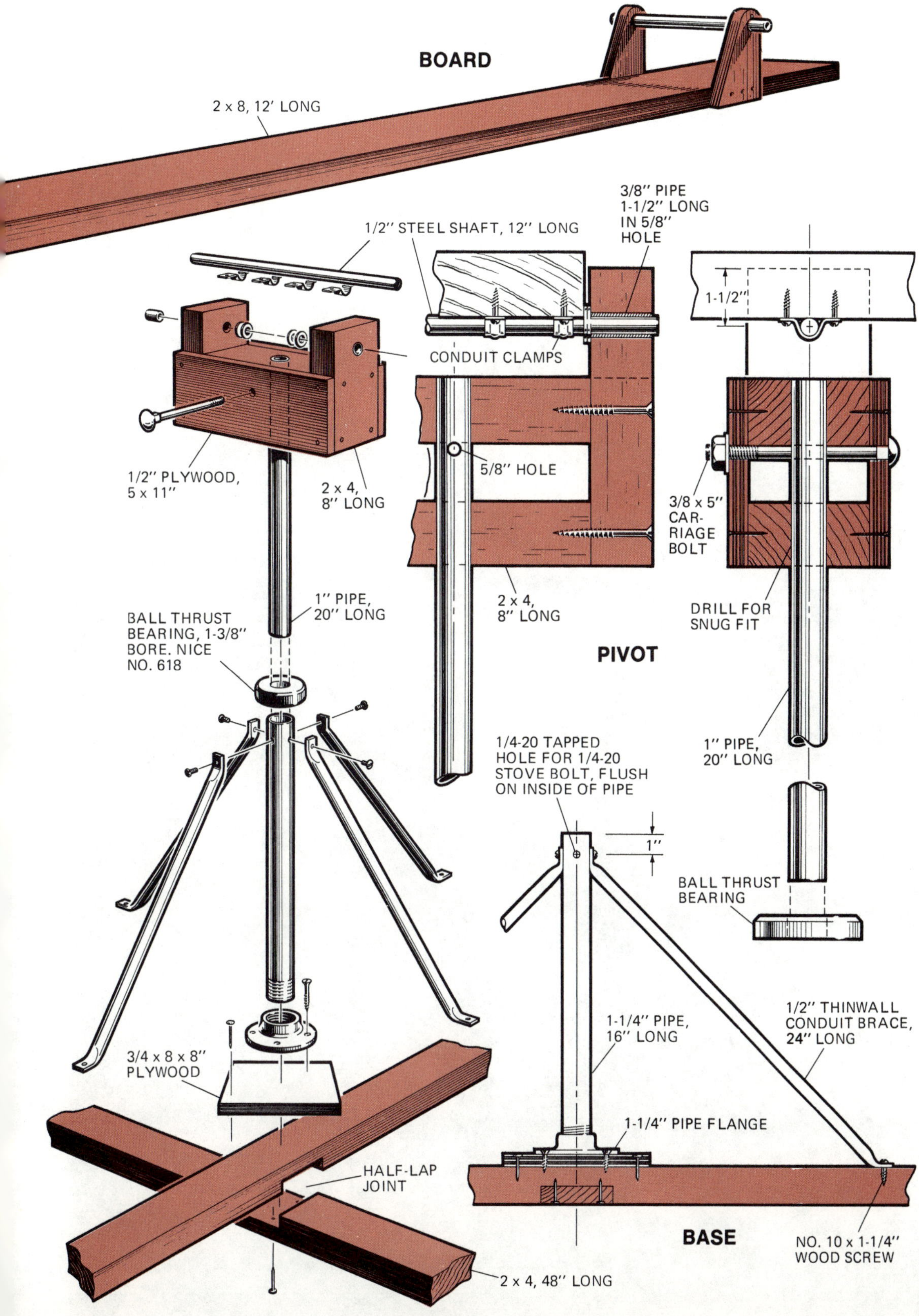
BOARD
2 x 8, 12' LONG
1/2" STEEL SHAFT, 12" LONG
3/8" PIPE
1-1/2" LONG
IN 5/8"
HOLE
1-1/2"
CONDUIT CLAMPS
1/2" PLYWOOD,
5 x 11"
2 x 4,
8" LONG
5/8" HOLE
3/8 x 5"
CAR-
RIAGE
BOLT
1" PIPE,
20" LONG
2 x 4,
8" LONG
DRILL FOR
SNUG FIT
BALL THRUST
BEARING, 1-3/8"
BORE. NICE
NO. 618
PIVOT
1/4-20 TAPPED
HOLE FOR 1/4-20
STOVE BOLT, FLUSH
ON INSIDE OF PIPE
1" PIPE,
20" LONG
1"
BALL THRUST
BEARING
1-1/4" PIPE,
16" LONG
1/2" THINWALL
CONDUIT BRACE,
24" LONG
3/4 x 8 x 8"
PLYWOOD
1-1/4" PIPE FLANGE
HALF-LAP
JOINT
BASE
NO. 10 x 1-1/4"
WOOD SCREW
2 x 4, 48" LONG

Here's back-yard summer fun

KIDS LIKE ALL KINDS of presents from the most complicated and expensive to the simplest and cheapest. But they're happiest when they know that you made the present yourself. The four games on these pages are easy to build, and one of them will suit your boy or girl (and some grownups if they get a chance to play), no matter what their age. You won't need any special tools to construct the stilts, swing, tetherball or basketball hoop. Since these games are played outdoors, you have to build them to withstand the weather. Make the swing out of solid oak stock and protect the pieces with two coats of spar varnish. All wood joints should be assembled with a waterproof glue or construction adhesive and all nails should be hot-dipped galvanized to prevent rust. For screws, use brass or aluminum.

The most complicated project, the basketball hoop, is worth the effort because the backstop adjusts to any height. The detail drawing (next page) shows how the heavy plywood backstop weights down the upper frame to get a clamping action between cross ties and 4x4 support posts. The cam action is so tight that 2x4 chocks under the cross ties on opposite sides of the posts will

YOUR KIDS are sure to enjoy the swing and stilts shown as much as the children in these photos are. Both projects have been made of durable hardwood for years of heavy, outdoor use

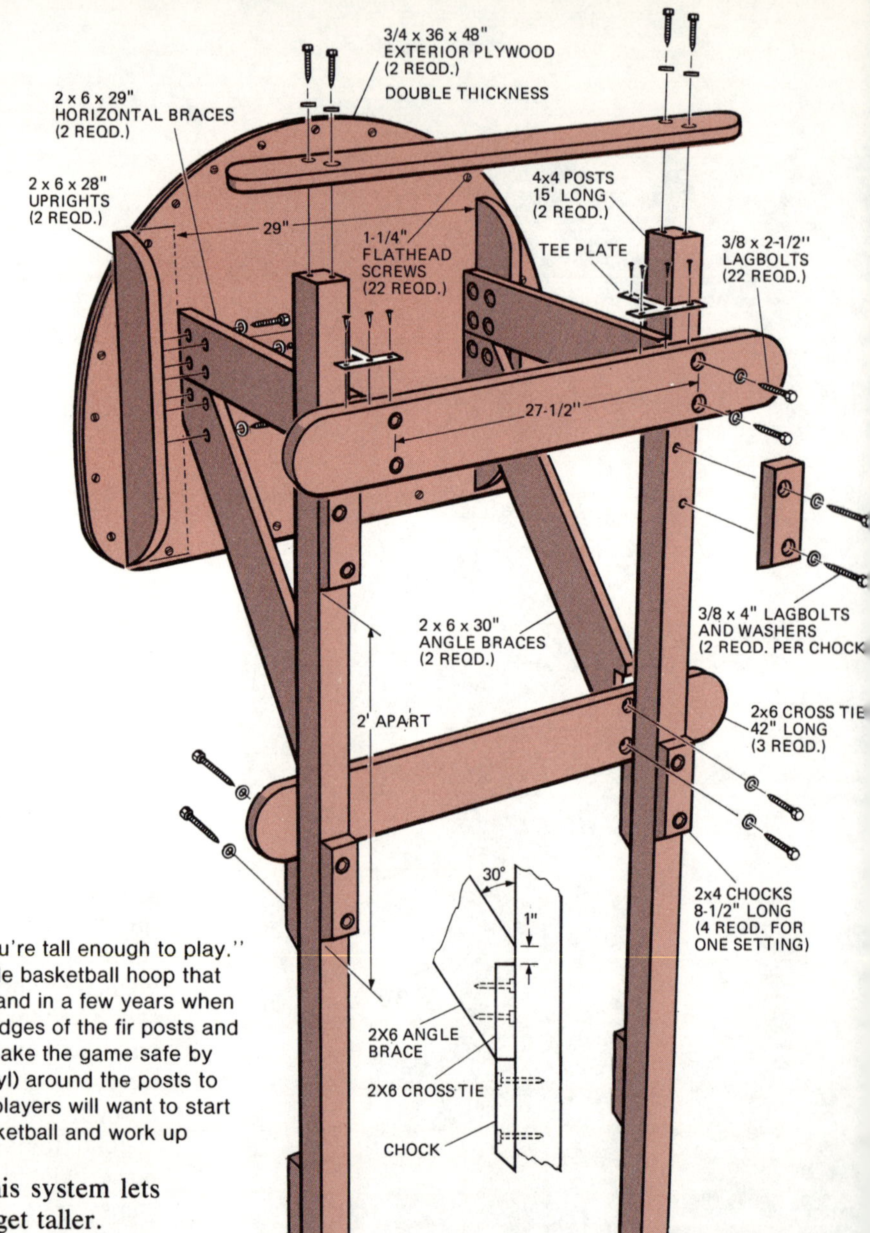

Basketball hoop

"**COME BACK** in a few years when you're tall enough to play." Why wait? You can build this adjustable basketball hoop that will be perfect for your kids right now and in a few years when they grow taller. Be sure to sand the edges of the fir posts and apply a sealer to eliminate splinters. Make the game safe by attaching bumpers (foam rubber in vinyl) around the posts to protect preoccupied players. Smaller players will want to start with a ball which is smaller than a basketball and work up

support the whole assembly. This system lets you raise the hoop as your kids get taller.

A pair of stilts is a great toy to develop balance and coordination. Use a hardwood like oak or maple for the stock and base pad. Exterior-grade plywood is fine for the foot platform that will easily support a 75-lb. child. For larger kids, add the alternate brace detailed in the drawings. To preserve the stilts and keep scrapes and bruises to a minimum, tell the kids to stay off hard surfaces.

Tetherball (page2199) is normally for two players. Each takes half of an imaginary circle around the center post for his court and tries to hit the ball past his opponent until the cord is completely wrapped around the pole. It's not easy because the other player is trying to do the same thing in the opposite direction. A metal sleeve, slightly larger than the pole, can be set in concrete at grade level so you can remove the pole to mow the grass or for winter storage. Your yard will be a special place for the kids after you've built one of these toys.

Child's swing

WHATEVER the object, kids will try to swing from it if it's possible. This good-looking design, assembled around a continuous rope loop, eliminates screwed joints that may split open under stress. The guard rails lift up along the ropes for easy access (you can face in either direction) and slide down to make an accidental fall next to impossible. Use nylon rope for a safer ride

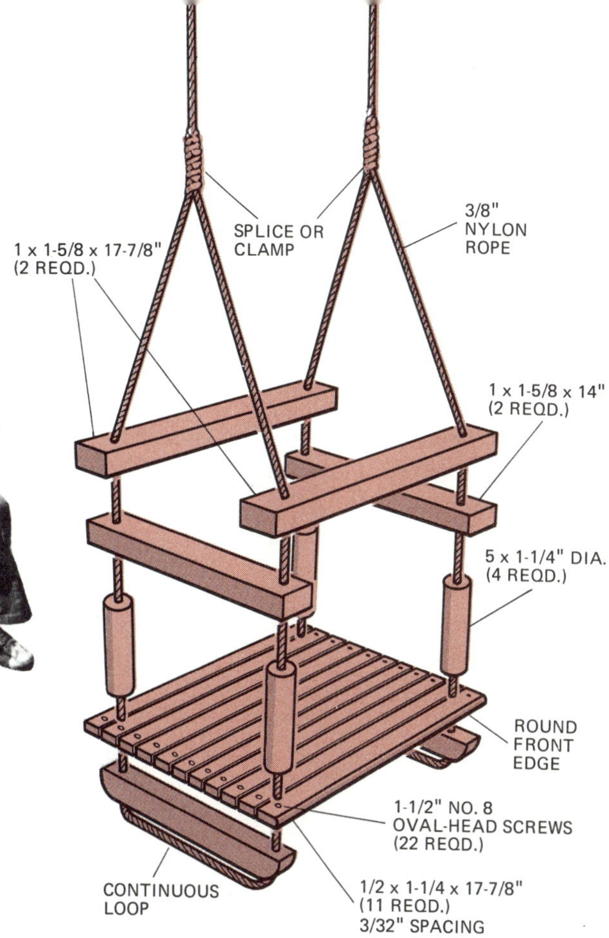

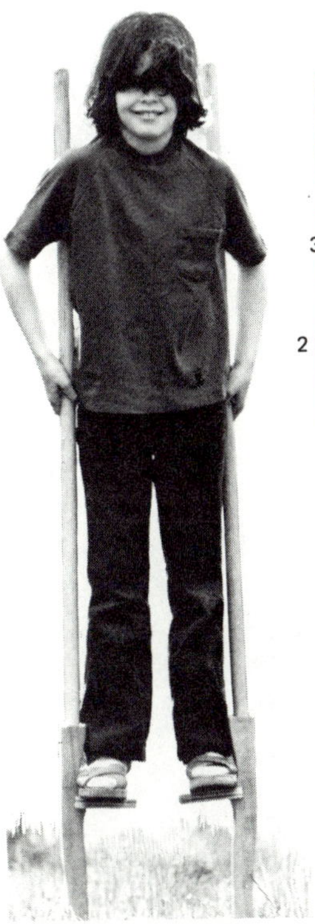

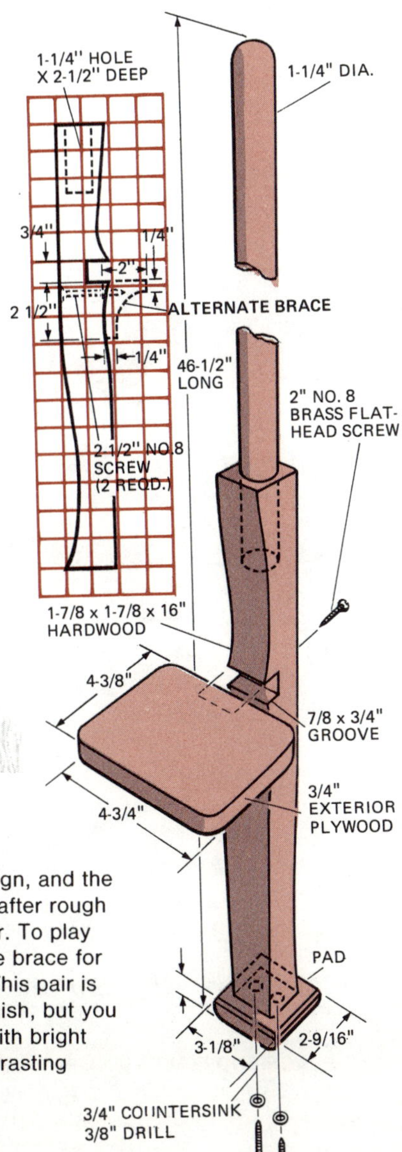

Stilts

WE TESTED this design, and the foot platform held up after rough use by a 150-pounder. To play safe, use the alternate brace for anyone over 75 lbs. This pair is sealed with clear varnish, but you can decorate yours with bright enamel colors or contrasting wood stains

Tetherball

THE TOUGHEST part of this project is locating a ball with a moulded loop on it. A 6-in.-diameter, concrete filled hole makes a strong, permanent base. Setting an oversize sleeve in the concrete will make the pole demountable. Tetherball is a game the whole family will enjoy

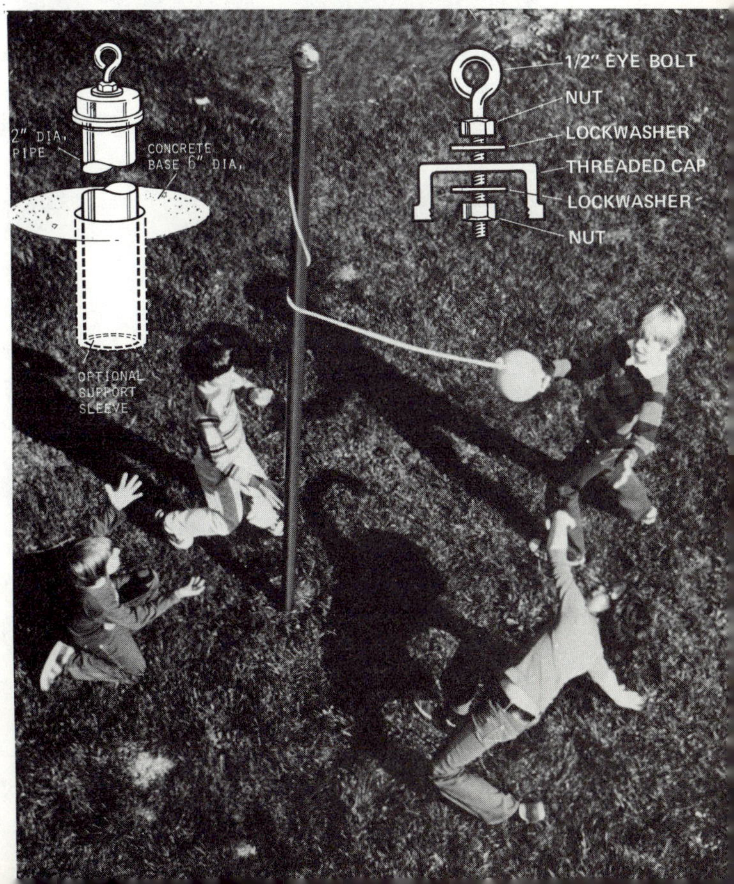

Build a pretty little playhouse

By BRAD SNYDER

This charmer can serve other roles, too—giving you much greater storage space for lawn toys and games and yard tools

■ WHETHER YOU NEED a playhouse for the youngsters, a summer office, pool cabana or more storage space for yard equipment, a lawn building lets you make greater use of your property.

Once we decided to build one, the next step was to decide its architectural style. This was solved by selecting the Western-style model shown which matched our home exterior. Elevations for it (and the alternate Western Side Door) are shown on these pages.

SEE ALSO

Cabanas . . . Garden shelters . . . Gazebos . . . Poolhouses . . . Summer houses

slab or piers are ok

Though the house could have been built on a slab, I elected to construct it on four concrete-block piers (in my area, exempt from tax assessment). After evaluating exactly what would be stored in the shed, I actually built it slightly larger than shown on the plans.

Extra attention to details—window boxes, cupola birdhouse and ornamental hardware—yields the touches that elevate this little house from the construction-shanty look frequently found in home-built yard structures. I kept complete labor and materials records while building the house; they show about 35 hours of labor.

SHED FRAMING rests on four piers (upper left). Then flooring is nailed to joists and trimmed in place.

SPEED CONSTRUCTION by assembling each wall on the ground (left), then hoisting it into place as a unit.

PLACE END WALLS (above) and hold them temporarily with diagonal bracing. Ends equal the platform width.

a pretty playhouse, continued

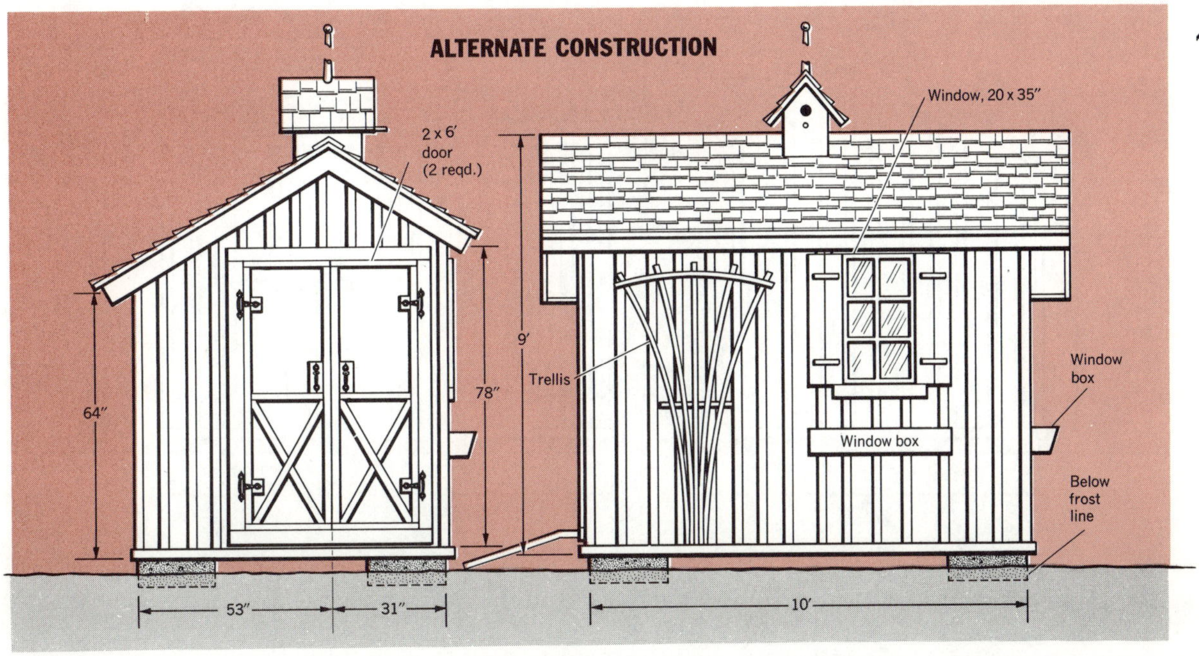

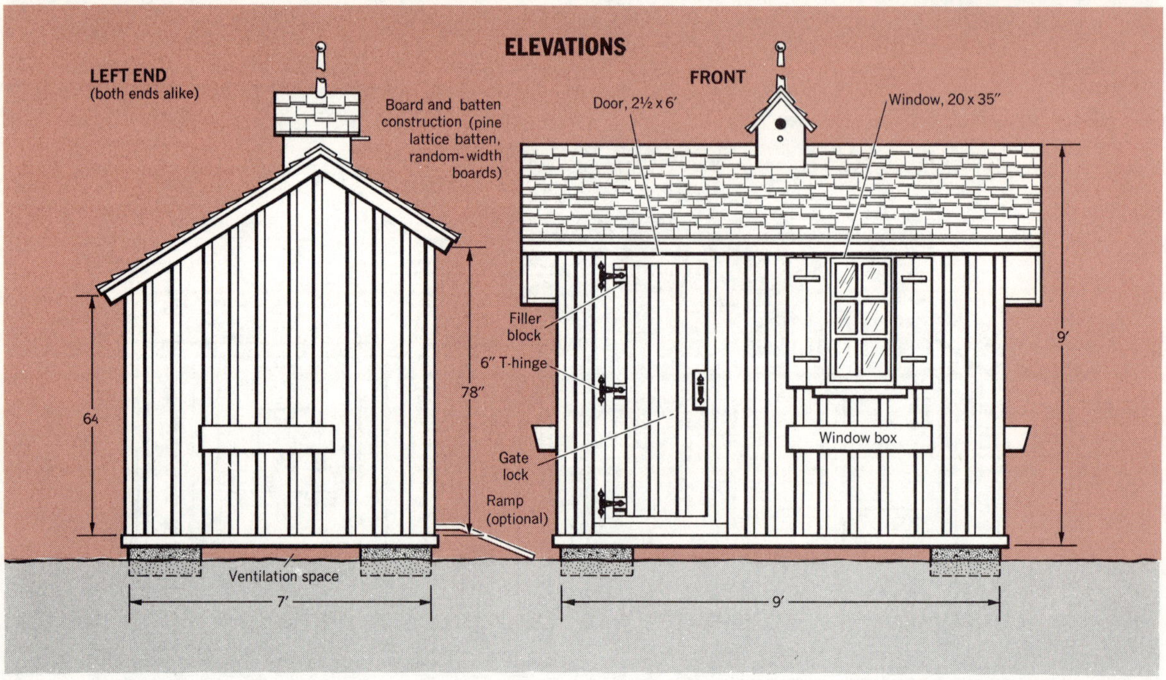
ELEVATIONS
LEFT END
(both ends alike)
Board and batten construction (pine lattice batten, random-width boards)
FRONT
Door, 2½ x 6′
Window, 20 x 35″
Filler block
6″ T-hinge
Gate lock
Ramp (optional)
Window box
64
78″
9′
Ventilation space
7′
9′

By JOHN L. KUIK

The fun of an outdoor playhouse moves indoors with this easy-to-build plywood version. Because it is easy to set up and knock down, it can be folded and stored conveniently out of the way for the night

Indoor playhouse

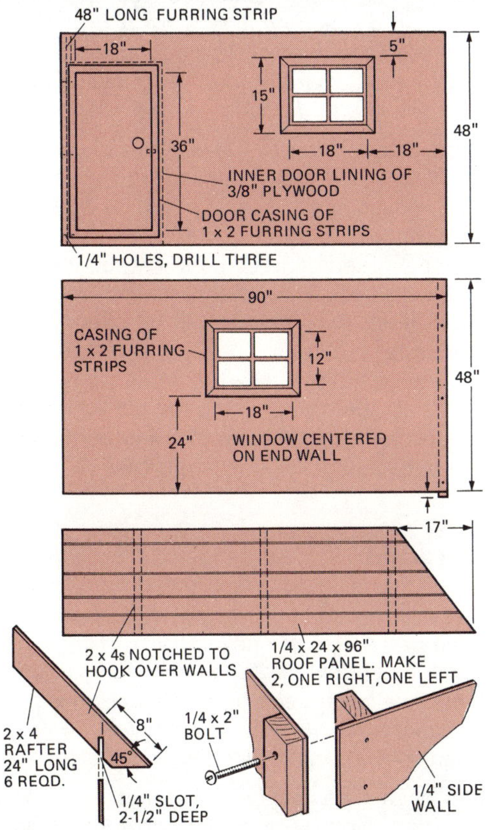

MATERIALS for the playhouse are ¼-in. plywood for the walls, a sheet of paneling for the roof, furring strips and 2x4 scraps, beveled and slotted for the roof supports. The corner is held together with three ¼-in. bolts through the furring strips on both plywood walls.

SEE ALSO
Pull toys . . . Toys

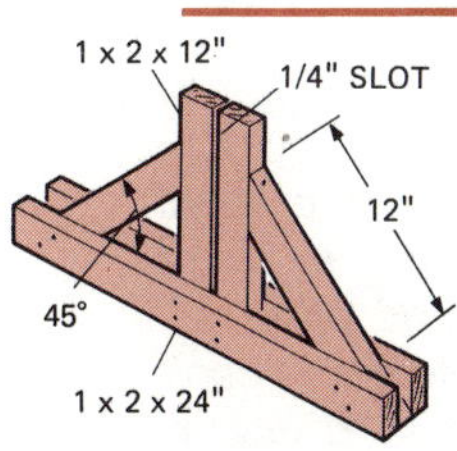

■ THIS QUICK-TO-SET-UP playhouse will delight your youngster. Walls can be ¼-in. plywood painted to suit or prefinished ¼-in. paneling. If the door opening is cut carefully, the cutout can become the door; window panes are also cut out, leaving muntins and bars. Furring strips for corner assembly and casing are glued and nailed; note that one longer corner strip serves to level walls held in end stands. Plywood strips lining door opening inside protrude ½ in. inward in order to keep the door from swinging in. Finishing touches are curtains and doorknobs, the latter made from thread spools.

Last resort

The cedar-shingled (four sides) hip roof of our house has a leak at the southeast hip line when the wind blows from the southwest. The roof has 16-in. prefabricated cedar shingles applied in what is called the Boston ridge method (alternating courses lapped). The slope is 4 in 12. To combat the leak, we have done the following to the southeast hip shingles:

1. Removed them and changed their shingle exposure.

2. Removed and added roofing felt.

3. Removed and snugly fitted the hip shingles.

After all that, the roof still leaks. I'm beginning to think my pitch is too low, but I don't know how to resolve this. The ceiling is finished with redwood and has 6 in. of insulation in the 2x8-in. framing. As I want the roof to breathe, I don't want to switch to an asphalt roof.—Roy L. Ellison, Cleveland, Okla.

I believe you should have stopped blaming the ridge shingles after you added roofing felt and it still leaked. Roof leaks are extremely difficult to locate if the underside isn't exposed. Water can penetrate in an area 10 feet away from the interior drip just by following the framing members to either a low spot or until it meets an obstruction (a nailhead or other framing member). It seems as if you have a leak somewhere else in your roof.

I suggest that you remove some of your redwood, possibly 3 ft. above where the leak appears to be, then look for telltale stains. Follow these stains until you come to the errant shingle. You can make the repair from the roof.

A well-installed cedar-shingled roof should last a long time. Don't allow leaves, pine needles or other wind-blown debris to accumulate. Incidentally, the Federal Housing Administration recommends a maximum exposure of 4½ in. on roof pitches of 4 in 12 and 5 in 12 in.

Undersize ceiling heights

When I build my new house, I'm going to make all ceiling heights 7½ ft. I realize I may pay more for labor by extra cutting for drywall and paneling, but I figure I'll make up for it in heating and cooling savings. Why isn't this mentioned in energy conservation articles? Do you know where I can obtain more data on the subject?—Ray Spencer, Iron River, Mich.

When the early settlers built their homes with low ceilings, a six-foot-six man was a rarity. If you are of average height and plan on keeping the house, you will notice slight savings on heating costs. Incidentally, a 7½-ft. average is the minimum ceiling height that is accepted by the FHA.

However, I do think that you should give serious thought to the resale value of your house and the availability of financing. Some lending institutions insist on a minimum ceiling height (excluding kitchens and baths) of 8 ft. Check this with a knowledgeable local real estate agent.

Since the heat loss is calculated in part on exterior wall area, you are really only cutting down 1/16th of your exterior wall height per lineal foot (90 sq. ft. versus 96 sq. ft. on a 12-ft.-long wall). You can check this out further with a licensed mechanical engineer. Considering resale value and tall guests, I would opt for extra insulation, insulating glass on storm windows and weather-stripping.

Curious woman

The rubber-backed, indoor-outdoor carpet in my kitchen is glued to the floor. It's too expensive to remove the carpet and sand the floor prior to putting down cushioned sheet vinyl. Can I glue the vinyl over the carpet? The edges would be covered by moldings and the carpet would add insulation.—Mrs. B. Jordain, Jerome, Idaho

I'm afraid you'll have to live with the carpet, or remove it to install cushioned sheet vinyl. The key word is cushioned, meaning that the material is already padded.

Additional padding, such as carpet, won't work. The vinyl will show all indentations (tables and chair legs). Eventually it will be pierced. A spokesman for the Armstrong Cork Co., Lancaster, Pa., verified this. It may pay to hire a neighborhood teen-ager to help strip the old adhesive off the floor. Although the carpet is warmer to the touch, the insulation value is negligible.

Flexible drains

Each time I've installed a new lavatory sink in my home (three to date) I've run into the same problem: The drain lines are never in line. There are flexible and bendable water supply tubings available, but I've never seen a flexible drain pipe to make my installation easier. Seems like an easy invention.—J. Marron, Point Lookout, N.Y.

There is such an item on the market. The flexible, acid-resistant line is made of polypropylene. It fits the standard sinks and traps. The makers say it works even if the drain and trap are up to 2 inches out of line. As the flexible section is kept to the vertical piping, it should not collect debris in its corrugations. Known as Flexi-Drain, it is manufactured by Webstone Co. Inc., 38 Harlow St., Worcester, Mass. 01605.

SHEETS of amber Plexiglas were used to make this handsome see-through coffee table, compatible with modern decors.

How to work with Plexiglas

■ ALTHOUGH MANY beginning do-it-yourselfers think otherwise, there's no ironclad rule that says an exciting, functional product must be hard to build. The well-designed, easy-to-make projects on these pages prove that's not so. Created from acrylic sheet plastic such as Plexiglas (TN), they are typical of the gleaming transparent, translucent, or opaque household items that are now so popular in the fashionable gift shops and better department stores.

SEE ALSO
**Coffee tables . . . Cutting boards . . .
Gifts, Christmas . . . House plants . . .
Internal carving . . . Magazine holders . . .
Occasional tables . . . Terrariums . . . Wine racks**

CLEAR PLASTIC has many applications. This fish tank is made of it. It can replace glass in doors, for safety, and can be used to make sliding cabinet doors.

While it looks like glass and comes in sheets like glass, acrylic plastic is as soft as hardwood—which means you can drill it and saw it to produce strong transparent joints, and you can heat-form it into interesting curves and shapes. The material is widely available from building supply dealers, hardware stores, paint and glass stores and wallpaper outlets.

The largest supplier of acrylic sheet plastic, Rohm and Haas, makes it in two forms: Plexiglas K (safety glazing grade), with thicknesses ranging from .080 in. to 3/16-in.; and Plexiglas G (safety glazing and decorative grade), with just two thicknesses—1/8-in. and 1/4-in. The only significant difference between the two, says the manufacturer, is that Plexiglas K, which is less costly, cannot be solvent cemented.

You can buy sheets in sizes ranging from 18x24 in. to 36x48 in. There are more than 40 standard colors of Plexiglas, in various tones and eight textured surface patterns.

The cost for 1/4-in. Plexiglas G at presstime was about $3.00 per sq. ft. for clear and 10 percent more for colors. Plexiglas K was about 25 percent cheaper.

Although acrylic plastic will scratch more readily than glass, it comes with a protective

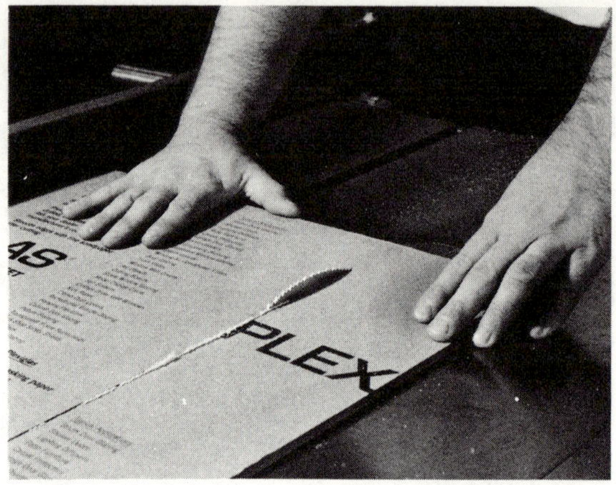

CIRCULAR SAWING: Use a fine-tooth "plywood" blade and set the blade a little higher than the thickness of plastic. Hold material firmly and work slowly.

SCRIBING: Plastic up to 1/8-in. thick can be cut by scoring with a pointed tool. Make the score along a straightedge, four or five times through the paper.

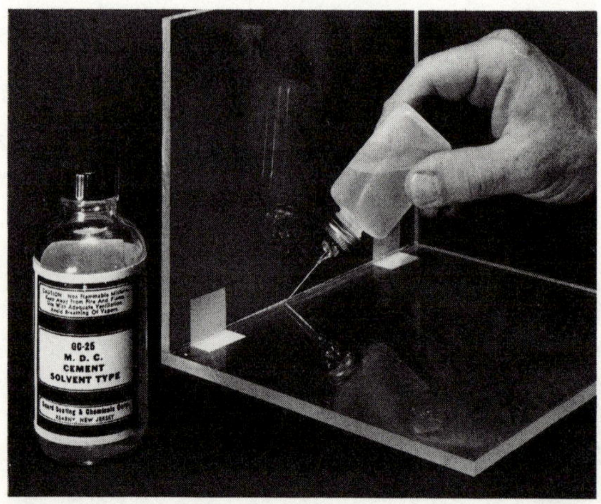

CEMENTING: Remove the paper and sand the surfaces to be cemented. Tape the work and apply solvent to joint with needle-spout unit.

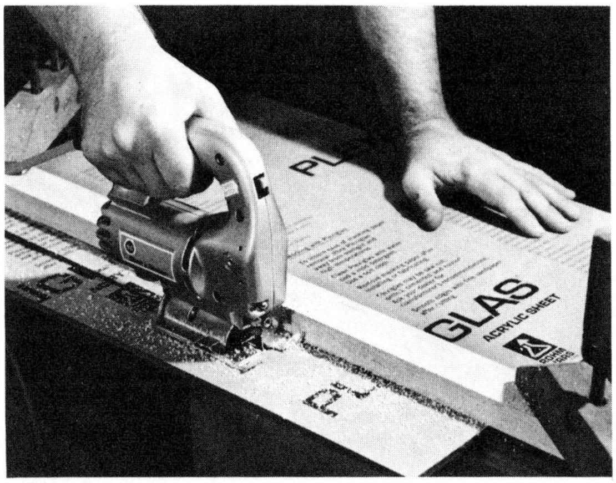

SABRE SAWING: The blade should have 14 teeth per inch. Use a strip to guide the saw in straight cuts and hold the work firmly on curves.

BANDSAWING: The blade should have a minimum of 10 teeth per inch. Pass the work slowly through the saw. Use protective paper to draw the cutting line.

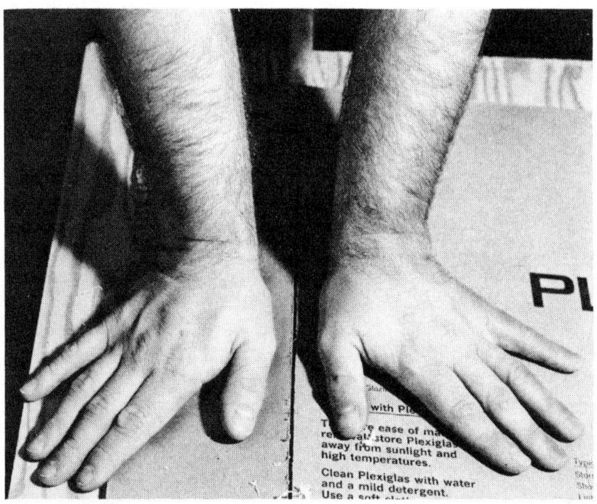

BREAKING: Position the score, face up, directly over a ¾-in. dowel. Hold sheet with one hand and press down with the other. Continue along the score.

DRILLING: Use a regular twist drill and press lightly. Back up the work with a wood block and a clamp. Drill slowly and don't remove the paper.

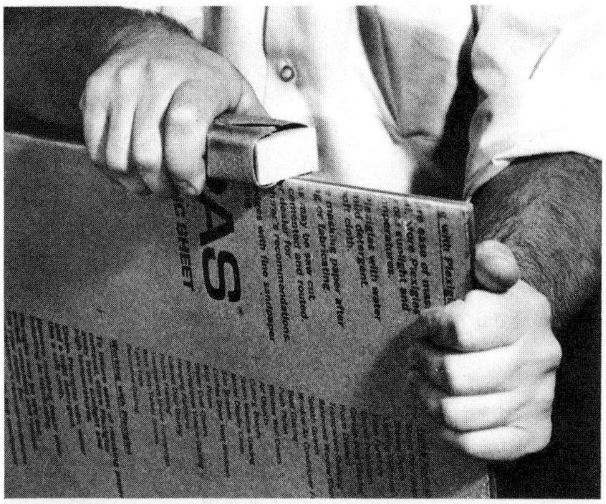

EDGE FINISHING: Marks are removed by scraping with a knife or by sanding with 60 to 80-grit paper, followed by 150-grit "wet or dry."

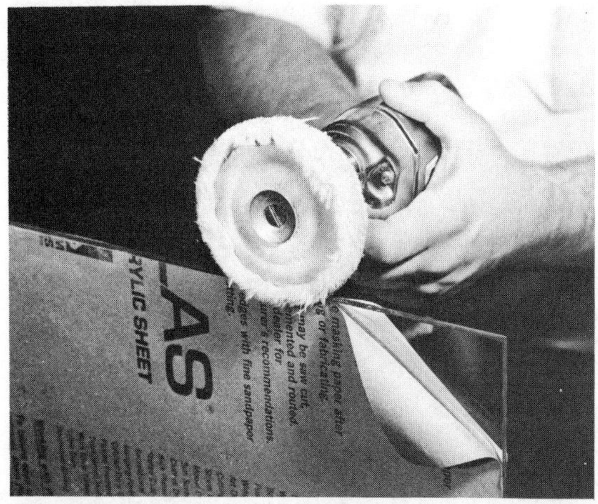

POLISHING: To produce a transparent edge, continue sanding with grits up to 400. Buff with a compound-coated muslin wheel and a cotton-flannel wheel.

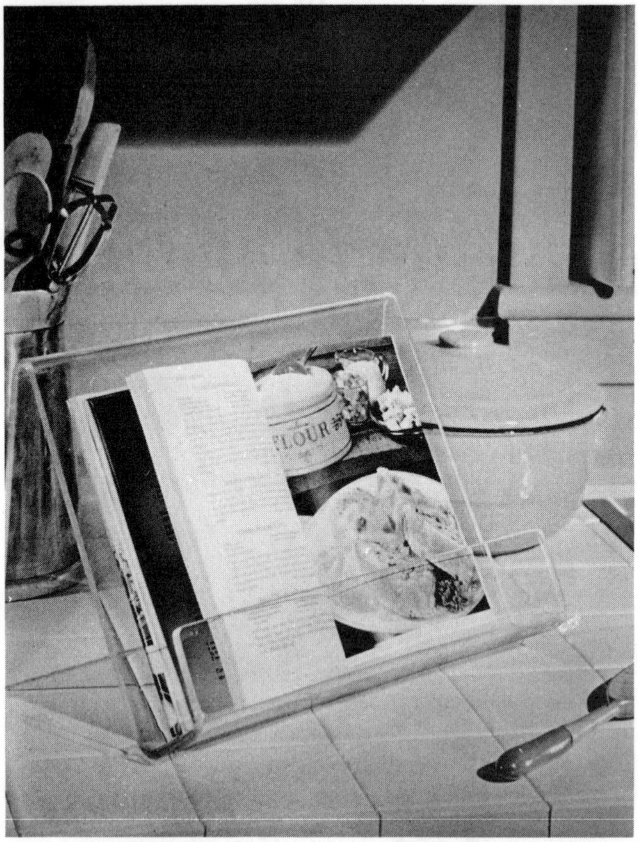

COOKBOOK HOLDER is heat-formed from one piece.

TRISECTED TABLE: Top rests on bent sheets.

TERRARIUM is a good project for beginner.

TELEPHONE STAND requires careful heat-forming.

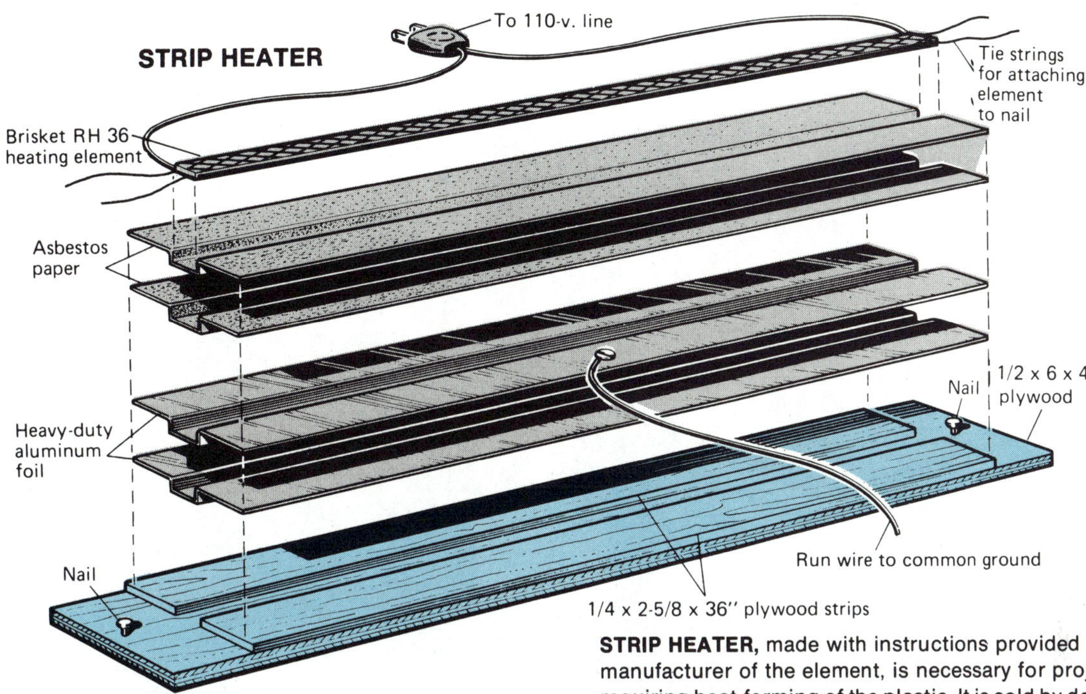

STRIP HEATER, made with instructions provided by manufacturer of the element, is necessary for projects requiring heat-forming of the plastic. It is sold by dealers who stock Plexiglas.

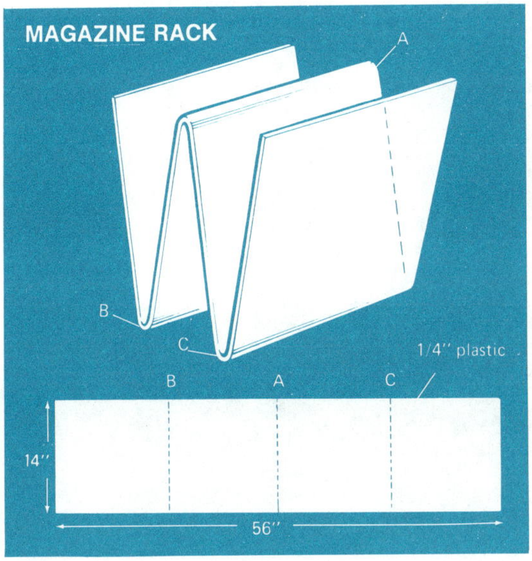

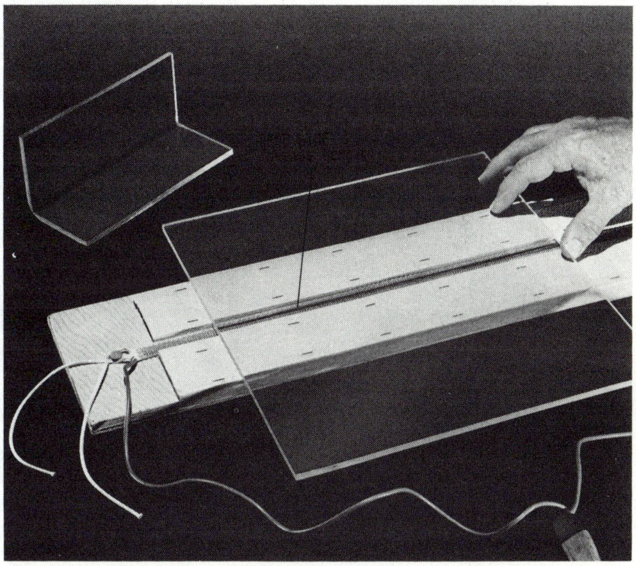

TO BEND PLASTIC, protective paper is removed and plastic is placed over heat tape in strip heater.

paper stuck to both sides which is usually left in place while the pieces are being handled and cut.

When working on the projects described on these pages, or one of your own designs, you will want to keep the following in mind:

• **Cutting.** Plastic up to ⅛-in. thick can be cut by scoring and snapping. After it is scored four or five times with a scratch awl, the scored line is centered face up over a ¾-in. dowel. Then the plastic is pressed down on each side to snap it. The minimum snap-off width is about 1½-in. Patterned plastic cannot be scored and broken; it must be sawed.

• **Sawing.** Use either a sabre saw equipped with a fine-tooth blade (32 teeth per inch) or table saw with a plywood-veneer blade. Hold the sheet down firmly and move it slowly through the saw; do not force. You can also make straight cuts

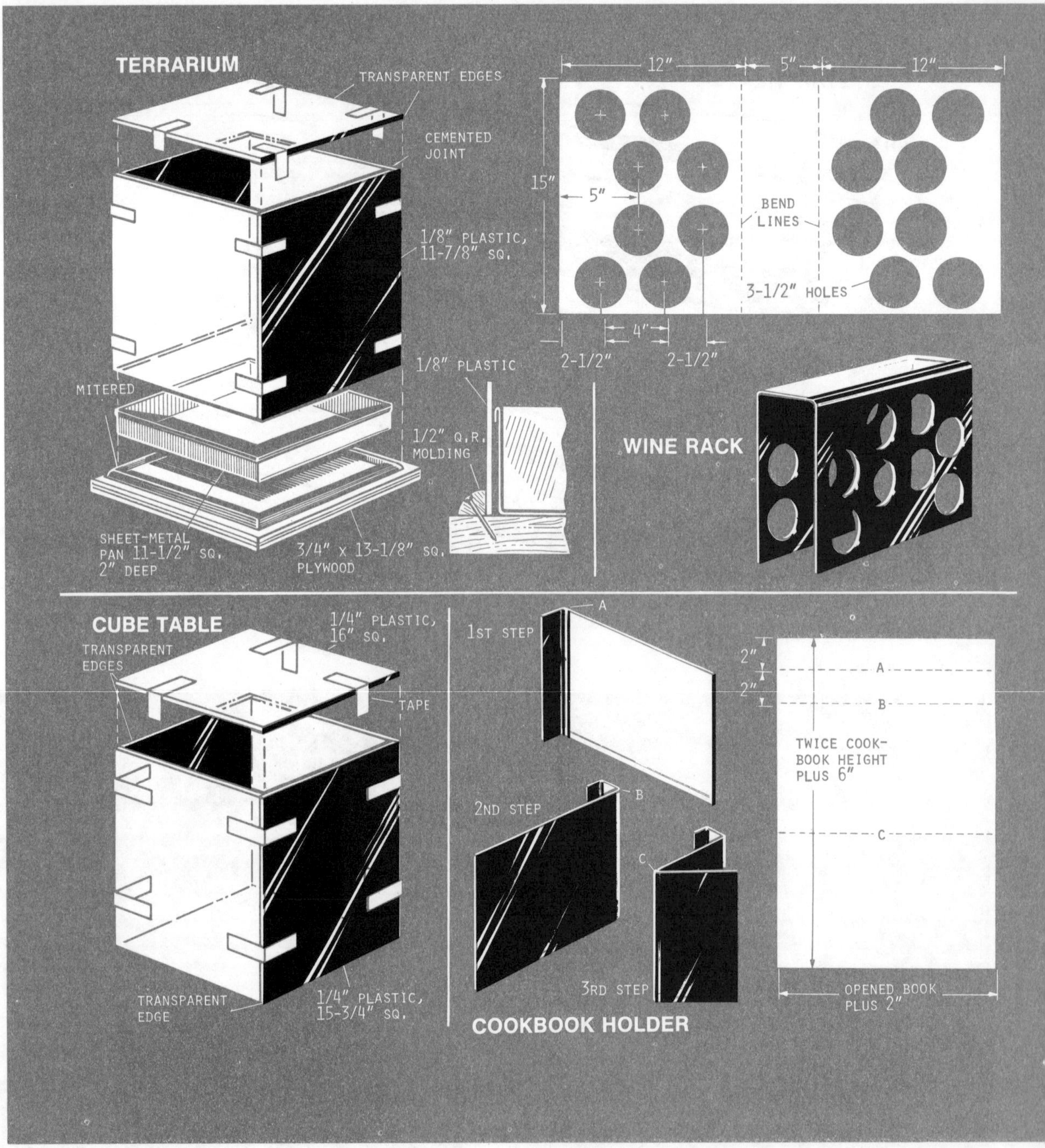

with a special hand tool obtained from the dealer who sold you the plastic.

• **Drilling.** You can use conventional twist drills to bore holes by hand. To do it, back the plastic with a clamped block of wood and be sure the drill is sharp.

To bore with power, use a specially ground high-speed twist drill (available from your sheet-plastic dealer). For best results, use a slow speed and minimum pressure: too fast and the plastic will spin with the bit, while too much pressure causes chipping on the back side of the hole.

• **Edge finishing.** Saw and other tool marks should be removed by scraping the edge smooth with a sharp knife or by sanding with a medium-grit (60-80) paper, followed by sanding with "wet or dry" (150) grit paper. For a satin finish, continue to sand with increasingly finer (220-320) wet-or-dry paper. For a transparent finish, sand with finer grit (400-500) wet-or-dry paper and

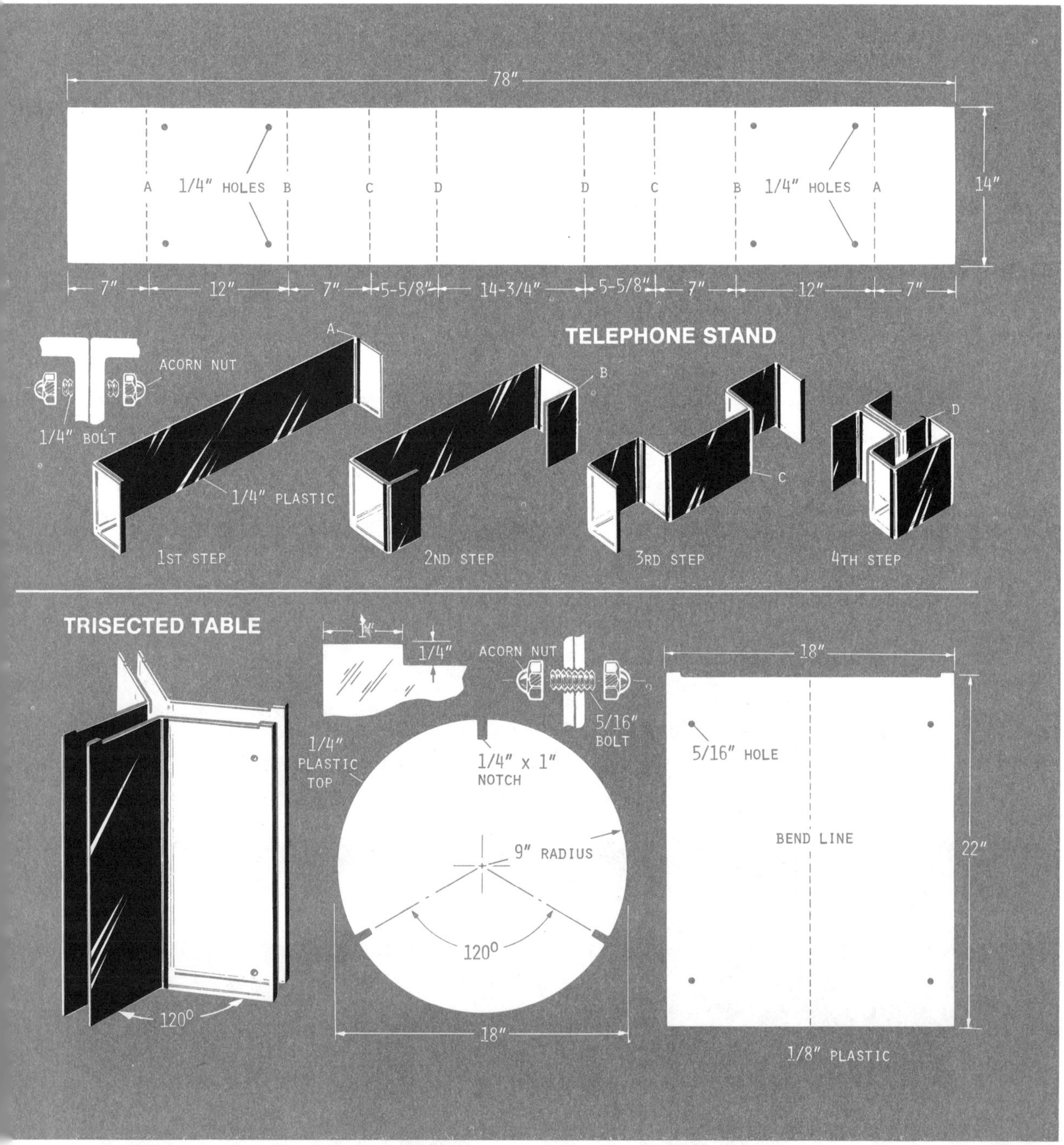

continued

then buff the edges with a clean muslin wheel dressed with a good grade of fine-grit buffing compound. (Note: Buffing kits, with compound, are sold at plastics dealers.)

• **Cementing.** Capillary cementing with a special solvent such as IPS #3 or methylene chloride is an easy and sure way of joining, literally fusing, two pieces of Plexiglas G and similar sheet acrylics. First, remove the protective paper from the plastic and sand the edges to a satin finish, as already described. (To save time, bind four panels together and sand the edges simultaneously.) Then place the workpieces together, hold the joint with tabs of masking tape and apply the liquid solvent with a needle-nose applicator made for this purpose (or use an eyedropper, syringe or small paintbrush—not as satisfactory). The liquid will quickly flow into the joint and create an immediate bond. Let it set 20 minutes before removing the tape.

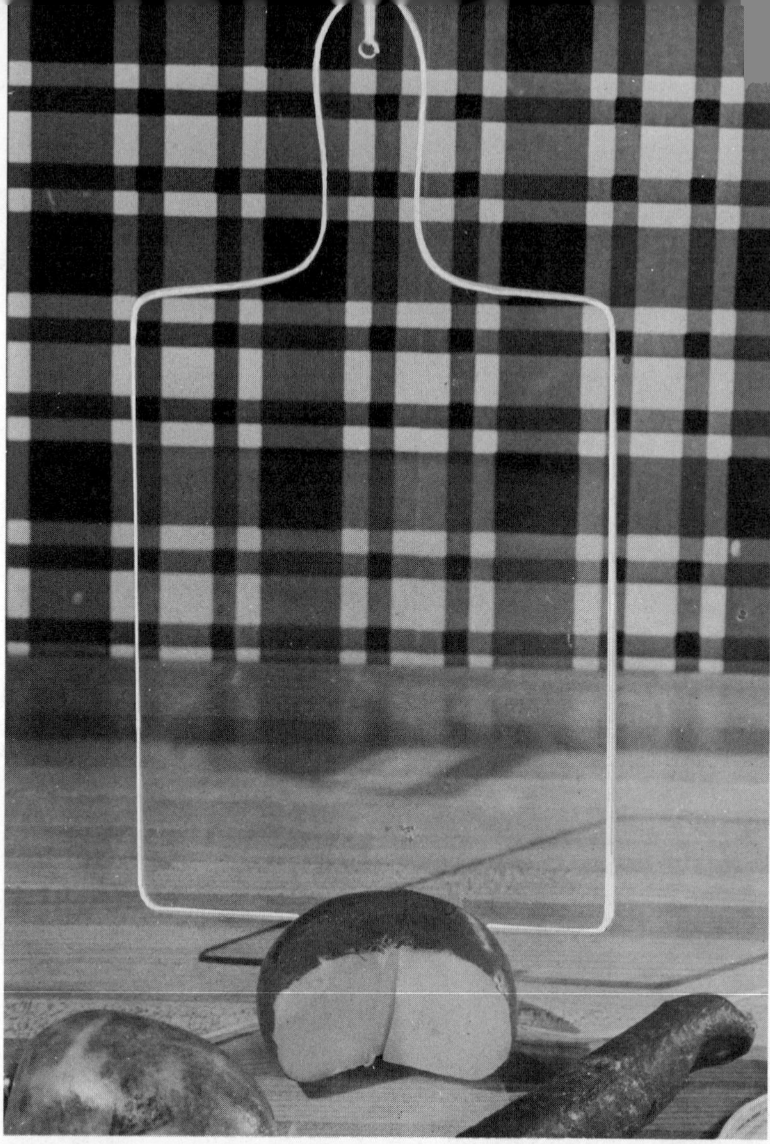

PLASTIC CUTTING BOARD is sanitary, non-absorbent, and is dishwasher-safe. The FDA and the USDA approve clear Plexiglas for such use.

DIAGRAM shows you how to make hat-coat rack shown on the opposite page.

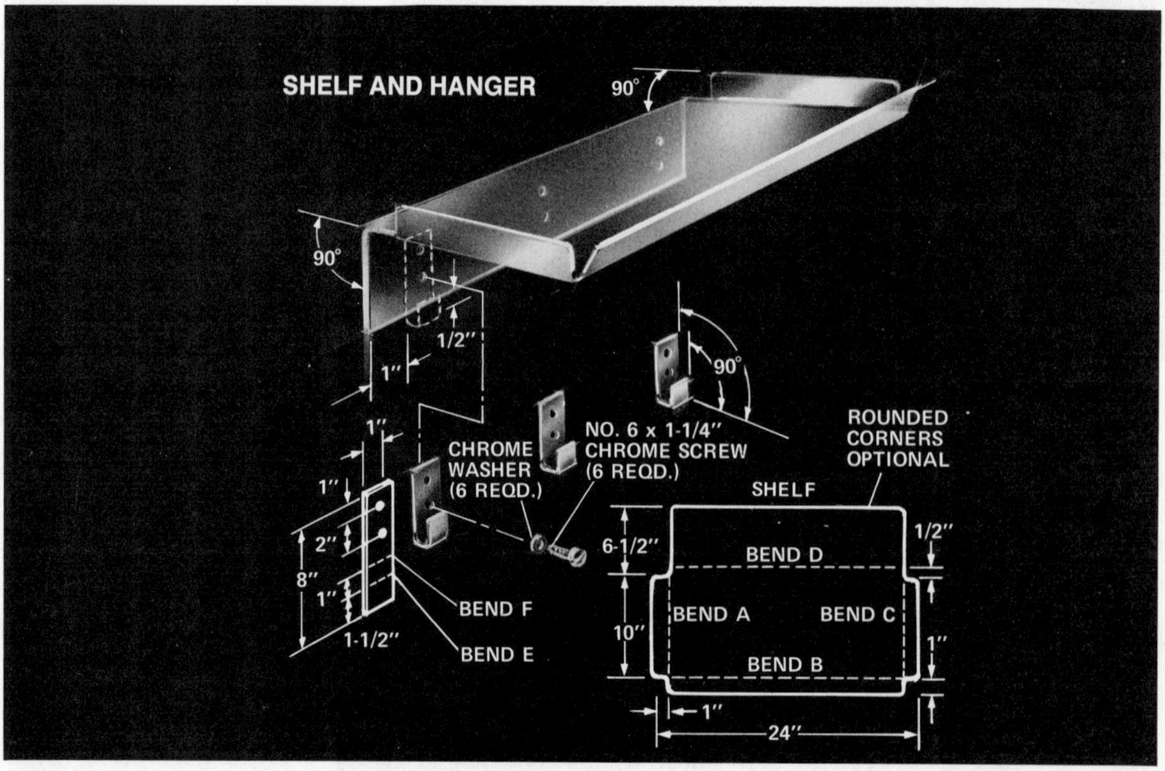

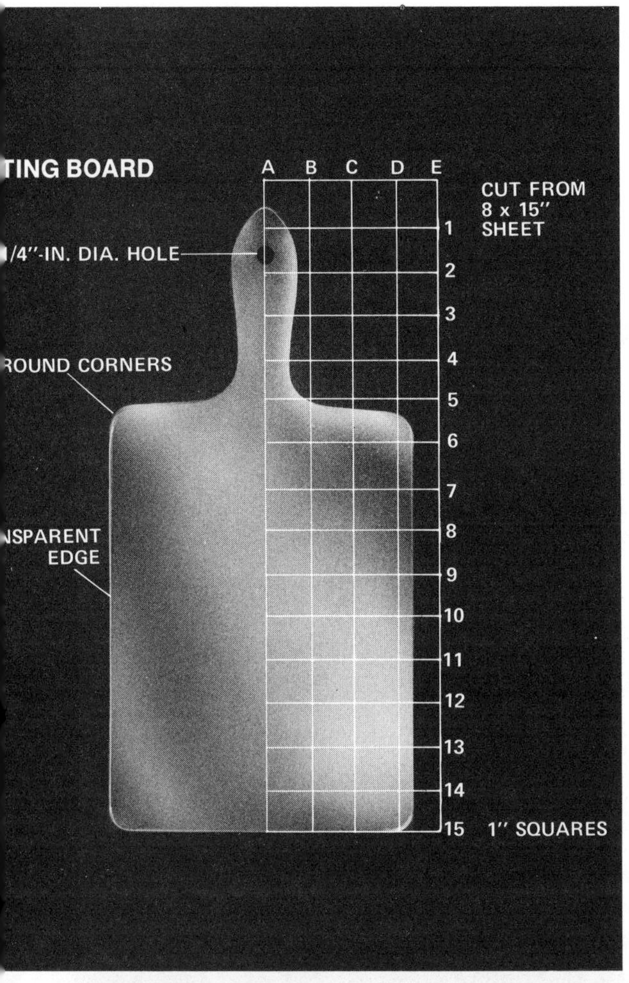

With type K Plexiglas, capillary solvent cannot be used. Follow the above directions, except use a thickened cement such as Daybond or IPS Weld-On #16 and clamp the joint for two hours.

Caution: Avoid dripping solvent on the surface of the polished plastic as it will deface it; also work in a well-ventilated room, as solvents may be toxic if inhaled for extended periods. Keep solvents away from flame and children.

• **Bending.** To make a bend, you will need a strip heater, such as the homemade unit shown on these pages that employs a heating element sold by plastics dealers. First, remove the protective paper from the plastic. Then use a grease pencil (''china marker'') to mark the plastic where it is to be bent and center the pencil mark over the heater element. It will take from 8 to 10 min. at the desired temperature of about 290°F to heat ¼-in.-thick plastic to a bendable state. Make the bend slowly, on the line, while the plastic is still on the heater. You'll find that the plastic has a tendency to ''spring'' back as it cools, so you must compensate a bit when forming a right-angle bend. Hold the bent material until the softened plastic cools and hardens.

Be careful not to overheat the plastic; it will scorch and bubble if you do. Bending it before it

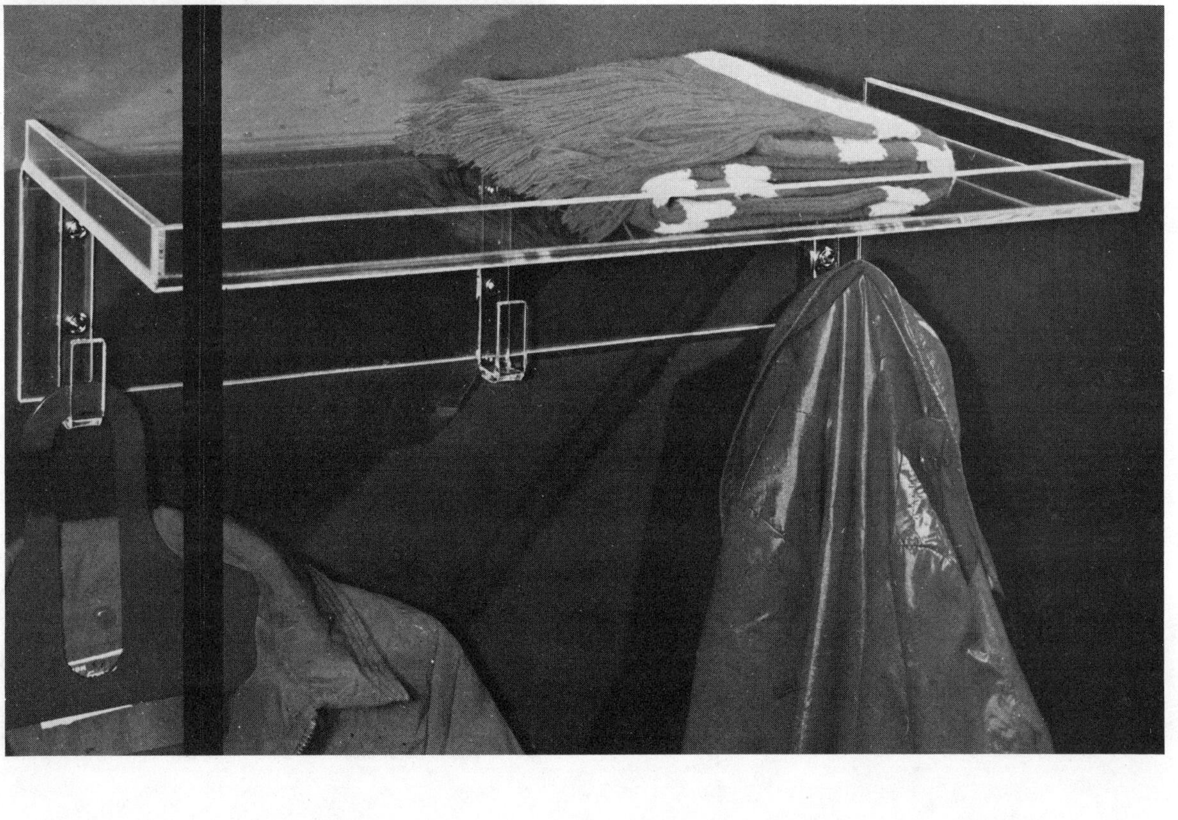

COFFEE TABLE, which stands 16 inches high, is made by combining a favorite wood with a pair of U-shaped legs fashioned of clear plastic. The result is an uncluttered, airy, floating effect.

is soft enough will cause stress crazing (small internal fractures) at the bend. Practice on a scrap first. The temperature of the plastic should not be greater than 340°F., and don't try to bend plastic more than ¼-in. thick with the heater. In any event, *do not* heat sheet acrylic in your oven; doing so could cause an explosion.

For more information about working with sheet acrylic, write to Rohm and Haas Co., Box 9730, Philadelphia, PA 19140. For a small sum they will send you a package containing a list of project plans, a do-it-yourself booklet of project designs and fabrication techniques, a booklet on the use of plastic as a safety measure in doors and windows, and a list of distributors. The firm also supplies a strip-heater kit and most of the special tools and cements mentioned here.

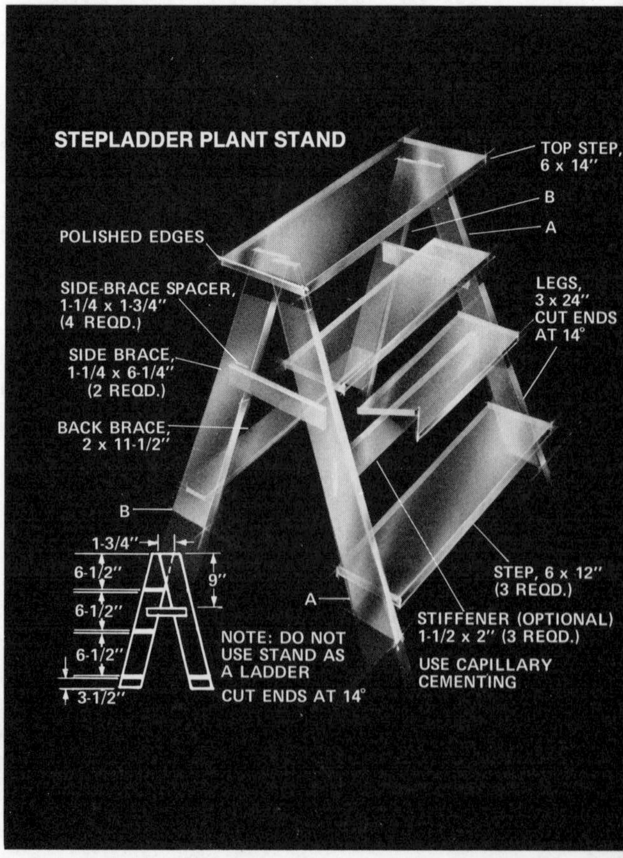

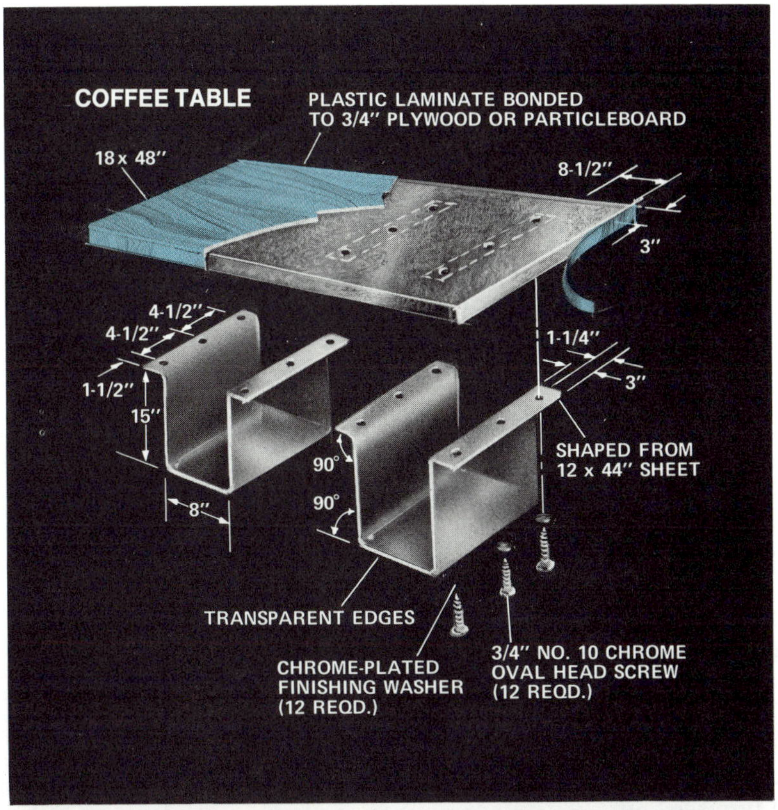

PLAN is for the coffee table shown on opposite page. The stepladder plant stand shown is excellent for displaying indoor plants; it can go anywhere.

Be your own home plumber

By RICHARD NUNN

■ HOME PLUMBING problems can be scary because the trouble is hidden in a tube of metal and you can't see it. The fact is that only two basic problems can exist: the pipes and valves spring leaks; the pipes and drains become clogged. The solution to any plumbing problem is strictly mechanical and follows a fairly simple repair procedure which is detailed below.

But before you tackle any plumbing problem, you should know how your home's supply and drainage systems work, and have a speaking acquaintance with their nomenclature.

The fresh water that comes into your home is supplied by either a public utility or a deep well in your yard. It is under pressure. If furnished by a public utility, the pressure is usually about 60 pounds per square inch (psi). If supplied by a deep well system, the water is pumped at 40 to 80 psi. The waste that goes out of your home flows into a public sewer or a septic system in your yard. Drains are not normally under pressure; gravity empties them.

Since fresh water is under pressure, you must always—*without fail*—turn off the water at the valve where it enters the house—or at the fixture—before you make repairs. You do not have to turn off the water to make repairs to drains.

The parts of a plumbing system are the *pipes* (copper, galvanized steel, cast iron, and/or plastic), the *valves* (faucets), and the *fixtures* (toilets, sinks, lavatories, bathtubs). The connections for the pipes, valves, and fixtures are called *fittings.* Plumbing accessories go by regular names such as pipe hangers, strainers, aerators, clamps, etc.

in and out of the house

The water coming into your home is controlled by a main valve which may be located in your

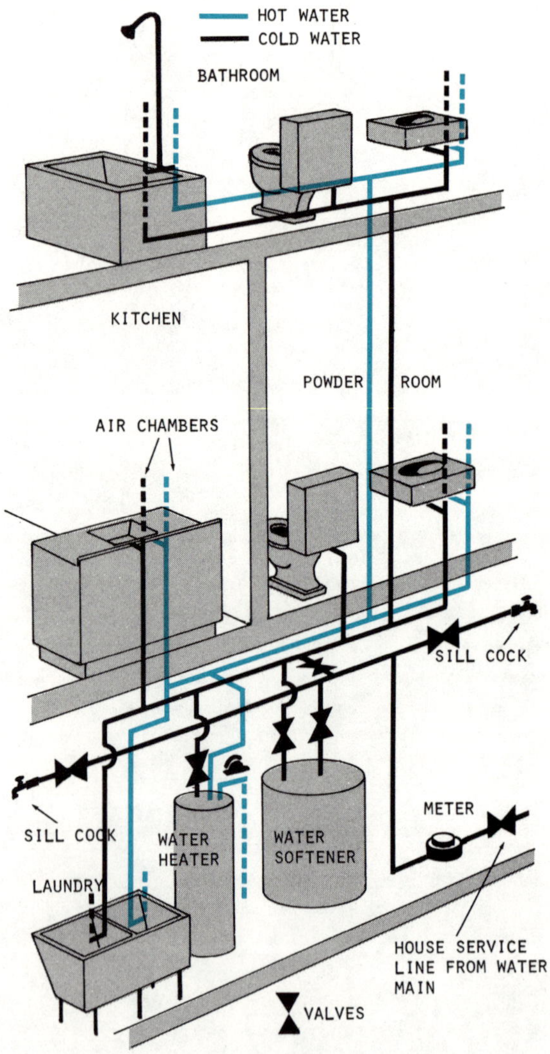

WATER DISTRIBUTION in a typical home comes through a water main and meter and then splits at the water heater. Under at least 60 pounds pressure per square inch, the water supply must be turned off before any repairs are made. Leaks at fittings and fixtures are the usual trouble spots.

SEE ALSO
Bathrooms . . . Bathtubs . . . Drains . . .
Garbage disposers . . . Heaters, water . . .
Plastic pipe . . . Sewage systems

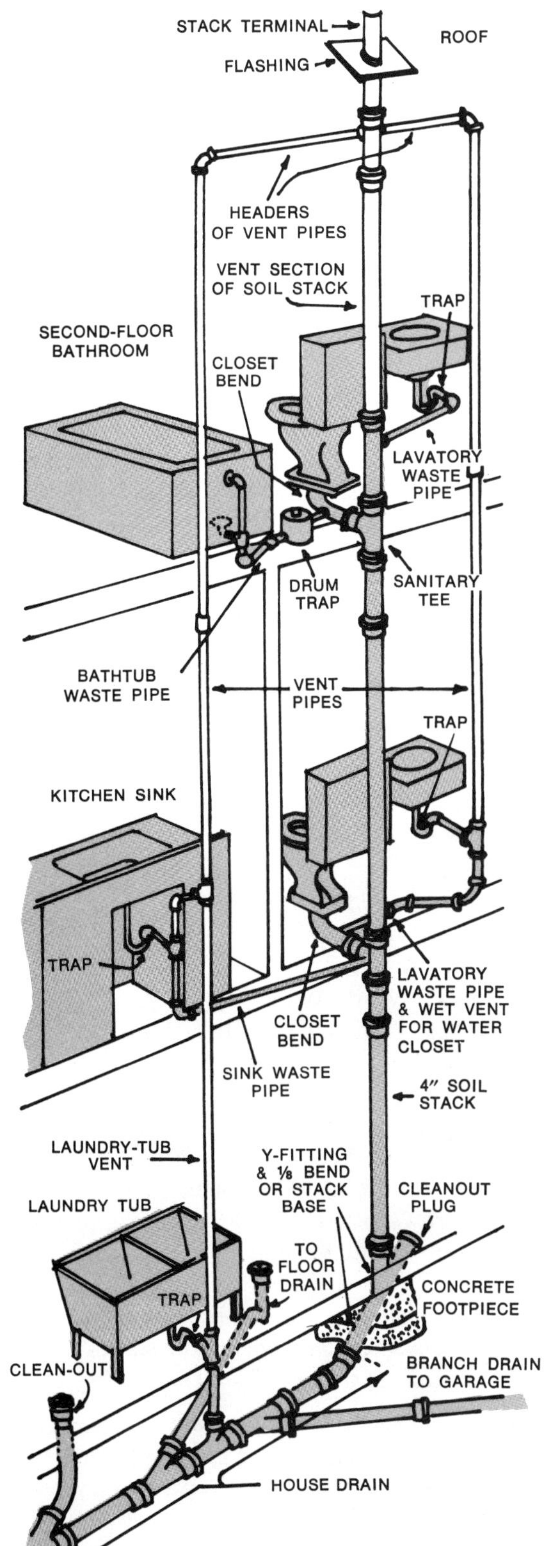

THE WASTE SYSTEM in a typical home involves a soil stack to which all waste fixtures (lavatories, sinks, tubs, toilets) are connected. Clogging is the No. 1 problem; especially look for trouble in the fixture trap area or at the base of the soil stack near the cleanout plug.

basement, a utility closet, or outside under the water meter. This main supply pipe splits at the water heater. One pipe continues on and branches off to supply the cold water to the sinks, lavatories, tubs, clothes washer, toilets. The hot water pipe, from the water heater, also branches off to the various fixtures that supply hot water; sinks, lavatories, tubs, and so forth.

While fresh water comes in below the house, drains start at the top of the house. The waste pipes slope from the fixtures and connect to a vertical pipe called the *main drain* pipe. Another vertical pipe called a *soil stack* runs vertically and parallel to the main drain. It is connected to the main drain and the top of it sticks out above the roof of the house and funnels away odors within the main drain. It also breaks a vacuum in the drain so the pipes connected to it from toilets, sinks, lavatories, etc., can flow freely. Main drains have a tee with a clean-out plug at the bottom of the drain pipe where it connects to the sewer. The clean-out plug is removed with a wrench.

Most drain pipes are *trapped,* ie., they have a sharp bend in them directly below the drain opening or several feet down the line. They are shaped like the letter "P" or "S." Another type trap, usually connected to a bathtub drain between the floor joists, is called a *drum trap* because it resembles a Civil War drum in shape. It is fairly small and has a clean-out plug.

The prime purpose of a trap is to form a kind of water "dam" between the fixture and the main drain. This dam prevents odors from the drain from working their way back through the drain pipe and out the opening in the sink, lavatory, toilet. Odors can't penetrate water barriers very

PIPE LEAKS can be stopped in an emergency with clamp devices which have a gasket that fits between the clamp and the leak in the pipe. The clamp is secured by bolts and nuts. Other leak stoppers include plastic electrician's tape for pinhole leaks and epoxy cement for leaks at fittings. All leak quick-fixes are temporary; replace the pipe or fitting just as soon as possible.

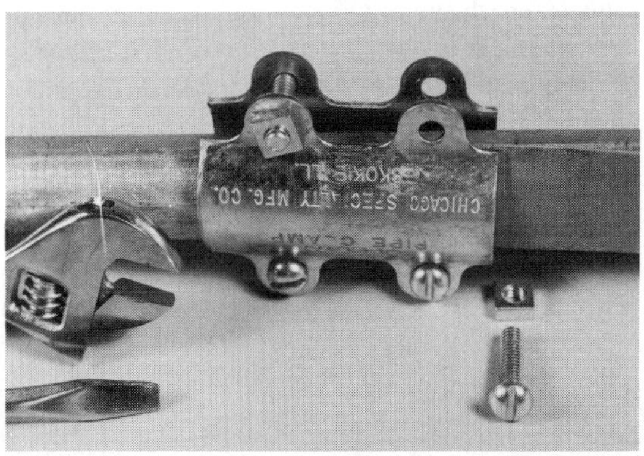

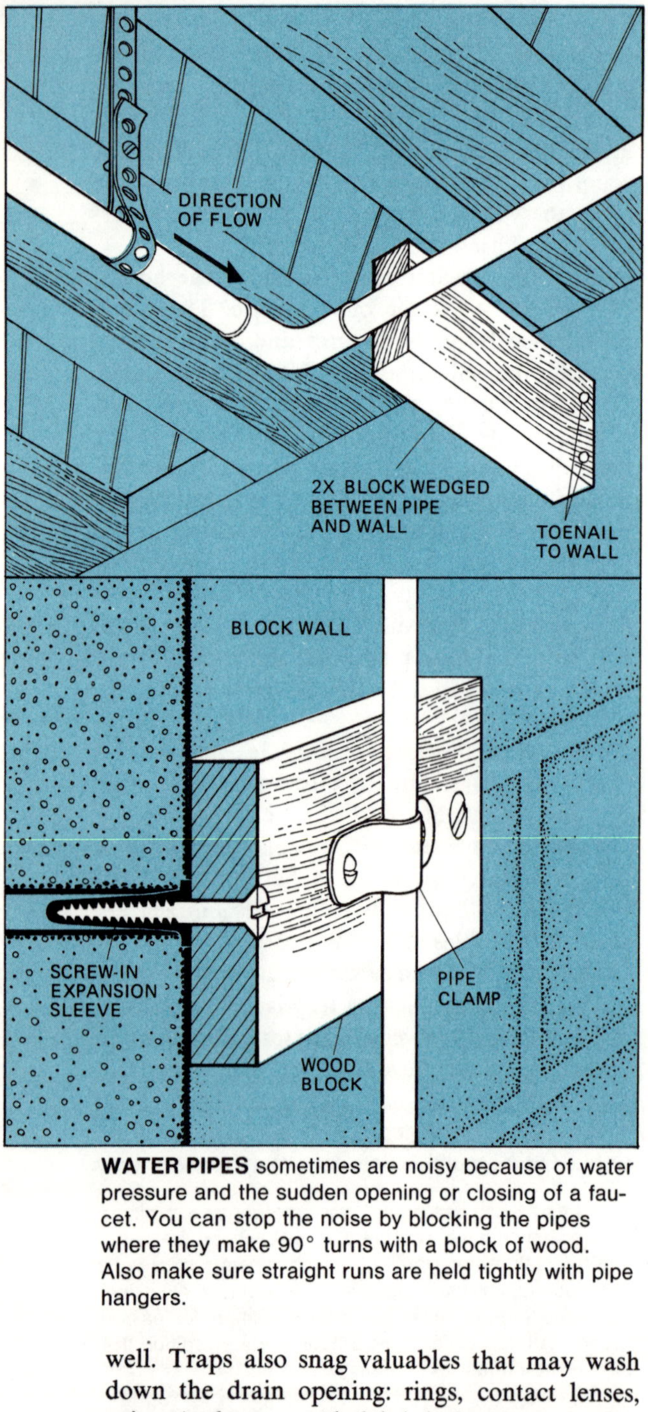

WATER PIPES sometimes are noisy because of water pressure and the sudden opening or closing of a faucet. You can stop the noise by blocking the pipes where they make 90° turns with a block of wood. Also make sure straight runs are held tightly with pipe hangers.

well. Traps also snag valuables that may wash down the drain opening: rings, contact lenses, coins. And traps catch debris before it can go farther into the system and seriously clog the pipes. It is easier to clean a drain than a sewer pipe, although debris sometimes finds its way into the main system.

So, like electricity, the plumbing in your home makes a circuit: fresh water in; waste water out. It sounds simple enough; and it is.

all about pipes

Water pipes can leak, freeze, rattle and pound. They almost never clog because they are under pressure and there is nothing in a properly-filtered water supply to cause clogging. If the water supply dwindles to a trickle or stops completely, look for trouble with the pressure: too many valves open at one time, pipes too small to handle the water demand, or a low pumping pressure at the utility or your own water supply well. The low pressure problem also can stem (but not often) from a leak in a pipe or fitting, a malfunctioning valve, or a frozen pipe. In some areas, the pipes can *lime* shut from mineral deposits in the water. To determine whether this is the case, first turn off the water. Then disconnect a pipe at the fitting. Lime builds up around the inside walls of the pipe. It is a hard, whitish deposit. If this is the problem, call in a professional plumber. Do not try to force chemicals through the pipes to remove lime.

Pipes most often spring leaks at the fittings. Corrosion is the problem. Or you may discover a leak in the wall of a pipe along its run. Actually this, too, is a corrosion problem. There are a couple of techniques to handle this situation quickly.

1. If the pipe is leaking at a fitting, try tightening the pipe into the fitting gently. Use two pipe wrenches on galvanized steel pipe—one on the fitting and one on the pipe; the jaws of the wrenches should be facing in opposite directions. If the leak is in copper pipe, the fitting will have to be resoldered or replaced. See the article on "How To Work With Copper Pipe" on page 2232. For plastic pipe, see the details below.

2. If the pipe is leaking along the run, you may be able to *temporarily* stop the flow of water with a clamp device, plastic electrician's tape, a self-tapping metal screw with a washer, and/or epoxy cement. All are available at most home centers and hardware stores. The clamp and gasket, which fits around the pipe in a clamshell configuration, usually is the most efficient. The metal screw/washer, tape, and epoxy sometimes work, but not always, depending on the size of the hole or crack in the pipe.

Caution: All leak-stoppers are for emergency use. Replace the pipe as soon as possible.

Noise in and from pipes is caused by water creating shock waves. What happens is that when a faucet is turned off—especially in a long horizontal pipe—a shock wave is created where the pipe changes its directional run. You hear a hammering or pounding noise caused by the shock vibrations. There are two ways to handle this; one technique is fairly easy and inexpensive; the other is more complicated and time-consum-

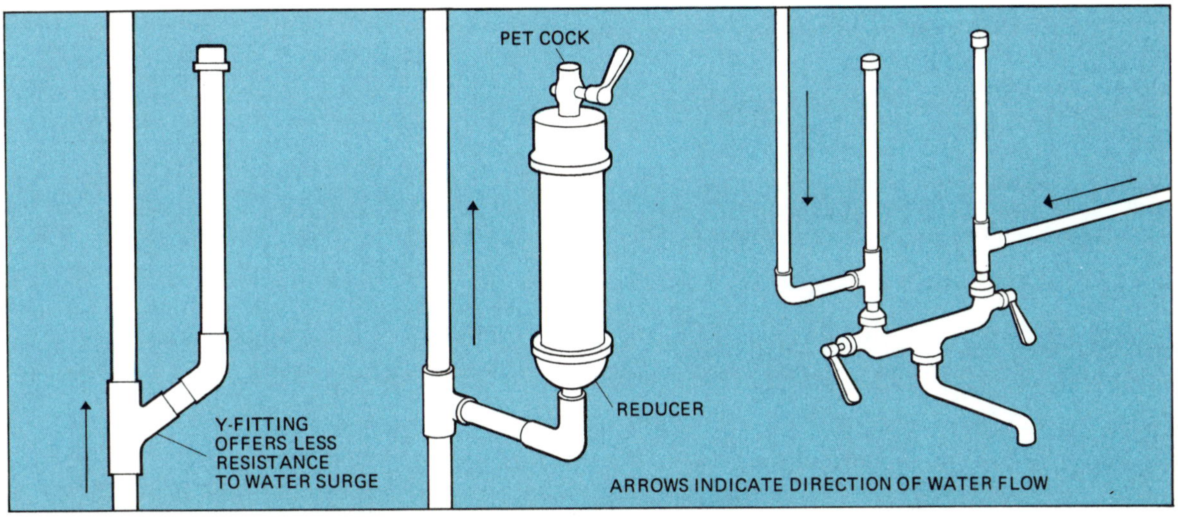

AIR CHAMBERS which you can make, or buy at home centers, stop the hammering noise in pipes. The hammer is caused by trapped air in the system; the chambers "pad" this noise. If the system has air chambers and you still hear hammering, check the chambers for sediment and scale.

ing, but not difficult.

1. Try adding pipe clamps (strap hangers) at about 4 ft. intervals along the pipe run. The clamps may be attached to joists, studs, and other framing members. Or you may have to insert blocks of wood behind the pipe, at 6 ft. intervals, and fasten the blocks to the wall then fasten the pipe to the block with a clamp.

A variation is to block the pipe with a piece of scrap wood wedged between a wall or framing member and the pipe where the pipe makes a directional turn. The wedge block (2x4, 2x6) should not put any stress on the pipe; a snug fit is adequate.

2. Add a noise-reducing air chamber; it absorbs an overflow of water. The chamber, which can be just a length of pipe capped at one end, contains air which helps cushion the thrust of the water when a faucet is closed quickly. Or you can buy a reducer chamber to solve the problem. Most reducers have a pet cock or valve to release any vacuum in the reducer. With the pipe chamber, you have to turn off the water and unscrew the cap from time-to-time to break the vacuum.

Prevention is the best cure for frozen pipes. If freezing is a frequent problem, you may be able to solve it by wrapping the pipes with pipe insulation. Also consider insulating with batt or blankets in the area through which the pipes run such as a basement or crawl space, between joists, or between studs.

If insulation is impractical, a length of pipe heat tape is inexpensive and easy to install. Heat tape is basically a heating element embedded in a sleeve of insulation. You spiral the tape around the pipes and plug it into regular housepower when temperatures fall. You can buy heat tapes with thermostats. When the temperature drops to about 35°F., the thermostat automatically switches on the tape.

Freezing sill cocks may be your biggest problem. Sill socks are the exterior faucet-like fittings to which you hook your garden hose. Just inside the wall, sill cock lines usually have shut-off valves. Thus you can close off that final leg in the system and drain it by opening the sill cock. If your plumbing system does not have this drainage feature, you can substitute a frost-free sill cock which has a compression valve 12 in. from the sill cock opening. The valve is inside the house.

Techniques for thawing frozen pipes depend on how accessible the pipes are. In any of the methods explained below, open the faucet nearest the frozen section of pipe before heat is applied to the pipe. The heat creates steam inside the pipe, which can break the fittings or damage the faucet.

If the pipe is horizontal in an open span, wrap the pipe with several layers of old toweling or burlap. Secure it with string. Then pour boiling water over the cloth until the ice in the pipe melts.

If the pipe is vertical in an open span, you can thaw it with a propane torch, if the flame from the torch is shielded so it doesn't scorch or set fire

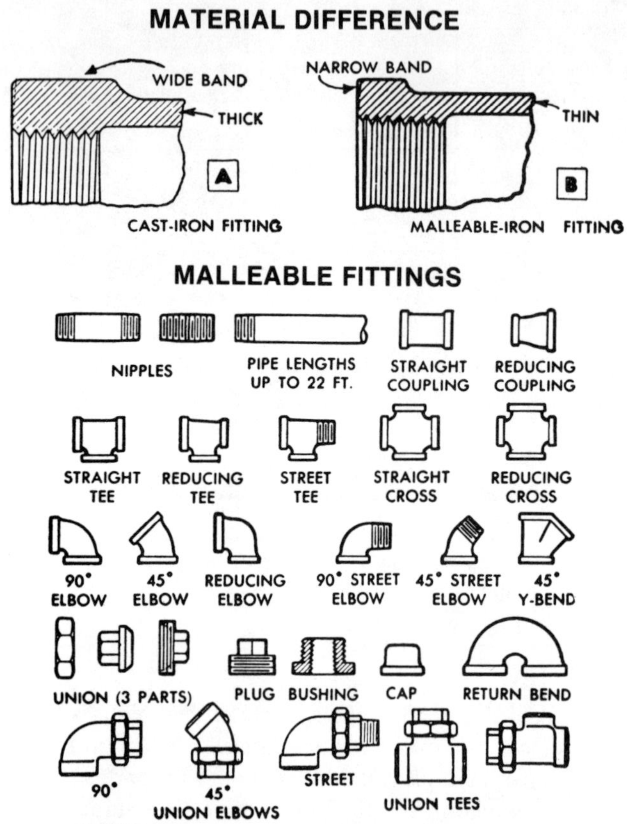

STANDARD plumbing fittings include these shapes for most copper and plastic installations as well as galvanized steel. Malleable-iron fittings are thinner than cast-iron fittings, if this is a consideration. Copper and plastic fittings are approximately the same thickness.

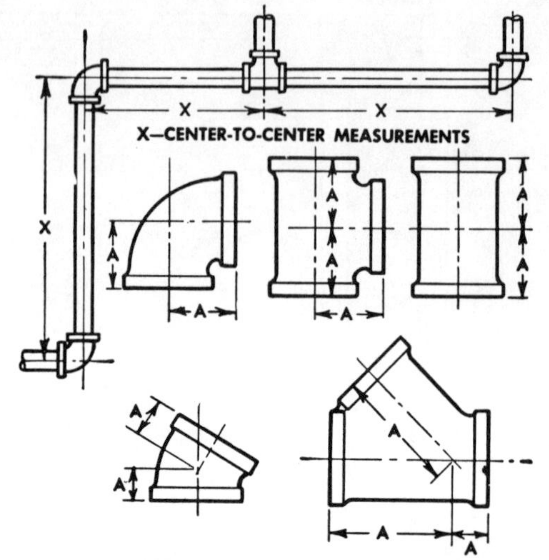

PIPE RUNS are measured from the center of the fittings. Or the run can be measured from the face of one fitting to the face of the adjoining fitting PLUS ½ or ⅝ in. at each fitting.

ALL PIPE—galvanized steel, copper, plastic—is measured by the inside diameter (ID) of the pipe. The fittings are sold by the ID measurement. Pipe goes into fittings ½-in. for copper and plastic and ⅝-in. for galvanized steel. Add this measurement when buying pipe.

to the materials near the pipe. This is dangerous under any circumstances; be very careful.

If the pipe is behind a wall, use a heat lamp to penetrate the wall covering and melt the ice. Melting will be slow because you must keep the lamp far enough away from the wall covering to prevent scorching. Heat lamps become very hot.

If a drain pipe is iced shut, pour hot water into the drain opening until the ice breaks free. Or you can remove the trap (where the ice block usually is located), and soak the trap in warm water.

working with galvanized pipe

Most home center, hardware, and plumbing supply stores stock and sell pre-cut and threaded galvanized steel pipe in a wide range of sizes and lengths. You'll also find a variety of fittings for all sizes. If special lengths of pipe are needed, you can have them cut and threaded at a plumbing shop.

Pipe diameters are *always* measured from the inside—not outside—of the pipe wall. Length of run is from one end of the threads to the other end of the threads—not where the threads stop on the smooth outer section of the pipe. Your measurement should be from the face of one fitting to the face of the opposite fitting PLUS 1¼ in. The extra length is for depth of threads in the fittings, which should be from about ½ to ⅝ in. Threads on galvanized steel pipe are slightly tapered. Therefore, when the threads are turned into a fitting, the threads have a "wedging" action that helps prevent leaks. Pipe sizes and fittings are standard. Example: if your plumbing system has ¾ in. galvanized steel pipe, any ¾-in. replacement pipe or fittings will match it. Steel and wrought iron pipe are sold in sizes from ⅛ in. to 6 in. in diameter.

Basic tools needed for galvanized steel pipe assembly include two 12 in. pipe wrenches, hacksaw, metal file, tape measure and a metal vise. Materials needed are pipe joint compound or plastic pipe tape, the pipe, and the necessary fit-

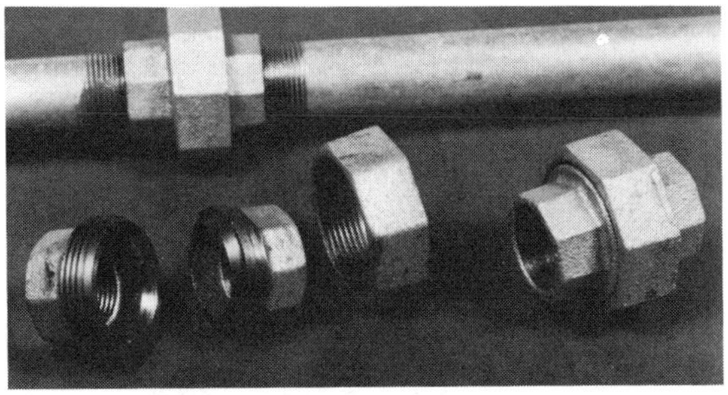

UNION FITTINGS are *always* needed when assembling galvanized steel pipe runs. The unions let you turn the pipe either direction in the standard fittings. This is necessary when replacing old pipe runs or assembling new pipe runs.

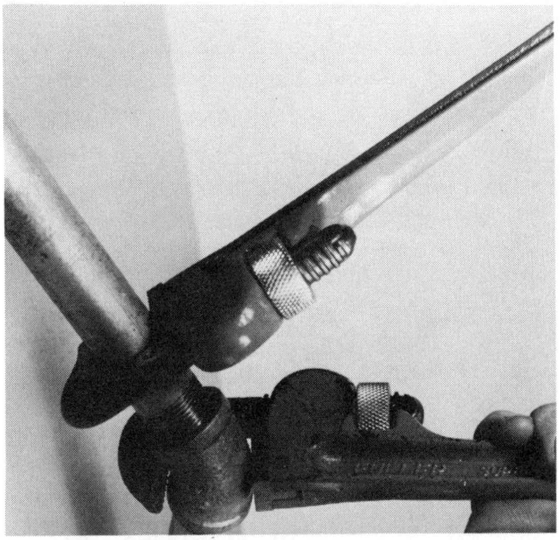

DOUBLE WRENCH galvanized pipe assembly and disassembly. The jaws of the pipe wrenches are opposed—opposite each other, as shown here. Keep one wrench on the fitting and the other on the pipe. To remove pipe in an existing run, use a hacksaw and cut the pipe at an angle—about 45°.

PLASTIC PIPE fittings have tiny shoulders inside the fittings against which the pipe butts tightly. If the pipe does not fit tightly against the shoulder, the connection probably will leak. Before buying and working with plastic pipe, make sure it conforms to your plumbing code.

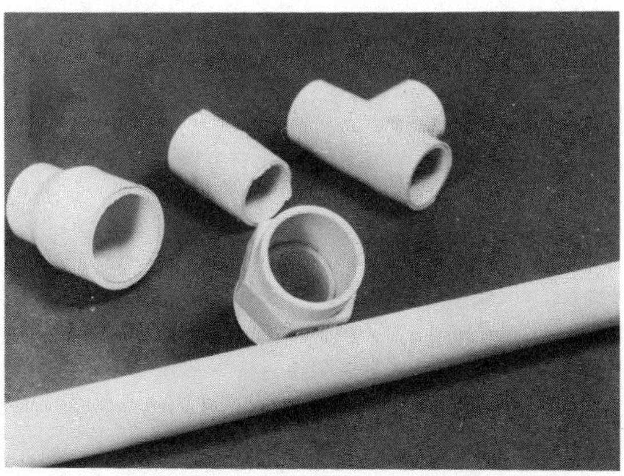

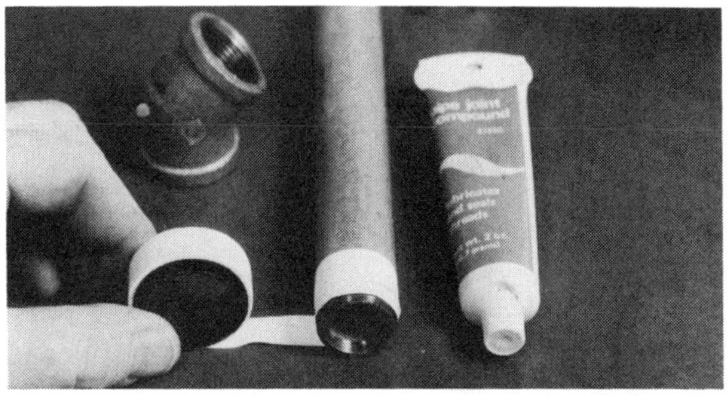

SEAL PIPE THREADS with either plastic threading tape or pipe joint compound, which has the consistency of putty. The tape should wrap around the threads in the direction the threads turn into the pipe fitting. Always put joint compound on the male threads of the pipe.

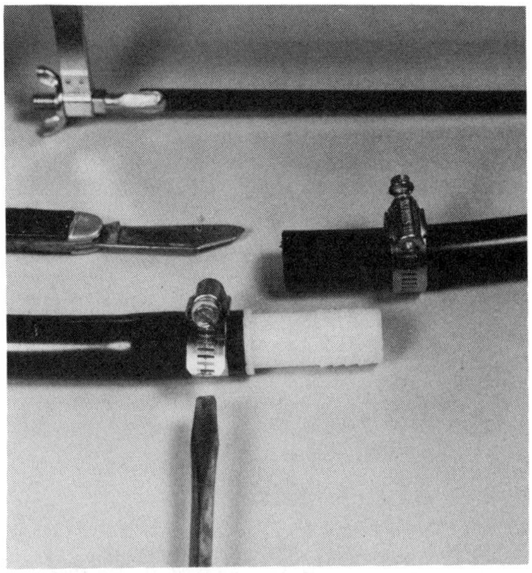

FLEXIBLE plastic pipe is assembled with straight or elbow connectors and clamps. The clamps slip over the pipe before the connectors are inserted. Clamps are similar to those used for radiator hoses in autos. They are turned tight with a screwdriver and/or wrench.

CUTTING plastic pipe may be done in two ways: with a hacksaw and miter box or with a tube cutter, which usually is recommended for copper pipe. Either way, the cut must be square and the burrs (cutting residue) on the pipe removed for a good, tight fit.

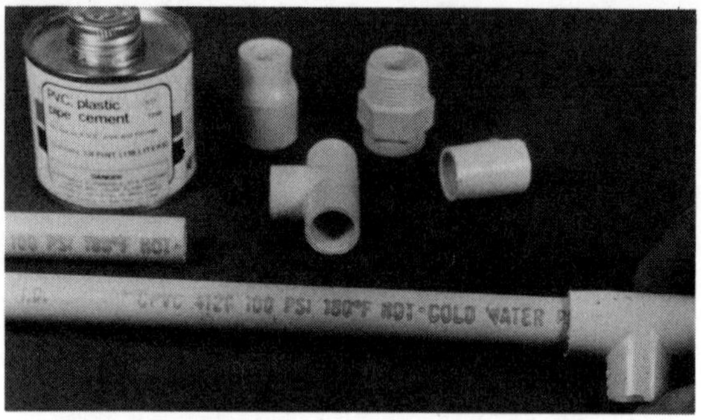

"DRY" ASSEMBLE the pipe run first—without the solvent. Put the pipe into the fittings tightly and set the pipe/fittings along the pipe run route. If the run does not fit, now is the time to cut and trim the pipe to fit the run perfectly.

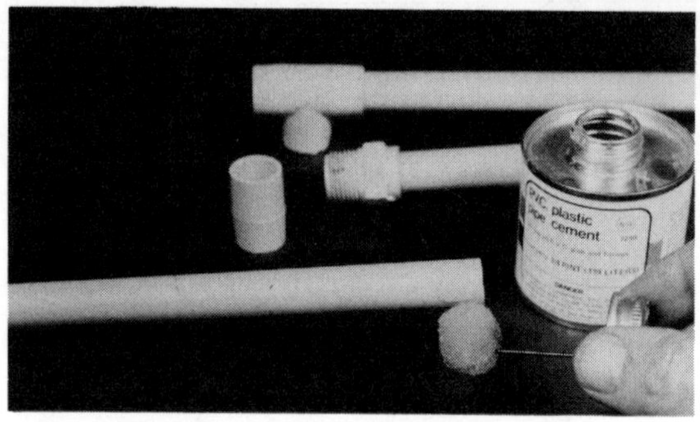

APPLY CEMENT to the pipe in a band about ½-in. wide. Use the type of cement recommended for the pipe. The cement should be spread fairly thin. Then slightly twist the pipe into the fitting so the cement forms a bead around the top of the fitting.

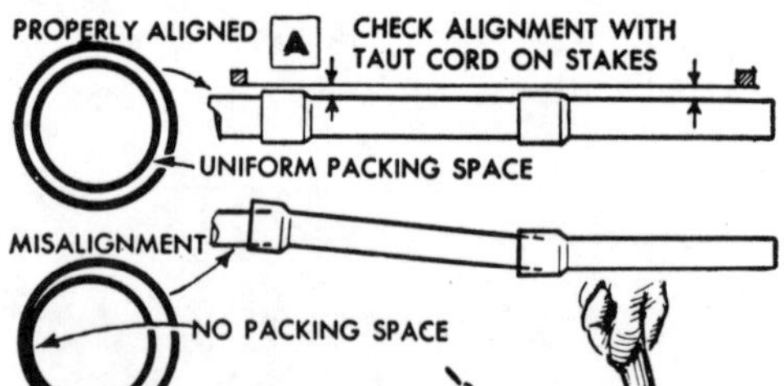

HUB-AND-SPIGOT drainage (sewer) pipe is assembled with oakum packing and molten lead. In vertical installations, the hub (thick end) faces "upstream". In horizontal installations, a joint runner is needed to fill the connection with lead. The hub also should face "upstream". Cast iron pipe is fractured by scoring it with a hacksaw and then breaking it at the scored line with a cold chisel and baby sledge hammer.

tings, i.e., tees, elbows, caps.

The one fitting that you *must* have is a union fitting. The union lets you turn the pipe being assembled in different directions.

Assembly procedures for steel pipe, illustrated in this article are extremely simple, but they take precise measurement and patience. Two pipe wrenches must be used to assemble (or disassemble) pipe runs: one wrench goes on the pipe fitting; the other wrench goes on the pipe. The jaws of the wrenches are opposite to provide better turning action.

Warning: pipe wrenches exert tremendous torque, so turn them gently. Too much pressure can crush the steel pipe. The jaws of the wrench are "loose" to conform with the diameter of the pipe. As the leverage is applied to the wrench handle, the jaws grip and hold the pipe tightly.

Pipe threads—*not* the threads inside the fittings—should be coated with pipe joint compound or covered with plastic tape to help deter leaks. Tape is less messy than joint compound, but it can be difficult to wrap. If you use tape, wrap it around the threads in the direction the threads will be turned into the fitting—usually clockwise.

Steel pipe in hot water runs should be kept as short as possible so the water will not lose heat in the run. Also steel pipe should not be used underground or under concrete walkways, driveways, patios, and so forth. Steel pipe should not be joined with copper pipe without an adaptor. The different metals set up a corrosive action.

working with plastic pipe

Local plumbing codes permitting, plastic pipe is a do-it-yourselfer's dream. It is lightweight, fairly inexpensive, and goes together in a flash with just plastic pipe cement.

Plastic pipe is manufactured from ABS (acrylonitrile butadiene styrene), PVC (polyvinyl chloride), and CPVC (chlorinated polyvinyl chloride). PVC and ABS are used mostly for drain, waste and vent systems and as an underground electrical conduit. You can use CPVC for hot and cold water systems under pressure; the pipe is pressure-marked as to pounds per square inch (psi).

Plastic pipe is available in a range of sizes and lengths, although the standard length is 10 ft., and the diameter sizes most popular are ½ and ¾ in. Standard fittings include elbows, tees, adaptors for steel and copper pipe, caps, valves and straight couplings. The parts are "welded" together with a brushed-on solvent.

Two cautions: Make sure that plastic pipe is accepted by the building codes in your community; do not mix two types of plastic (ABS with CPVC for example) in the same installation.

Tools for working with plastic pipe are simple: a hacksaw and/or tube cutter, miter box, tape measure, small file, sandpaper, pocketknife and clean wiping cloth. Materials include the pipe, fittings and cement recommended for the type of plastic being used. If flexible plastic pipe is used, clamps will be needed to secure the pipe to the fittings.

Procedures for installing almost any plastic plumbing run include these:

1. Carefully measure the run. Add 1 in. of pipe length between each fitting; the extra pipe allows for the distance it goes into fittings.

2. Make a drawing of the plumbing project on graph paper showing the direction changes of the pipe and the number and type of fittings needed. Double check all measurements.

3. Cut the pipe to fit the run, using a hacksaw and miter box or tube cutter. Clean away any cutting debris on the pipe.

4. Dry assemble the pipe and fittings and match the assembled pipe to the plumbing run. Make any necessary adjustments.

5. Cement the pipe run, starting at one end of the run. Do not cement the entire project. Working piece-by-piece allows any adjustment if you have made a measuring mistake. Once cemented, the pipe has to be cut to be removed. It can not be pulled apart at the fittings like copper or galvanized steel pipe.

drainage pipe

Working with drainage pipe looks frightening. It's large and heavy, and appears complicated. Actually, drainage pipe is easy to assemble—especially "no-hub" pipe which is connected with gaskets and clamps. Old-fashioned hub-and-spigot pipe is more difficult to handle because the pipe sections have to be filled with oakum and molten lead. This requires a heater for the lead and a "joint runner" to funnel the lead into the joint when the pipe is along a horizontal run.

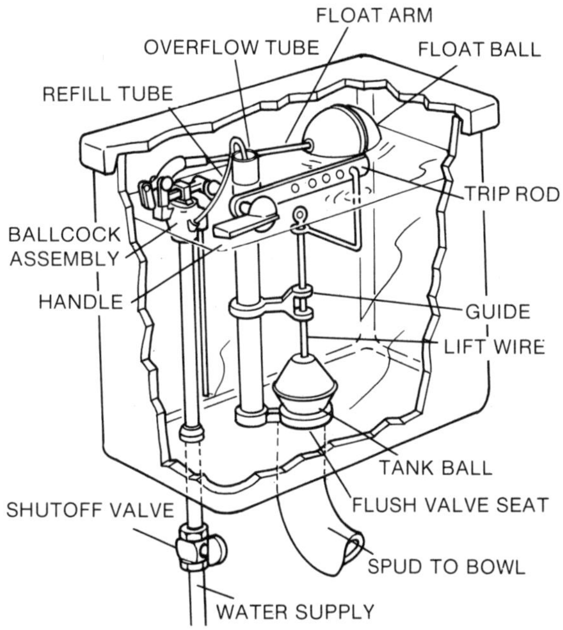

PARTS LOCATER for a typical flush tank. The tank may sit right on the back of the toilet bowl, or be connected to the bowl via a spud (shown).

You can cut cast iron pipe with a hacksaw. Or you can rent a roller cutter for small diameter pipe or a chain cutter for large diameter pipe. With a hacksaw, score the pipe about ⅛-in. deep around its circumference at the cut-off point. Then, at the scored line, tap the pipe with a baby sledge hammer to fracture it. The edges may be left rough since they will fit into a spigot or gasket. However, if the edges are really rough, smooth them with a cold chisel. Properly scored, the fracture will be smooth.

If hub-and-spigot pipe is used, the joint (hub) in a vertical run should face upward. The joint is first packed with oakum and then filled with molten lead. If the joint is on a horizontal run, it also is packed with oakum and filled with molten lead that is placed with a joint runner that you can rent.

If no-hub pipe is used, a no-hub gasket serves as a connector. In assembly, the pipe is cut and butted together. A clamp and sleeve is slipped onto the pipes after you are satisfied that the pipe joint is a fairly tight fit. The sleeve is centered on the joint and the clamps are tightened with a screwdriver or T-wrench. Elbow and tee fittings are assembled the same way.

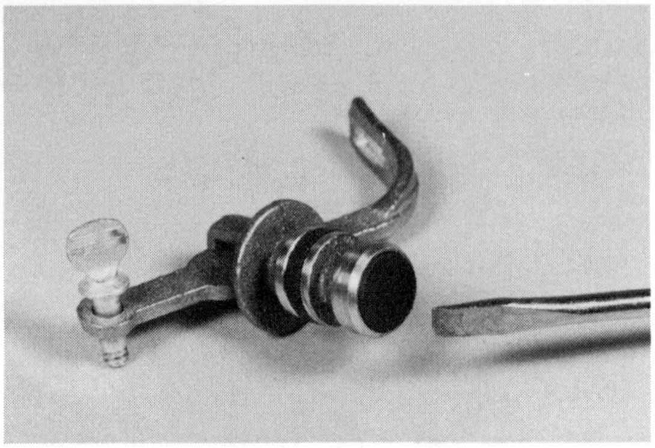

TWO REPLACEABLE washers are in the ballcock valve: one in a groove (O-ring) around the stem and the other at the bottom of the stem. You can remove the washers with the tip of a screwdriver and press the new ones back in position.

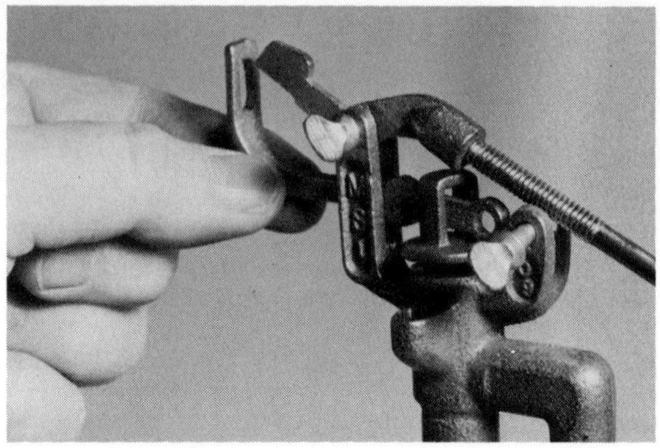

WORN WASHERS in the ballcock assembly can cause a noisy toilet. In this type ballcock, remove the thumbscrews that hold the float arm assembly. Then remove the lifting arm. If the ballcock is the plastic type remove the valve cover. You will see an O-ring. Replace it.

solving flush tank troubles

A flush tank is a water reservoir for the toilet. The tank contains an assembly of valves and floats that regulate the flow of water into the toilet bowl. The water in the tank is perfectly clean; don't be concerned about putting your hands into it for minor flush tank adjustments.

The best way to solve a flush tank problem is to isolate the problem. Below is a list of typical flush tank malfunctions and what you can do about them.

Inadequate flush. There's not enough water in the tank to complete the flush in the toilet bowl. Small ballcock assemblies have a screw on top of the ballcock at the float rod joint. Turn this screw up or down to lower the float arm and float ball. By lifting the float, you add water to the tank; by lowering the float, you lower the water. If the ballcock is the low profile type or has the float on the ballcock assembly, a knurled screw on top of the ballcock regulates the water, or a spring clip on the float is adjusted to raise or lower it. The water level should be about ¾ in. below the top of the overflow tube.

If the ballcock does not have an adjustment, try bending the float rod down for high water or up for low water. Bend the rod gently. Then flush the toilet to test the water level. You may have to bend or unbend the rod to get the water level needed.

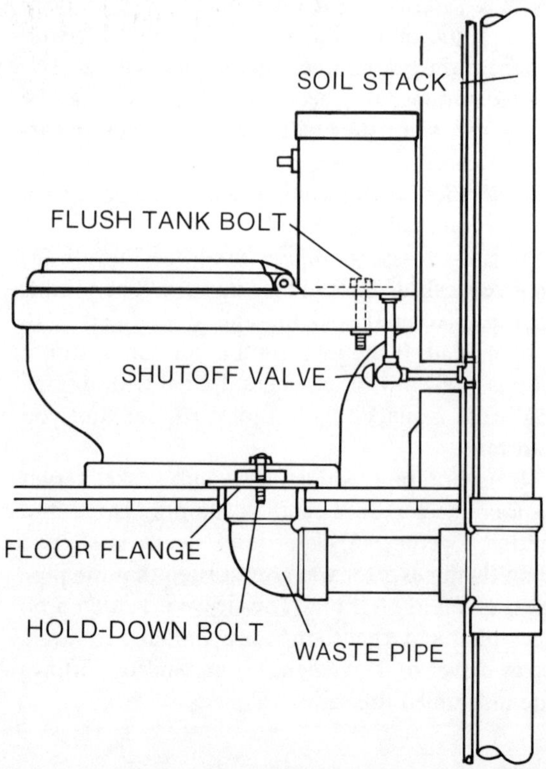

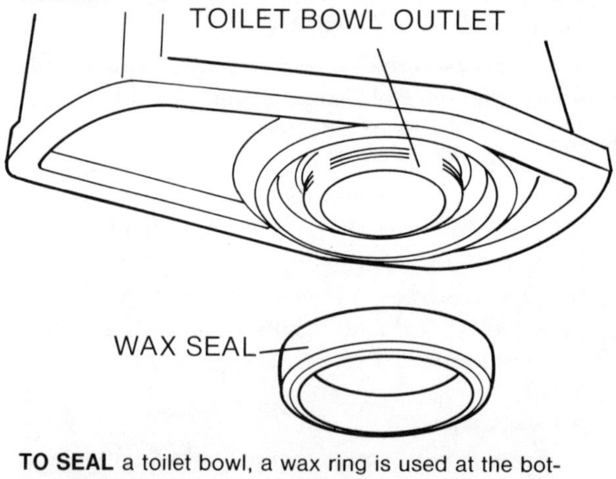

TO SEAL a toilet bowl, a wax ring is used at the bottom where the bowl slip-fits into the waste pipe. Do not assemble the bowl without the wax ring or the toilet will leak. It's a good idea to replace the hold-down bolts and caps (if any) when you change a bowl or even repair the seal.

CRITICAL MEASUREMENT for new toilet bowl is from the wall to the center of the waste pipe. Determine this by measuring from the wall to the center of the hold-down bolt. Or remove the toilet bowl and measure from the center of the pipe to the wall.

Constantly low water in the tank. The float ball may contain water which won't let it rise high enough to supply the necessary water supply. You can remove the float ball by unscrewing it counterclockwise from the rod. Or the tank ball, at the bottom of the tank, may be leaking so slowly that you can't hear the water. See "running water" category.

Splashing sounds. Chances are the refill tube is not discharging directly into the overflow. This water is used to form a seal in the toilet's trap to prevent odors from escaping from the main drain. Simply flush the toilet to check the water flow and reposition the tube into the overflow to solve the splashing problem. Splashing also may be caused by a worn inlet valve atop the ballcock assembly. Flush the toilet and look for leaks at this point while the tank is refilling. If the valve (actually its washer) is the problem, turn off the water and remove the valve. It is screwed to the ballcock housing. Inside, you will see a flat or O-ring washer. Replace this part and reassemble the unit. Then flush the toilet. If the problem still exists, replace the entire ballcock assembly. The cost is not prohibitive.

Tank is hard to flush. Look first at the lift wire guide attached to the overflow tube. Is the guide in alignment with the lift wire on the tank ball? If not, the lift wire can bind in the guide, causing a hard flush. The problem also can cause a running toilet because the tank ball doesn't seat properly in the flush valve seat.

Check also the flush handle and its linkage with the tank ball lift wire. There may be too much slack in the linkage. You can correct this by shortening the chain on the end of the trip lever, or repositioning the wire linkage in the holes in the trip lever. Look for corrosion at the base of the handle on the inside of the tank. Remove this with steel wool and tighten the nut that fastens the handle to the tank.

Singing flush tank. The sound can be caused by a faulty gasket in the ballcock assembly, or restricted water flow to the ballcock assembly. Washer replacement is detailed above. If the problem is restricted water flow, try opening the fixture valve completely. If not, look for corrosion at the valve or at the water opening to the ballcock unit. Both the valve and the ballcock may have to be changed.

Moisture on or around toilet. Condensation usually can be blamed. If the flush tank "sweats" during the summer months, try installing a foam liner or tank cover to stop this. Leaks at the bottom of the flush tank most likely are caused by loose locknuts at the bottom of the ballcock assembly where the water supply connects. Try tightening this connection. Go easy; too much heft can crack the tank. If tightening doesn't stop the leak, turn off the water and replace the washers and gaskets at the bottom of the ballcock assembly.

Leaks around the base of the toilet bowl could be condensation, but, unfortunately, the trouble probably is a leak at the wax ring gasket between the bottom of the toilet and the sewer pipe. First try tightening the hold down bolts at the base of the toilet. If this doesn't work, you will have to replace the wax ring, which is detailed below. Don't delay this repair: the water leak can cause lots of damage to the structural members of the house.

A cracked flush tank or toilet bowl sometimes is the source of leaks and moisture. Here, the tank and/or the bowl must be replaced immediately. You cannot satisfactorily repair the cracks.

Unstopping a clogged toilet is not a pleasant project, but the following procedures can save you some time and trouble.

Do not flush the toilet, even though some of the water has drained from the bowl. Instead, bail out the excess water in the bowl so the water height is slightly below its normal level. The best way to bail is to wrap your hand and arm in several plastic garbage bags. Tie the tops of the bags loosely around the top of your forearm. The bags protect your hands and arms from the toilet mess.

Position a plumber's friend suction cup made especially for toilets in the bottom of the bowl. Work the plunger *extremely* hard and fast up and down in the bowl. Use all the muscle you can; 50 strokes is minimum. A pattycake action won't work. You should feel and hear the blockage break loose as the plunger travels up and down.

If the plunger doesn't work—after you've given it a fair try—use a closet auger to remove the blockage. This tool is threaded down through the bottom opening of the bowl and up and over a trap configuration and out the sewer pipe connection. You can either snag the blockage (usually a wash cloth or toy) and pull it out or force the blockage (paper and waste) down into the sewer pipe. Do not force an insoluable object into the main sewer. It will block the entire system.

Reseating or replacing a toilet bowl is easier than it might sound, although it requires patience.

First, make sure that it isn't against local codes for you to do the job. Some communities require

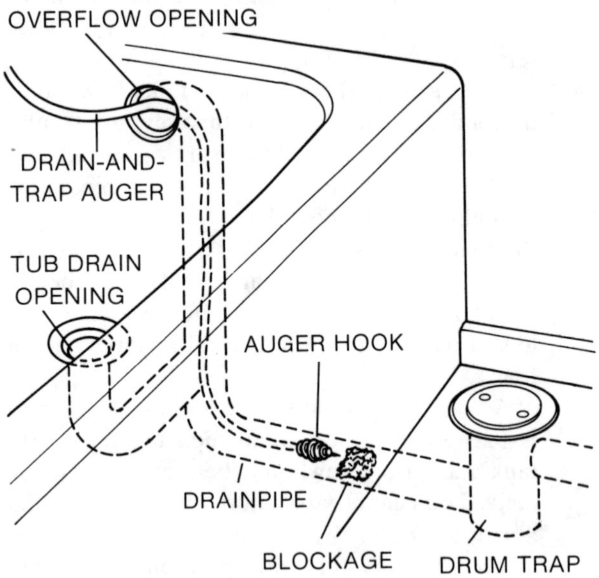

BATHTUB DRAINS sometimes respond to auger cleanout rather than suction. But try suction first. The auger can be inserted through the tub drain opening or down the overflow. Or, the trap may be opened (in older homes) and the auger worked back (or forward) from the trap.

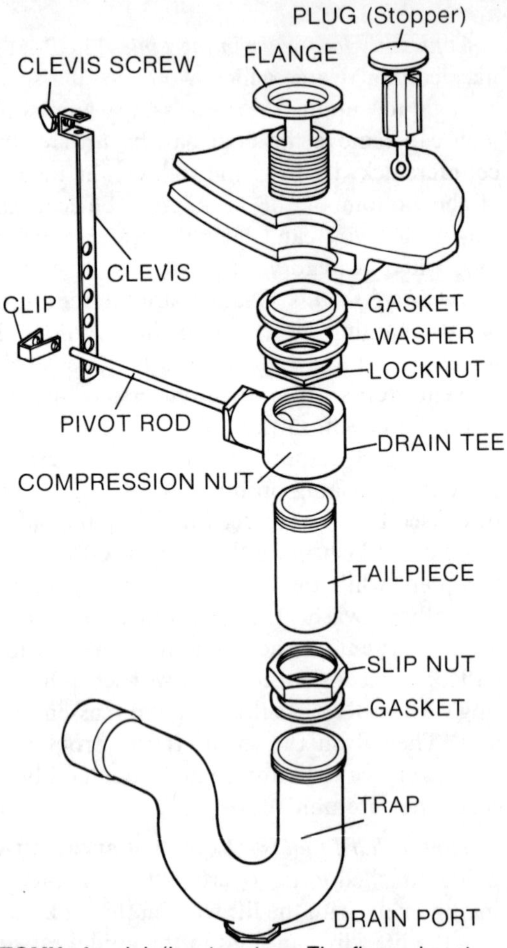

ANATOMY of a sink/lavatory trap: The flange is set with plumber's putty. The trap is connected with slip nuts and O-ring gaskets. By unscrewing the compression nut, the pivot rod can be released from the bottom of the plug so the stopper can be removed.

a licensed plumber to make repairs/replacements.

Replacement and reseating is essentially the same. In replacement, you need to know the measurement from the wall in back of the toilet to the center of the toilet drain pipe. This is easy if the old bowl has been removed. If not, find the measurement from the wall to either of the toilet bowl hold-down bolts. If only one bolt (each side) holds the bowl, measure from the wall to the center of this bolt. The plumbing supply retailer can determine what size replacement unit is needed from these measurements.

To remove the old toilet bowl, pry or lift off the caps that hide the bowl bolts. Then turn out the bolts counterclockwise. Of course this should be done only after the water has been turned off and the flush tank and bowl have been emptied.

If the bolts won't budge, slide a hacksaw blade between the bottom of the bowl rim and the top of the floor and saw the bolts loose. Or if you intend to replace the bowl, simply break the bowl into small pieces with a baby sledge hammer. Wear safety glasses during this operation; gloves are a good idea, too.

Once the bolts are free, you can lift the bowl straight off the floor flange and what's left of the wax ring seal. Carefully examine the area around the opening for wood decay. Rotted framing or flooring must be replaced before the bowl is reseated. The floor flange is fastened to the framing/flooring. Check it to see if it is in sound condition. If not, replace it; the cost is minimal.

A wax ring or wax sealer is used to waterproof the connection between the bottom of the bowl and the pipe. Turn the bowl upside down and fit the wax ring on the bowl projection. Or, if the floor flange is recessed slightly below the floor, install a wax ring with a plastic sleeve on the bowl. The sleeve faces toward the pipe since it sets into the pipe. With a putty knife, spread toilet-bowl setting compound around the edge of the bowl rim. Thickness should be about ⅛- to ¼-in.

Lift the bowl, turn it over, and set it down over the pipe and onto the floor. Twist the bowl slightly so both the wax ring and compound "seats" properly. At this point, set a carpenter's level across the bowl and level the bowl by pushing it gently downward into the wax ring. If level can't be accomplished by pressing, you will have to shim under the bottom rim of the bowl with cedar shingle wedges. Keep the edges of the wedges under the rim so they don't show. A bead of tub caulking around the rim at the floor will hide any gaps.

Once in place, secure the bowl to the floor with hold-down bolts. Tighten the bolts carefully; too much pressure on the wrench can crack the bowl. Install the flush tank on the back of the bowl to complete the job.

Toilet seat replacement is simply an unbolt-the-old and bolt-down-the-new project. The locknuts fastening the seat to the bowl are directly under the hinged lids. Toilet seats are standard; one size usually fits all. Be careful tightening the new locknuts; too much pressure can crack the bowl.

opening clogged drains

Like most plumbing problems, opening a clogged sink or tub drain involves a procedure: first try one technique, then move to another if the first one fails.

If water in the bowl is slow draining but not completely clogged, try a chemical drain cleaner, following the manufacturer's instructions.

If the drain is completely blocked, a plumber's friend (suction cup) may open it. Bail out most of the water in the bowl, leaving about ¾-in. If the bowl has an overflow, stuff a wet cloth into the overflow opening. Wedge it tight. Remove the strainer or stopper from the drain opening. Place the suction cup of the plumber's friend over the drain opening and seat the rim of it against the bottom of the bowl. Now bend over the handle of the plumber's friend and, without lifting the suction cup off the surface of the bowl, work the handle in an up-and-down action just as hard and fast as you possibly can. Use plenty of heft with the weight of your shoulders over the handle. Give the handle at least 50 downward strokes. Don't give up.

During the plunging process, you probably will hear and/or see the drain open and the water run out. When the drain is clear, flush fresh water through the pipe and add chemical drain cleaner following manufacturer's directions.

If, after an honest try, the drain will not open, place a bucket under the trap of the bowl and

ANATOMY of a faucet: Designs may vary, but the working parts are similar. If the faucet is leaking at the top, the washer or packing probably is the cause. If the faucet is leaking out the spout (body), the stem washer may be the problem.

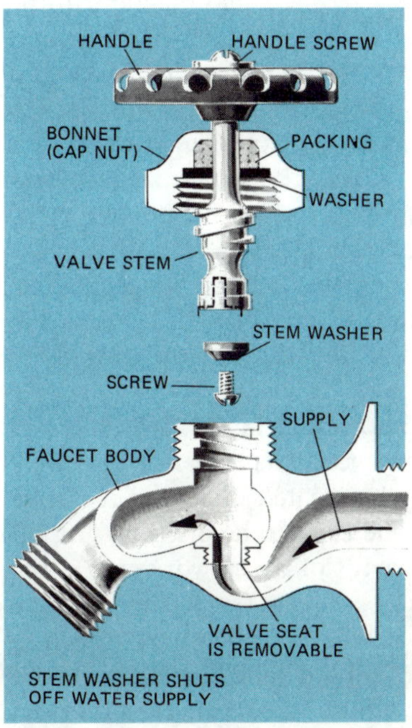

O-RING WASHERS are used along the stem of some late model faucets. The washers snap into a channel or groove machined into the stem; they may be removed with the tip of a screwdriver or nail. If the faucet is leaking around top, this washer may be the cause.

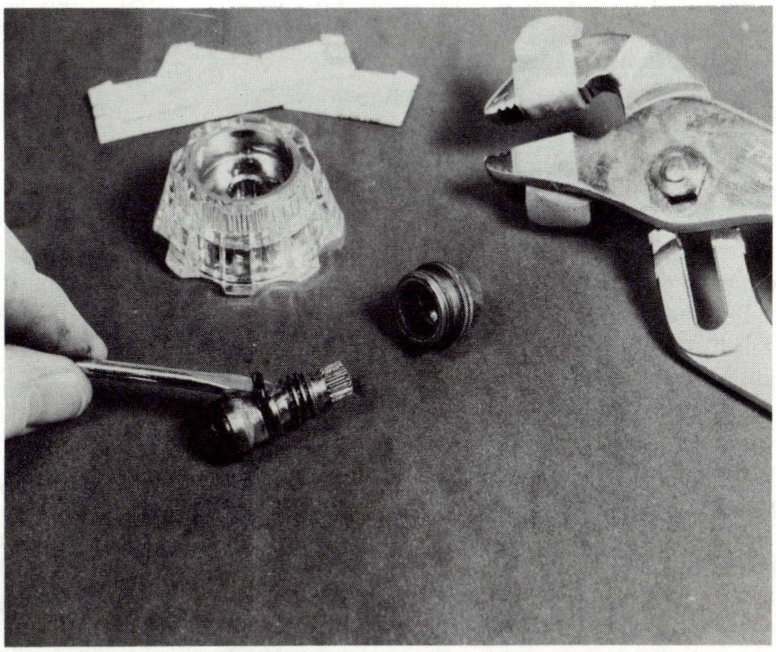

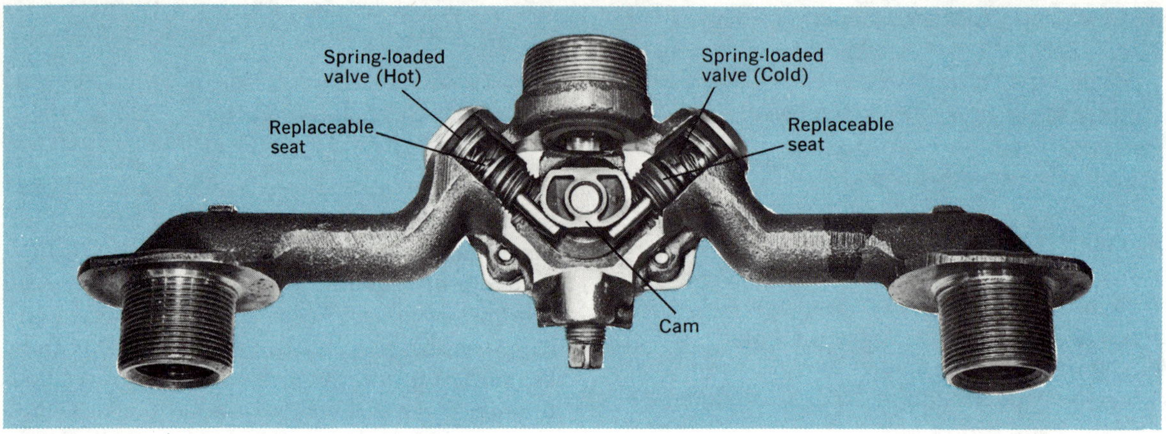

SINGLE-LEVER FAUCETS that are cam operated have spring-loaded valves and replaceable seats. The seats are removed with a screwdriver after the valves are removed—also with a screwdriver and/or wrench. If this type faucet is leaking, it's possible that dirt is lodged on the seat.

with a wrench remove the large nuts that hold the trap pipe to the tailpiece of the drain and the drain extension pipe. The water from the bowl will go into the bucket along with the clog which usually is stuck in the trap.

The clog may be beyond the trap. In this case, thread a plumber's snake or flexible auger into the drain extension and rod out the pipe. If the drain is still plugged after you reassemble the parts, the trouble is in the main drain, and it will have to be cleaned out at the clean-out plug. You can tell whether this main is stopped because the other drains in the household also will fail to flow properly—including the toilets.

Clogged bathtub drains often can be opened by using the same technique as for sink and lavatory drains. However, if the plunger treatment won't work after you have given it a fair chance, remove the escutcheon plate that covers the overflow and, usually, the trip lever that operates the tub's stopper.

Thread a flexible auger down the overflow pipe so it inches into the main drain pipe. Then twist the auger until you feel the clog break. Flush the system with fresh water and add chemical drain cleaner.

Bathtubs in older homes have a drum trap which usually is located near the tub between joists under the flooring. There is an access opening in the floor to get at this trap. It could be in the bathroom next to the tub, or in a closet that fronts or backs the tub. The cover over the trap may be fastened by screws, or you may have to just pry the cover up and off with the tip of a screwdriver. On top of the trap is a lug which can be turned with an adjustable wrench. Remove the top and clean out the trap. If the debris is not in the trap, you can run the auger through the pipes that connect to the drum trap and open the drain.

when faucets develop sniffles

Leaky faucets not only waste water and the energy to heat water, but get on your nerves with a steady dripping sound. Repairing leaky faucets, and those with other problems such as rattles and excessive moisture, is an easy job that shouldn't take over 30 minutes to complete if you follow these procedures for repair.

First, turn off the water at the shut-off valve below the fixture or at the main water valve.

There are two basic types of faucets: compression and cartridge. Some of the cartridge faucets are claimed by their manufacturer to be "washerless," but they still utilize O-rings and gaskets which can wear out, causing leaks and other problems.

Compression faucets are the single handle or lever type that have a packing nut, packing, and a threaded stem with a washer on the end of it. The washer compresses against a valve seat in the faucet housing and shuts off the water. Hence: compression faucet. What goes bad here is the packing or washer. This is normal, caused by wear.

To repair a compression faucet, regardless of its design, first remove the handle. It is held by a screw which may be located under a decorative escutcheon cap. The cap can be pried up and off the handle with a tip of a screwdriver. Or the handle screw may be a set-screw located in back of the handle. You will need an Allen wrench to loosen the screw. Pull the handle straight up and off the stem. Use a little force, if necessary, from

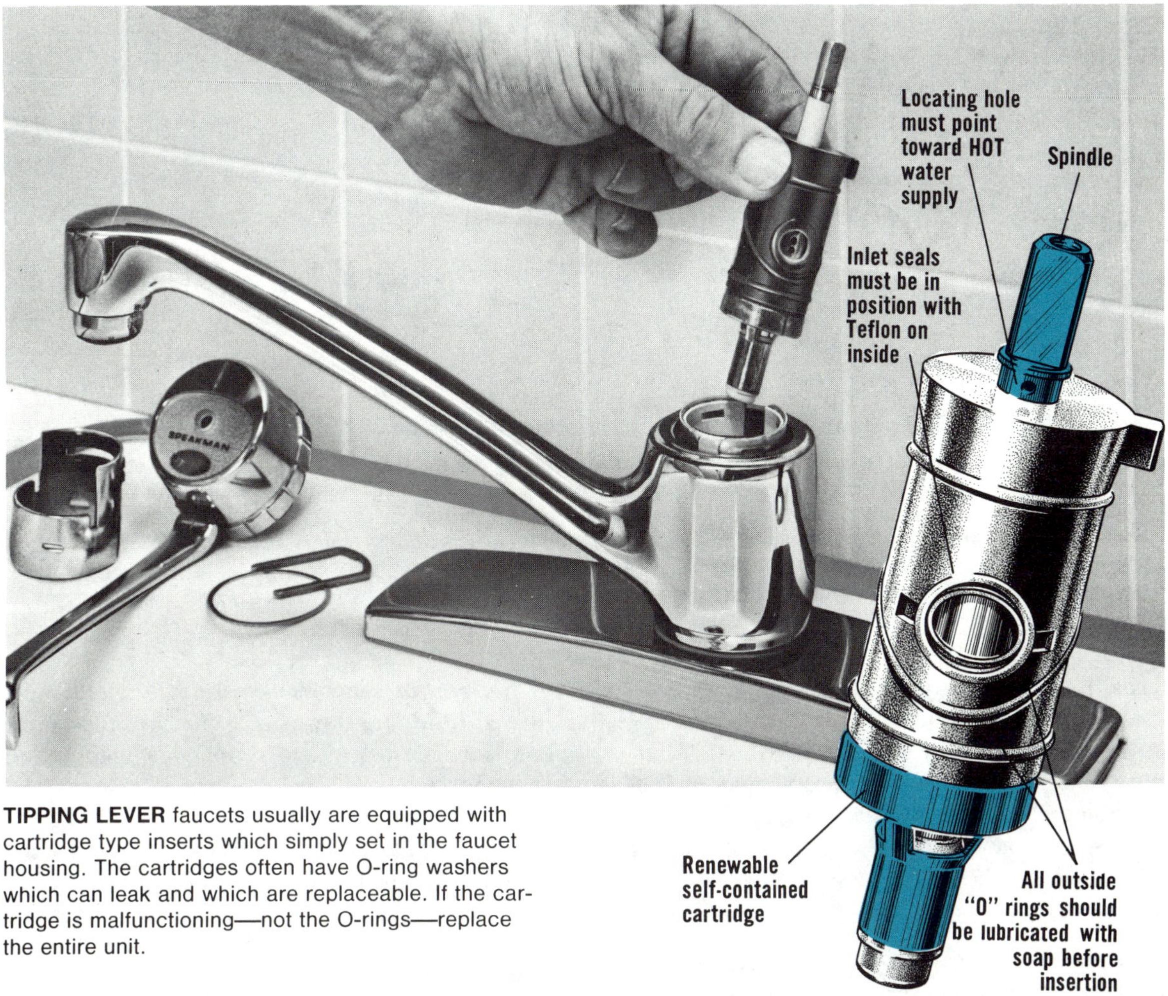

TIPPING LEVER faucets usually are equipped with cartridge type inserts which simply set in the faucet housing. The cartridges often have O-ring washers which can leak and which are replaceable. If the cartridge is malfunctioning—not the O-rings—replace the entire unit.

a screwdriver. Remove the packing nut, which unscrews counterclockwise. An adjustable wrench does the best job without marring the chrome finish. Then, with the handle back on the stem (but not fastened with the screw), turn out the stem. At the top of the stem you will see either a washer or packing string; at the bottom of the stem you will see a washer held by a screw.

If the faucet is leaking around the cap, replace the packing washer or gasket or string. If the unit is leaking out the spout, change the stem washer. It is recommended that you use new replacement parts, which are very inexpensive. Don't try to make-do. When you change one part, change the other at the same time. Also, while the stem is accessible, polish it with steel wool to remove any corrosion. Pay special attention to the stem washer. If it looks ragged and chewed, instead of worn smooth, chances are the valve seat against which the washer compresses is rough and pitted. You can smooth this seat with a seat dressing tool on sale at most home center and hardware stores.

Or you may be able to replace the valve seat, which screws into the faucet housing. A hex-type wrench is used for this; it also is sold at home centers and hardwares.

To complete the job, reassemble the faucet in reverse order and turn on the water.

Cartridge faucets have four basic designs: tipping lever or valve; ball; disc; cartridge. Replacement parts usually are sold in kits for the specific brand of faucet. Sometimes you can find individual parts, but the kits are the best buy. Know what type of faucet you have before you shop for parts. Delta faucet parts, for example, will not fit Peerless faucets.

Single lever faucets (tipping lever type) have spring-loaded valves for both hot and cold water. The valves are located in a V configuration next to the spout. To remove the escutcheon housing, unscrew the spout of the faucet and lift both off. A cap covers each valve and it may be removed with a screwdriver or adjustable wrench. Problems with this faucet are worn valve stems and

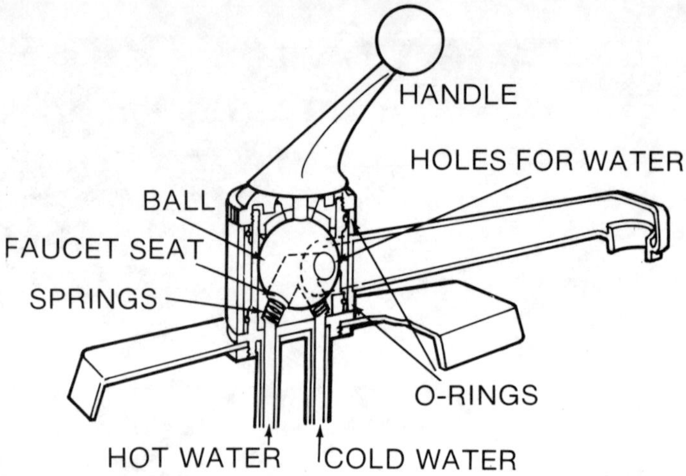

DISASSEMBLED ball faucet is shown above left. The springs are under the washers (O-rings) at the bottom of the faucet. You pry out the washers with the tip of a screwdriver and press them back into place with your fingers. The large end of the washer should be in an "up" position. Washer and spring kits are available; take along the old parts for a match. Above right, ball faucets are also the tipping type. The handle (lever) is removed by releasing a set screw at the base. Unscrew the faucet cap to get at the ball and seat assembly. The parts simply lift out of the housing. If the faucet is leaking at the cap, try tightening the cap. If this doesn't work, replace the gasket or O-ring at the cap.

seats. Both parts may be replaced; they are removed from the faucet housing with a faucet seating wrench which you can buy for this purpose. The procedure is extremely simple: just remove the old stems and seats and replace them with similar new ones. If the spout is leaking where it joins the handle assembly, replace the O-ring washer.

DISC FAUCETS are self-contained. However, they do have three seals at the bottom of the cartridge which can work loose. Remove the handle assembly, escutcheon, and cartridge screws. Then lift out the cartridge. Push the seals into place; reassemble the faucet.

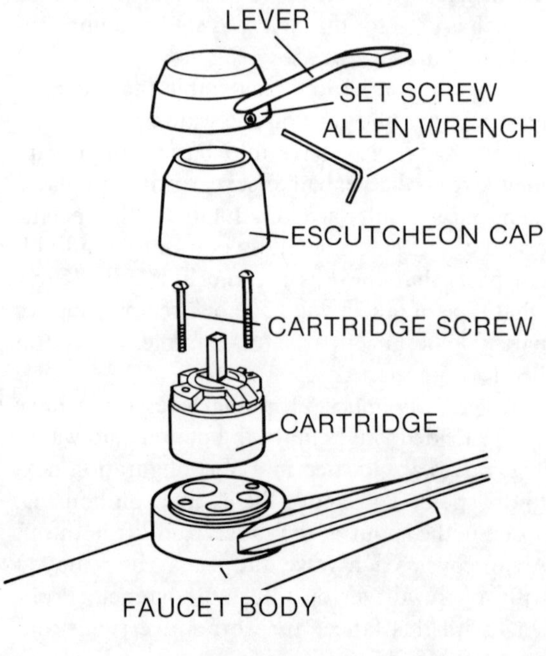

Ball cartridge faucets have a single lever handle that tips up and down to open/close the faucet and moves sideways to supply hot/cold water. The faucet handle is held to the ball assembly by a setscrew usually found on the handle at the front of the faucet. Loosen this screw, remove the handle, and then unscrew the knurled cap counterclockwise to get at the ball parts. Under the cap you will find a cap and cam assembly, an O-ring washer to seal it, and the ball. Lift out the ball and look down at the housing. There are two or three faucet seats that are topped by O-ring washers pinched into the housing and springs under the washers.

You can remove the O-ring washers with the tip of a screwdriver (be careful) and then flip out the springs. Just install the new springs and reseat the O-ring washers. Then replace the ball, cam, cap and O-ring washer. Reassemble the handle parts.

A disc faucet has three cartridge seals at the bottom of the cartridge; these can become worn and cause the faucet to leak or drip.

A setscrew holds on the handle; loosen it with an Allen or hex wrench. Lift off the handle and the escutheon cap underneath the handle. The cartridge is held by two or three screws. Remove these and lift up the cartridge. You will see the O-ring seals at the bottom of the cartridge. Remove and replace these; a screwdriver is the best tool.

If the seals are not causing the problem, it is recommended that you buy a new disc cartridge replacement; don't try to repair the old one.

Cartridge sleeve faucets usually are single-lever, and the lever or handle is turned to the hot or cold water selection and then tipped up to turn on the water. To get at the cartridge, the lever is pushed down past the "off" position and the escutheon is pried off with a screwdriver after the lever screw at the top of the escutcheon is removed. This screw may be hidden by a decorative escutcheon plate which is a friction fit on top of the lever housing.

Once off, you will see a retaining nut. Remove it with a screwdriver, adjustable wrench, or pliers. Lift out the grooved sleeve directly below the retaining nut. At the top of the cartridge you will see a tiny clip that holds the cartridge in the faucet housing. Pull this clip straight out with pliers or the tip of a screwdriver. The cartridge now may be removed by pulling it straight up with pliers. If the cartridge has O-ring washers, replace these, which may be the cause of the leak. Or replace the entire cartridge and then reassemble the faucet. As a rule, it is best to replace the cartridge instead of trying to repair it. The cost is minimal.

Bathtub faucets operate almost the same way as sink and lavatory faucets except they are horizontal instead of vertical. If the tub faucet is a cartridge type, it may have several retaining clips that have to be pulled before the cartridge can be released from the housing. Also, the cartridge may be color coded so you can insert it properly into its housing. This will be noted on the replacement cartridge package (usually) or you can match the cartridge configuration of the old part with the new for the proper assembly.

other plumbing connections

Shower heads, kitchen sink spray hoses, and washing machine connections fall into this category, and you'll find these parts easy to replace. Since new parts are not costly, it is recommended that you work with new parts instead of trying to repair the old ones. You will save time and effort.

Shower heads are connected to a riser type pipe that works off the bathtub faucet. The shower head is simply screwed onto this pipe; an adjustable wrench is used to remove or install it.

Troubles with shower heads usually are lime build-ups in the nozzle of the unit. By removing the shower head from its pipe, you may be able to disassemble the unit by removing the faceplate. It will turn counterclockwise. Once inside the head, you can clean the water holes in the face plate and the lime deposits in the water channels. Try soaking the head overnight in white vinegar, which will loosen and remove the minerals.

Kitchen sink spray hoses usually go bad at the nozzle. Unfortunately, most spray nozzles are permanently attached to the hose, so the entire hose unit must be replaced if it doesn't work. But before you buy a new hose, try removing the nozzle. If it can be removed, you turn a coupling nut between the hose and the nozzle which exposes a snap ring and washer assembly. Remove these parts and the spray nozzle will disconnect from the hose.

If the unit must be replaced, it is coupled to the kitchen sink faucet directly under the spout of the faucet under the kitchen sink. You may need a basin wrench to turn the hex nut that attaches the hose to the faucet. Be sure to turn off the water before removing the hose. Also, insert the new hose through the hole in the sink before you connect the hose to the faucet fitting.

Washing machine connections are flexible hoses (similar to a garden hose) which connect to faucets with threaded spouts (similar to an exterior sill cock). The hoses usually have small screens at both the faucet and machine connections. If the washer won't fill with water, or the washer is slow-filling, check these screens to make sure they are not clogged with sediment from the water system. Often they are.

water heater maintenance

The water heater probably is the most neglected appliance in any home. It goes right along heating water and you don't know it even exists—until the hot-water faucet flows cold. Water heaters actually take little maintenance, but there are a couple of checks you should make on a regular schedule.

Every month or so, press down on the relief valve of the heater, which is located on top of the unit. Let a little water trickle out so you know the valve is functioning properly. Also, open the heater drain every two months or so and let a couple of gallons of water flow out. This will remove any sediment from the bottom of the tank. If the tank is old, don't drain it. Draining could cause leaks.

If the water won't heat and the heater is electric powered, check the fuse box or circuit breaker at the main power entrance. If the heater runs on gas, the pilot light may be out. Instructions for lighting the pilot are embossed on the front of the heater near the pilot light panel. If, after checking these points, the heater still won't function, the problem probably is a malfunctioning element or thermocouple. Call a pro to fix this.

How to work with copper pipe

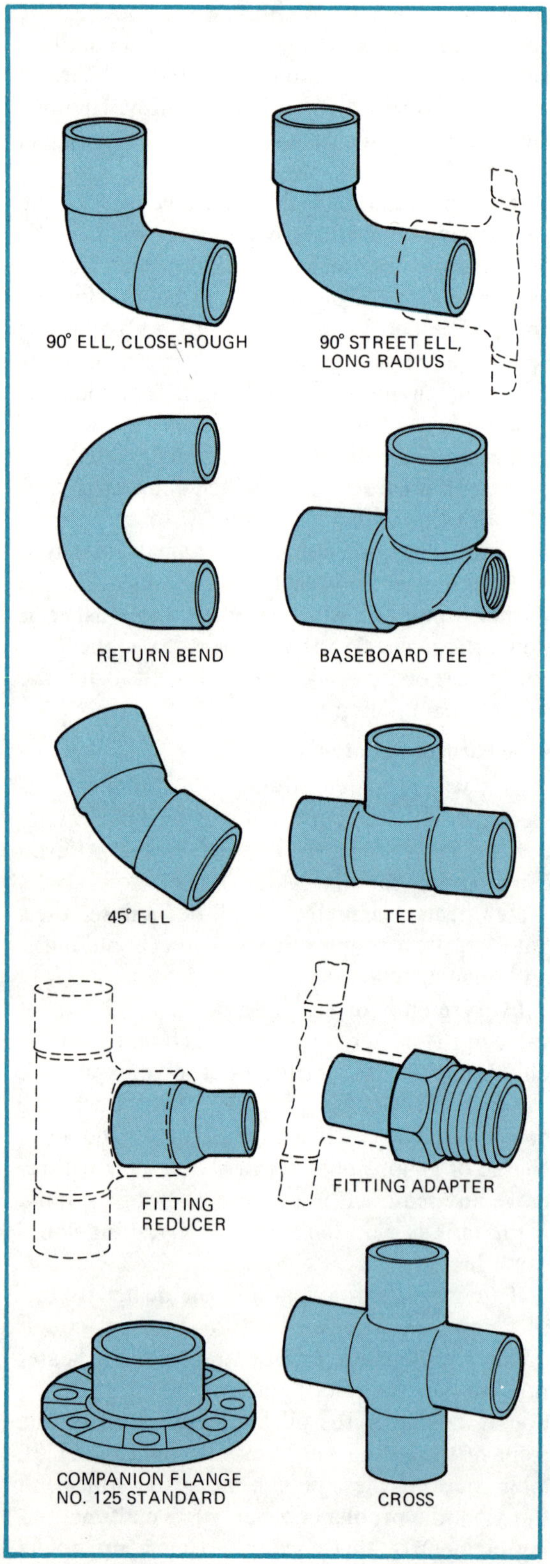

■ COPPER PIPING is light and extremely durable, requires no threading of the ends to join it, comes in varying diameters, wall thicknesses and degrees of hardness, and is suitable for both hot and cold-water systems. To join copper piping, there are many types of fittings to cover every part of the plumbing layout. A number of common fittings are shown at the left.

Copper pipe can be joined using either soldered (also called capillary or ''sweat'' joints) or screwed (compression fitting) joints. Compression joints are of two types. With the first, called a ''bead'' fitting, the tubing is pushed into the fitting, a bead of jointing paste is applied around the tubing in front of a compression nut, and the compression nut is tightened onto the fitting. The result is a watertight fit. The second type is called a ''flare'' fitting because the end of the tubing is funnel-shaped with a special flaring tool (below). This shaped end receives the male end of the fitting; the compression nut is then tightened to finish the connection.

SEE ALSO
Bathrooms . . . Bathtubs . . . Drains . . .
Garbage disposers . . . Plastic pipe . . .
Sewage systems . . . Soldering . . . Torches

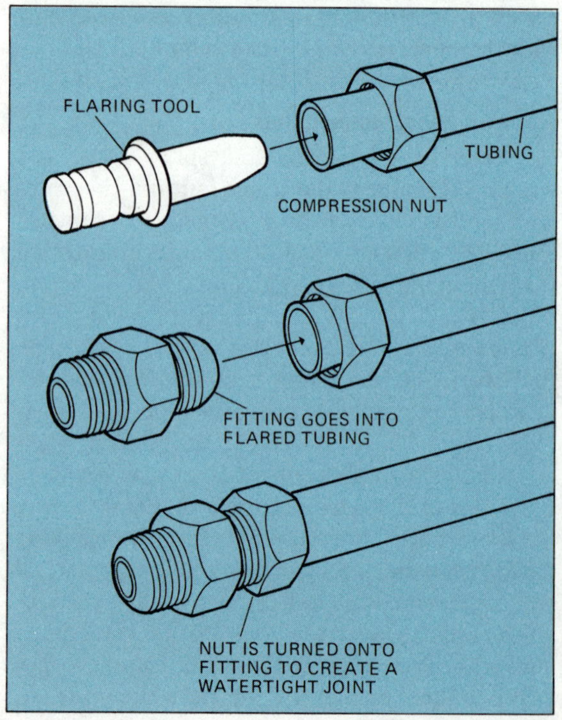

Types of copper piping

Type	Temper
K	Hard (rigid) or soft (flexible)
L	Hard or soft
M	Hard only

To be sure the type of copper piping that you use for a specific application complies with local plumbing code, always check with your local building department. In general, Type L can be used below ground, Type M above ground. For a superior installation, use Type K below ground and Type L above ground.

Equipment needed

- Propane torch
- Hacksaw
- Smooth file
- Tubing bender (also known as a "hickey")
- Tubing cutter with reamer
- Sandpaper or fine steel wool
- Solder
- Flux

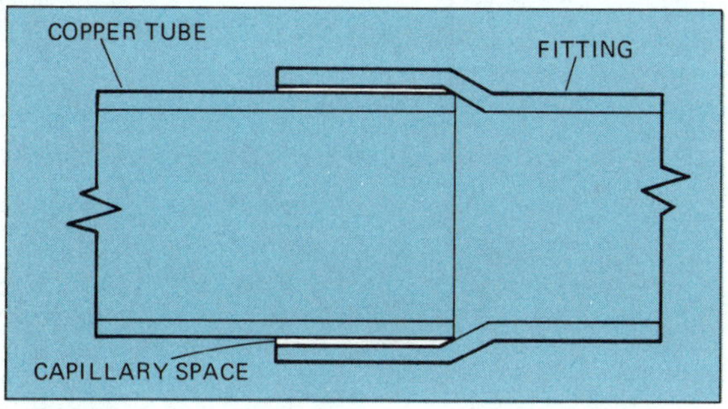

Capillary or 'sweat' joints

Properly prepared, a sweated joint will provide many years of troublefree (nonleaking) service. Although your joint may leak the first couple of times you attempt to sweat pipe, you'll soon be sweating copper pipe just like a pro by getting a little practice under your belt and by following the rules outlined on these pages.

To understand the principles of sweating pipe, you should understand how capillary action works. When the end of a copper pipe is inserted as far as possible into a fitting, a small amount of space will remain between the inside wall of the fitting and the outside wall of the pipe. When the fitting is heated with a propane torch and solder is applied around the pipe at the outer edges of the fitting, the solder will be drawn into this space by capillary action, bonding the pipe and fitting together securely. Such action will be the result regardless of whether the piping will be running horizontally or vertically.

If you're repairing or adding to an existing copper piping system, remember that all parts to be joined first must be completely dry. After the soldering is done and the joint cooled to room temperature, test the work for possible leaks.

Cutting and cleaning

Cut pipe to length using a tubing-cutter (1) or a fine hacksaw blade. Make sure the cut is square and the pipe remains round and true. Cutting with a hacksaw blade leaves rough edges on the inside and outside of the pipe, while a tubing cutter leaves rough edges on the inside of the pipe. Remove burrs on the outside of the pipe with a smooth file or sandpaper and on inside with a reamer (2) or rattail file. Clean the end of pipe with steel wool or a strip of sandpaper (3).

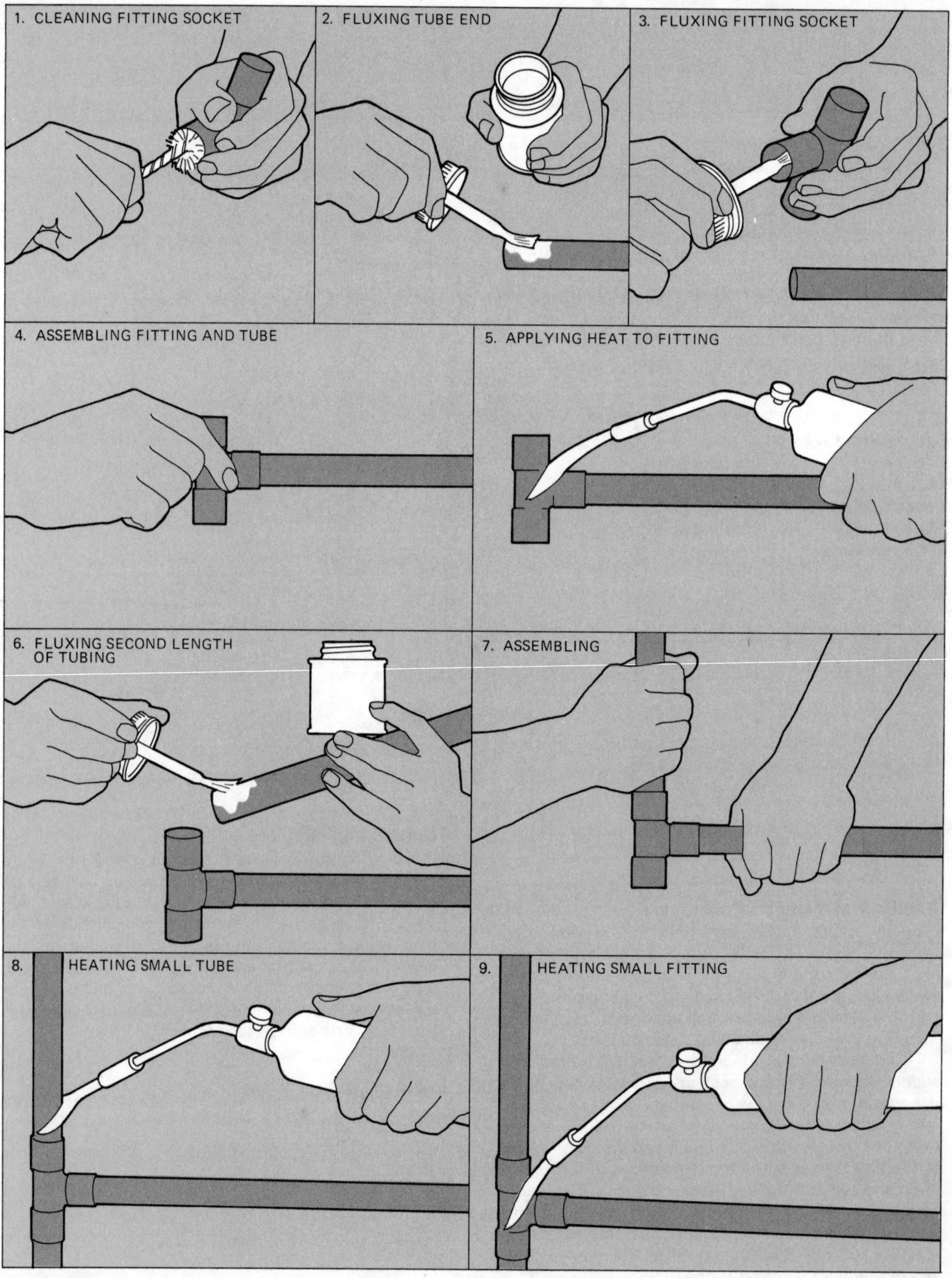
1. CLEANING FITTING SOCKET
2. FLUXING TUBE END
3. FLUXING FITTING SOCKET
4. ASSEMBLING FITTING AND TUBE
5. APPLYING HEAT TO FITTING
6. FLUXING SECOND LENGTH OF TUBING
7. ASSEMBLING
8. HEATING SMALL TUBE
9. HEATING SMALL FITTING

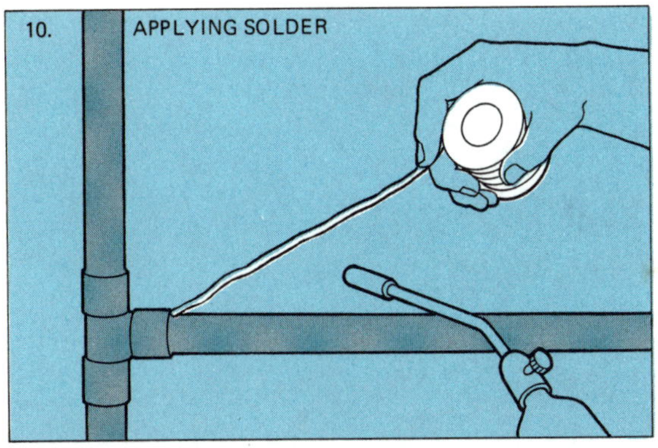

Assembling copper system

After you have thoroughly cleaned the inside of the fitting socket (Step 1, left), apply a thin coat of flux to the end of the pipe (Step 2) and the inside of the fitting (Step 3) with a small, clean brush. Then push the tubing tightly into the fitting (Step 4) and twist the pieces slightly in order to distribute the flux evenly. Wipe off any excess flux that remains and apply heat with a propane torch to the fitting (Step 5).

In the same manner, apply flux to the second length of tubing (Step 6), insert in the fitting (Step 7) and apply a flame to both the tubing (Step 8) and fitting (Step 9). Melt the solder from a spool of soldering wire around the tubing-fitting joint (Step 10, above).

Flux for soldering is mildly corrosive. It contains zinc and ammonium chlorides in a petroleum base, and is used as a protective coating on the metal and as an agent to help the solder flow. Always stir flux before you use it.

The cardinal rule in choosing a solder is to buy a quality solder. Most solders for household plumbing jobs are composed of 50 percent tin and 50 percent lead. If the joint requires a solder of greater strength, use one comprising 95 percent tin and 5 percent antimony.

Do not clean, flux and assemble more copper piping than you can solder in about two hours.

Soldering tips

Remember to align joints with adequate support before soldering, and to place no strain on them. When soldering, use torch with sweeping motion—tubing and fitting should be at same temperature for best flow of solder into joint. If solder forms lumps, joint is not hot enough. If there is no question that the joint is hot enough but solder still does not flow freely, overheating resulting in burned flux is likely, and the joint must be started again from Step 1. As soon as solder has set, use a wet brush or rag to crack and remove flux (remove it from inside of pipes by flushing with water); remove all flux before pressure-testing the joint—if necessary use a wire brush. If you have to redo a joint, reflux the entire joint area before applying heat to unsolder.

Ten steps for assembling copper piping

Clean the inside of the fitting with a wire brush. A thorough cleaning is absolutely necessary because a "sweat" joint relies on capillary action and *any* dirt, grease, or surface oxidation on the pipe or the fitting will hinder the joining action. Because the pipe should fit tightly into the fitting, do not remove too much metal when sanding or the capillary space will be enlarged and the joint weakened.

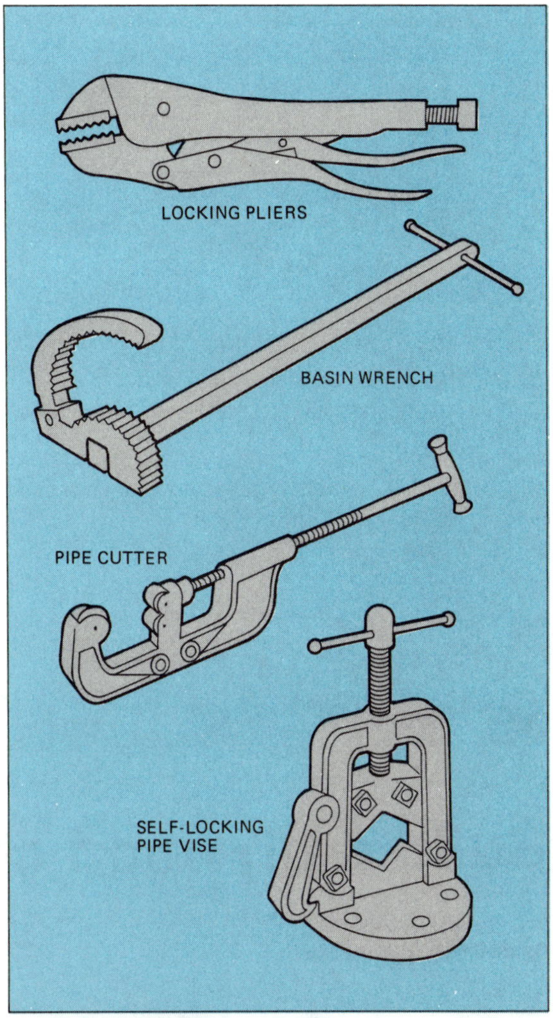

Toolbox additions

If you plan on doing most of your own plumbing jobs, the four tools shown above can be valuable additions to your toolbox. The two pictured at the top are available at most hardware stores, while you may have to visit a plumbers' supply house to find the lower two.

Vise-grip pliers, with serrated jaws and locking nut, are especially useful when working with small-diameter pipes. A basin wrench, whose gripping head is adjustable, will save you many bumps and knocks on head and hands when you are installing a basin where there is little room for swinging ordinary wrenches.

A pipe cutter, which is faster and more accurate than a hacksaw when cutting iron or galvanized pipe, is operated simply by starting the cutter over the pipe, and, as it is revolved, tightening the handle gradually to deepen the cut. Thread-cutting oil should be applied to both the cutter and the pipe.

A self-locking pipe vise has V-shaped jaws that grip the pipe from both top and bottom. It eliminates the need for a helper to hold the pipe while you do the cutting.

Build a plywood cutoff jig

By EBEN H. GUSTAFSON

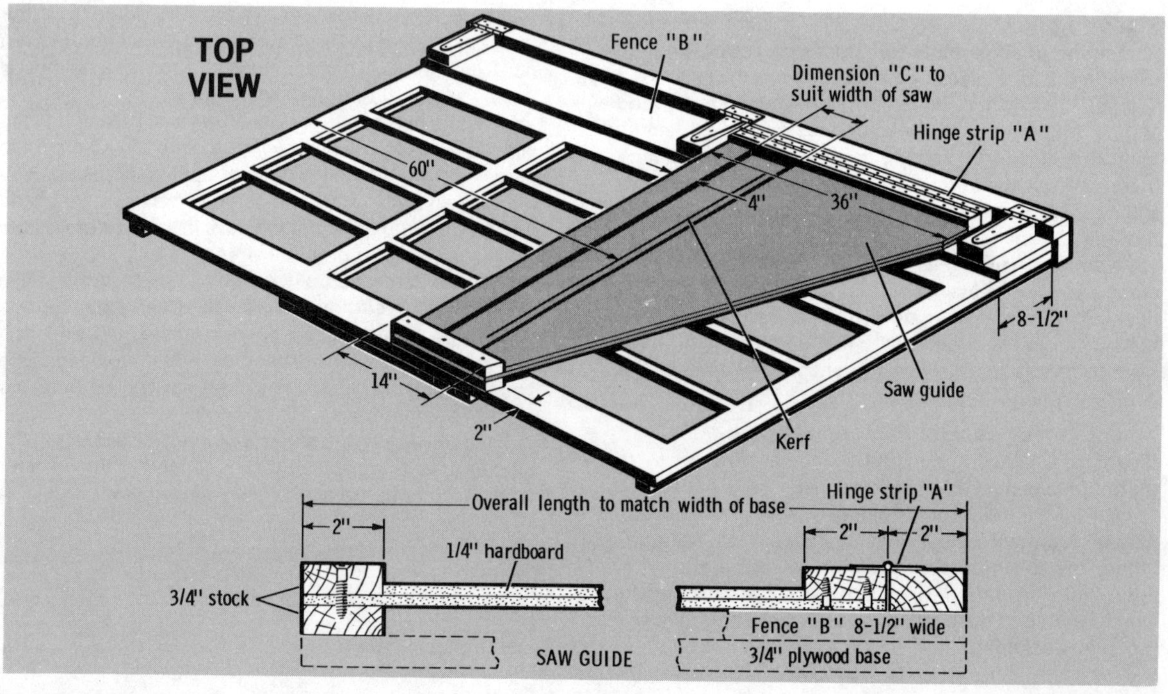

■ IF YOU NEED to cut up a full sheet of plywood only once in a while, you aren't going to bother making this cutoff jig. You'll first saw it roughly to a size that's fairly easy to handle and take it from there, not caring particularly if you waste some material in doing so.

However, if you run a small cabinet shop where you are working daily with these big, awkward sheets, it will pay you to make this handy labor-saver.

It consists of a 60x96-in. base on which the plywood sheet is placed, and a saw guide which is hinged to swing down on top of the work. A built-in track and kerf in the guide, which is made to fit your particular portable electric saw, lets you zip across the sheet in nothing flat, resulting in a perfect 90° cut.

When not in use, the jig is swung up against the wall, clearing the benchtop for other use. You can either attach the jig directly to the wall or bolt it to the rear edge of the bench on which it's used. A 1x2 handle hinged under the front of the jig is fitted with a spring-loaded bolt latch and chain to make it handy to swing the jig up against the wall and lock it securely in place. As an extra precaution, a king-size turnbutton will give added assurance that it won't come crashing down accidentally.

The details clearly show how it's made. The base is a 4x8-ft. sheet with a 20-in. piece splined to it to make it 68 in. wide, then cut as shown to make it lighter and self-clearing of sawdust. It's important in hinging the hardboard saw guide to be sure that it is exactly 90° to fence "B."

JIG STORES AGAINST WALL when not in use. Note latch-fitted handle to raise and lower jig.

The jig will accommodate both plywood and lumber up to ¾ in. thick. Thinner stock is cut by shimming it up with scrap pieces. The track for the saw is made just wide enough to let it slide smoothly, yet without any side play.

SEE ALSO

Circular saw blades . . . Circular saws, portable . . . Paneling, plywood . . . Power-tool stands

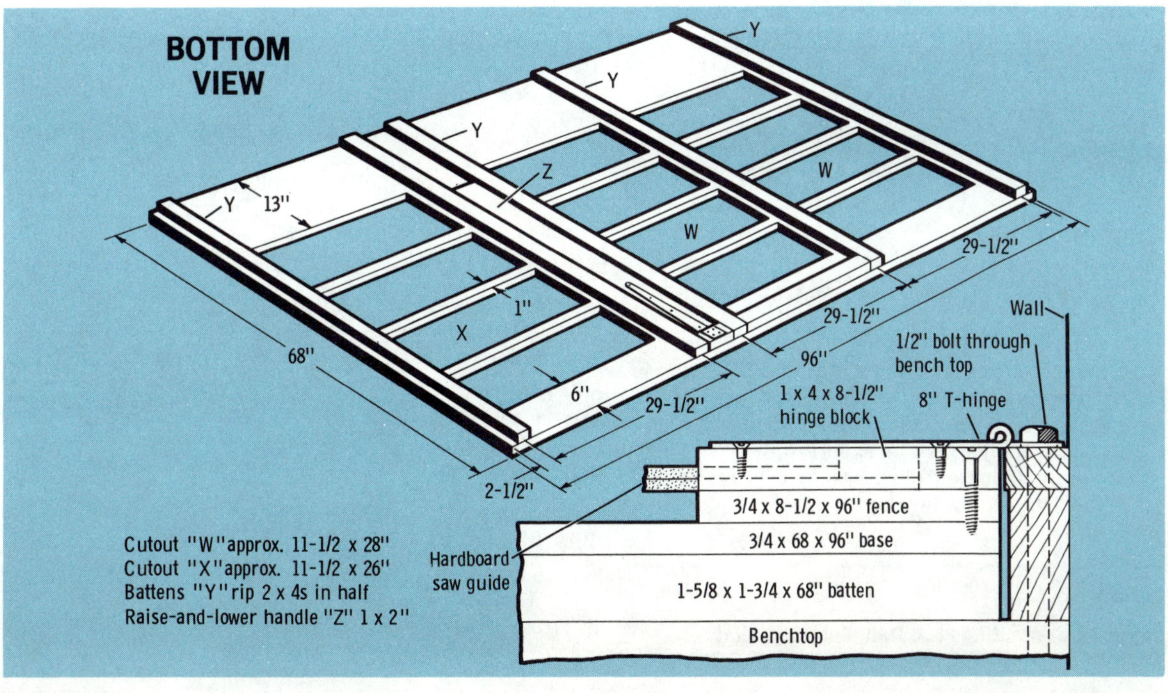

16 ways to hide plywood edges

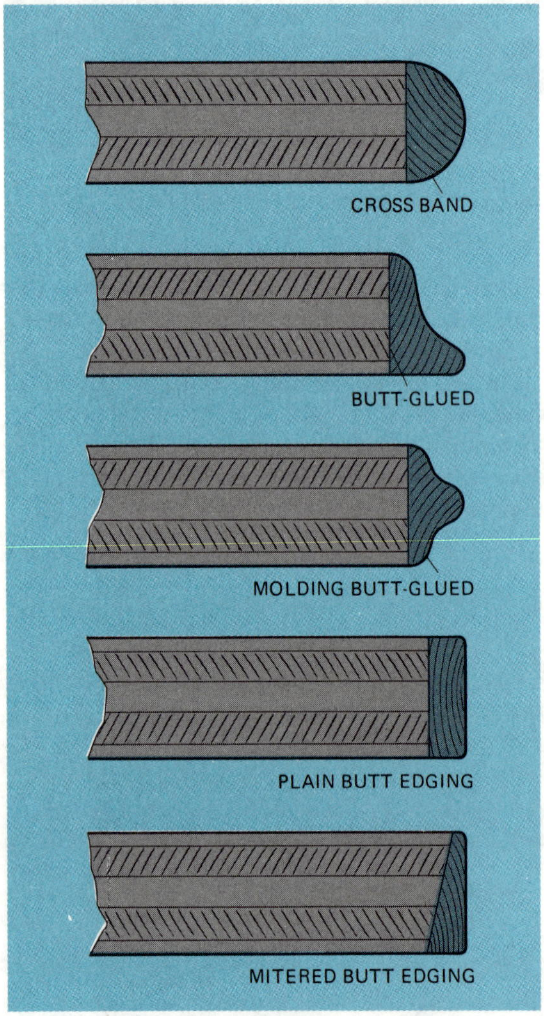

■ PLYWOOD HAS long presented the home workman with the problem of hiding the material's laminated edges from view. The simplest do-it-yourself technique has been to cover them with paper-thin wood tape. It's sold in rolls in a choice of woods and merely glued on. This is okay for book shelves and perhaps the square edges of a tabletop, but it's not too durable a solution if the project will get lots of handling and wear. And wood tape, limited to plain square edges, is no help when you want shaped edges on a piece of furniture. But here are many ways to hide the laminations and add eye appeal at the same time. They range from comparatively simple to more involved approaches.

SIMPLE BUTT-GLUING moldings to straight plywood edges can dress them up. Five approaches are shown at left. Small finishing nails or brads are added, their heads set and puttied over. For the ultimate in hiding nails, a small gouge is often used to lift a chip of wood first. The nail or brad is then driven and the chip is glued back in place over the head. On fairly small projects, rubber bands cut from a large inner tube are handy for clamping molding to the plywood edge.

SPLINES FORM exceptionally strong joints. They're popular where there is room for them, as with wider moldings such as those at the right. With a table saw, run kerfs in both the molding and plywood and rip thin wood splines to fit the kerfs. A rabbet in the molding (top right), plus the spline and glue, makes a joint so strong that the edge stiffens the plywood.

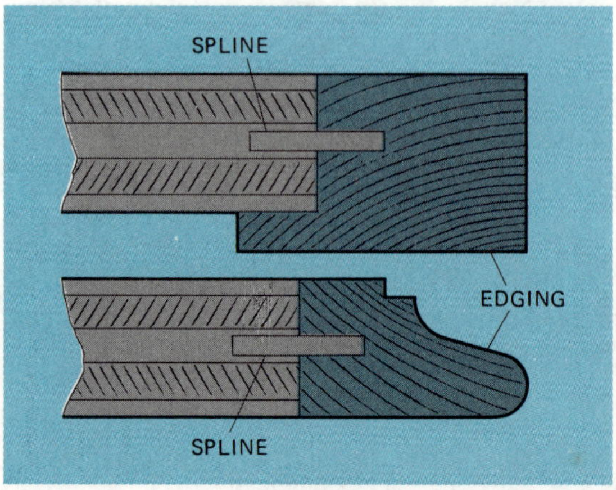

SEE ALSO

Joinery . . . Moldings . . . Paneling, plywood

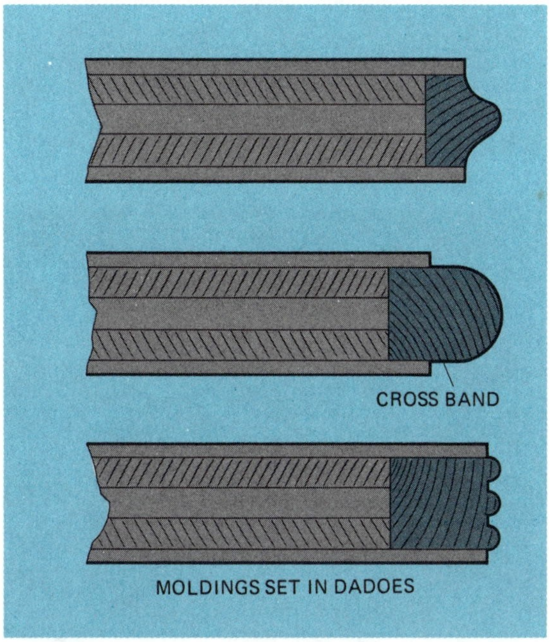

INSETTING MOLDINGS in dadoes turns the plywood veneer plies into a part of the decorative edge. A dado in the core laminations gets a depth to suit the molding. At the top, that depth brings the veneer ply flush with the molding, but the outer veneers can also make decorative shoulders. Pinch clamps will hold surface veneers against the molding while glue sets.

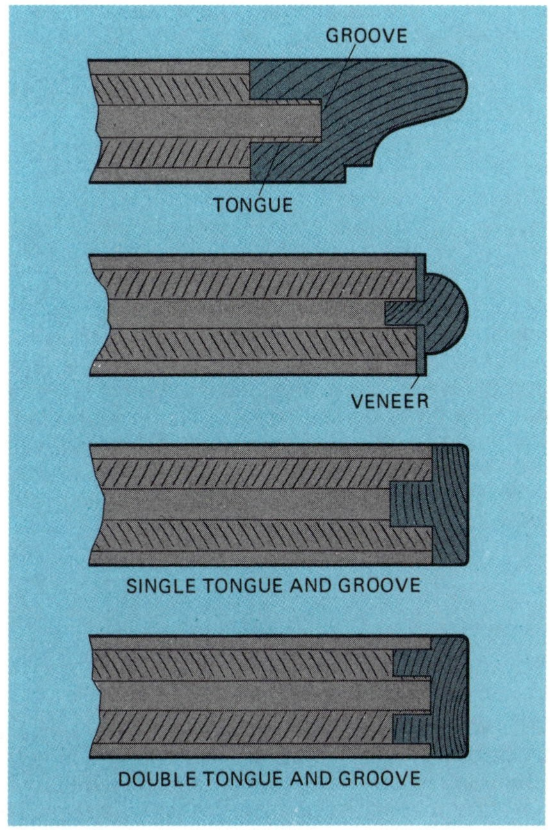

TONGUE-AND-GROOVE joints are far less likely to pull loose. Grooves can be cut in the plywood, as in the center examples above, or in the molding. The second drawing shows how an edge treatment can be built up, with narrow molding added to a veneer strip.

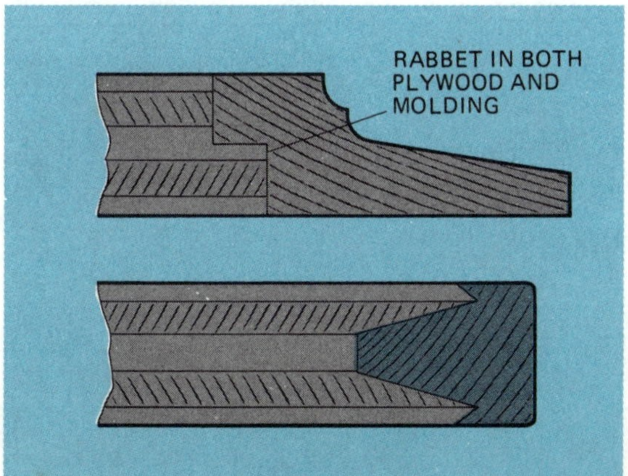

IN SPECIAL approaches at the left, you see how fancy, wide picture-frame molding can be the edging (top). Below it is perhaps the strongest joint of all—but one that takes special cutters to form both the plywood groove and the molding. After such a start, you might end up by shaping the exposed face of the molding itself.

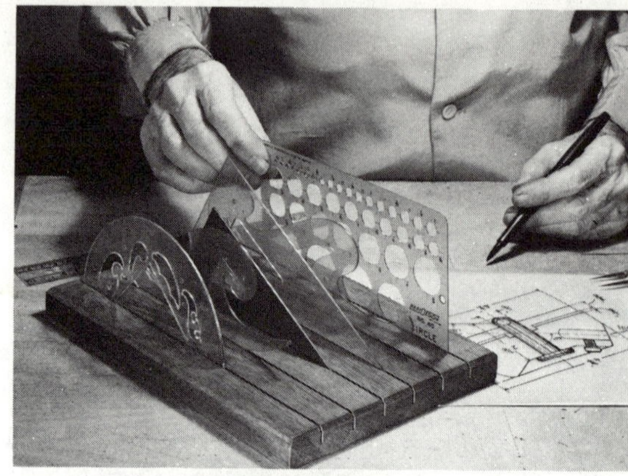

A SLOTTED BLOCK to hold drafting templates and triangles upright was one draftsman's solution to a couple of common problems. Picking up such drafting tools is often difficult—especially when they're lying flat on a drawing board or table. It's also hard to keep them clean when they're slid from one end of the board to another. The slots are simply saw kerfs.—*Victor J. Lamoy.*

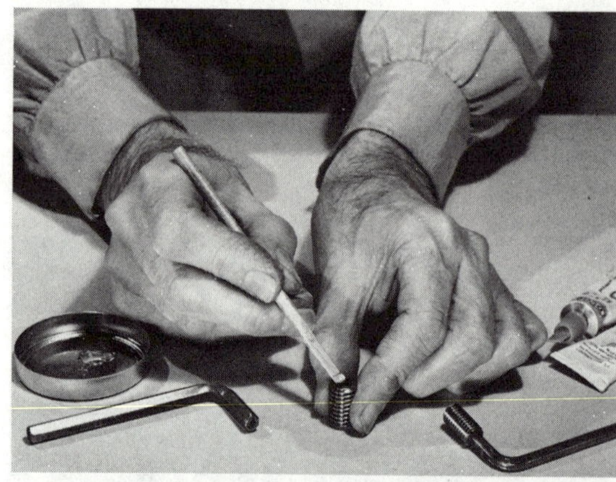

ALLEN SCREWS are often used as temporary adjusting screws or setscrews with power tools such as jigsaws, belt-disc sanders or Unimat lathes. I often find it advantageous to epoxy the Allen wrenches permanently to the setscrews to avoid the problem of searching for the right-size wrench. Before applying a drop or two of epoxy, however, tighten the screw to make sure the handle of the wrench will remain out of the way.—*Jay K. Wallace.*

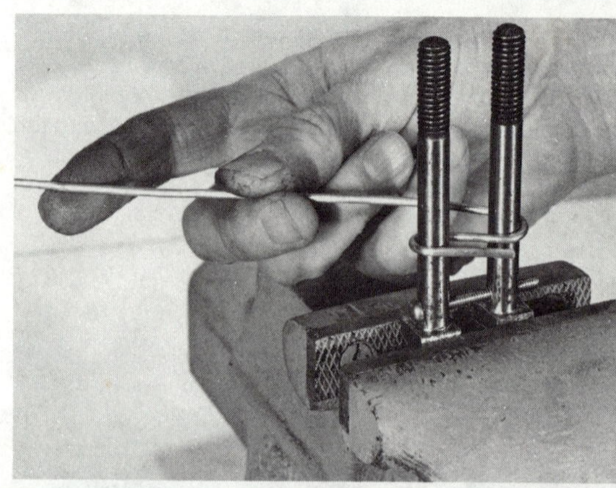

THIS WIRE BENDER is easily made and can be used for bending wires of different sizes when gripped in your vise. It consists of two square-headed bolts, each having one side of its head cut flush with its flank. The bolts are clamped with the cut sides together; then a hole is drilled through the shank's sides. One is reamed for a slide fit, the other tapped for the adjusting screw. The bolts are spaced for the size of the wire to be bent; then the jig is clamped in a vise.—*Peter Legon.*

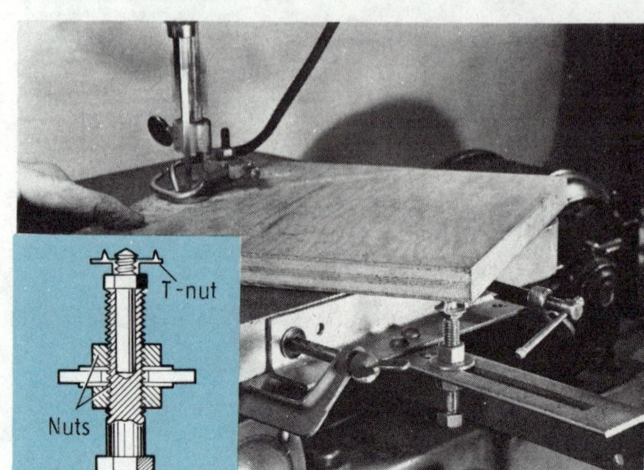

AN ADJUSTABLE PIVOT sliding in a slotted length of angle iron that's attached to the table of your jigsaw makes a handy fixture for cutting true discs. The detail shows how the pivot and its Tee-nut point rests in a blind hole drilled in a machine screw. This permits removing the pivot and driving it into the underside of the work. How the fixture is attached to the machine depends on the table itself. If it has a lip, like the one shown, it can be attached with C-clamps.—*Peter Legon.*

METRIC CONVERSION

Conversion factors can be carried so far they become impractical. In cases below where an entry is exact it is followed by an asterisk (*). Where considerable rounding off has taken place, the entry is followed by a + or a - sign.

CUSTOMARY TO METRIC

Linear Measure

inches	millimeters
1/16	1.5875*
1/8	3.2
3/16	4.8
1/4	6.35*
5/16	7.9
3/8	9.5
7/16	11.1
1/2	12.7*
9/16	14.3
5/8	15.9
11/16	17.5
3/4	19.05*
13/16	20.6
7/8	22.2
15/16	23.8
1	25.4*

inches	centimeters
1	2.54*
2	5.1
3	7.6
4	10.2
5	12.7*
6	15.2
7	17.8
8	20.3
9	22.9
10	25.4*
11	27.9
12	30.5

feet	centimeters	meters
1	30.48*	.3048*
2	61	.61
3	91	.91
4	122	1.22
5	152	1.52
6	183	1.83
7	213	2.13
8	244	2.44
9	274	2.74
10	305	3.05
50	1524*	15.24*
100	3048*	30.48*

1 yard =
.9144* meters
1 rod =
5.0292* meters
1 mile =
1.6 kilometers
1 nautical mile =
1.852* kilometers

Fluid Measure

(Milliliters [ml] and cubic centimeters [cc or cu cm] are equivalent, but it is customary to use milliliters for liquids.)

1 cu in = 16.39 ml
1 fl oz = 29.6 ml
1 cup = 237 ml
1 pint = 473 ml
1 quart = 946 ml
= .946 liters
1 gallon = 3785 ml
= 3.785 liters
Formula (exact):
fluid ounces × 29.573 529 562 5*
= milliliters

Weights

ounces	grams
1	28.3
2	56.7
3	85
4	113
5	142
6	170
7	198
8	227
9	255
10	283
11	312
12	340
13	369
14	397
15	425
16	454

Formula (exact):
ounces × 28.349 523 125* = grams

pounds	kilograms
1	.45
2	.9
3	1.4
4	1.8
5	2.3
6	2.7
7	3.2
8	3.6
9	4.1
10	4.5

1 short ton (2000 lbs) =
907 kilograms (kg)
Formula (exact):
pounds × .453 592 37* =
kilograms

Volume

1 cu in = 16.39 cubic centimeters (cc)
1 cu ft = 28 316.7 cc
1 bushel = 35 239.1 cc
1 peck = 8 809.8 cc

Area

1 sq in = 6.45 sq cm
1 sq ft = 929 sq cm
= .093 sq meters
1 sq yd = .84 sq meters
1 acre = 4 046.9 sq meters
= .404 7 hectares
1 sq mile = 2 589 988 sq meters
= 259 hectares
= 2.589 9 sq kilometers

Kitchen Measure

1 teaspoon = 4.93 milliliters (ml)
1 Tablespoon = 14.79 milliliters (ml)

Miscellaneous

1 British thermal unit (Btu) (mean)
= 1 055.9 joules
1 calorie (mean) = 4.19 joules
1 horsepower = 745.7 watts
= .75 kilowatts
caliber (diameter of a firearm's bore in hundredths of an inch)
= .254 millimeters (mm)
1 atmosphere pressure = 101 325* pascals (newtons per sq meter)
1 pound per square inch (psi) = 6 895 pascals
1 pound per square foot = 47.9 pascals
1 knot = 1.85 kilometers per hour
25 miles per hour = 40.2 kilometers per hour
50 miles per hour = 80.5 kilometers per hour
75 miles per hour = 120.7 kilometers per hour